Chester D. Geller

Geller

ANALYTIC GEOMETRY

PRENTICE-HALL MATHEMATICS SERIES

Albert A. Bennett, EDITOR

PRENTICE-HALL INTERNATIONAL, INC., *London*
PRENTICE-HALL OF AUSTRALIA, PTY., LTD., *Sydney*
PRENTICE-HALL OF CANADA, LTD., *Toronto*
PRENTICE-HALL OF INDIA (PRIVATE) LTD., *New Delhi*
PRENTICE-HALL OF JAPAN, INC., *Tokyo*
PRENTICE-HALL DE MEXICO, S.A., *Mexico City*

ANALYTIC GEOMETRY

SECOND EDITION

PAUL K. REES

Professor of Mathematics, Louisiana State University

PRENTICE-HALL, INC., Englewood Cliffs, N.J.

Third printing.........June, 1964

Library of Congress Catalog Card No. 63-7194
Printed in the United States of America
03424 C

PREFACE

Although the essential features of the earlier edition have been
retained in this revision, the new edition differs in that some new
material, some modernizing, a considerable bit of touching up, and a
complete set of new exercises have been included.

Definitions and new principles are clearly stated, explained, and
illustrated. The equation of a set of points is introduced early and
used often throughout the book. Conics are still developed from three
separate definitions, but Art. 4.9 gives the eccentricity definition as
does Art. 8.9 in the chapter titled "Polar Coordinates."

Domain and range are discussed with functions. Only about
70 per cent as much space is devoted to conics as formerly, because
only one article instead of three is included on reduction to standard
form. In removing the product term, we use cot 2θ instead of tan 2θ.
Thus the only case ruled out is the one in which $B = 0$, and in such
a case no rotation is needed.

The chapter on *Higher Plane Curves* has been expanded and
divided into two chapters called *Algebraic Curves* and *Transcendental
Curves*. In the first of these chapters, there are new articles on
"Polynomials in x," "Functions of the form y^2 equal to a rational
function," and "Composition of ordinates."

There are forty-four exercises in this edition, which number approximates the number of non-quiz class periods in a semester. A considerable amount of planning was required to insure that the exercises be spaced a normal lesson apart. The problems in each exercise are arranged in groups of four; the problems in each group are of nearly the same level of difficulty and involve the same principles. Such an arrangement makes it possible for the instructor to check lesson coverage by assigning every fourth problem. Answers are given in the book to all of the 1300 problems except those whose numbers are divisible by four. Answers not given in the book are available in pamphlet form.

The criticisms and suggestions of my colleagues and others are appreciated, for they have helped to make this a better book than it would have been without their friendly help.

Paul K. Rees

CONTENTS

3. THE CIRCLE   53

4. THE CONICS   69

essentially skip

5. THE GENERAL SECOND DEGREE EQUATION   91

1 *INTRODUCTORY CONCEPTS*

1.1. *THE FIELD AND METHOD OF ANALYTIC GEOMETRY*

Analytic geometry differs in procedure from the geometry studied in high school in that the former makes use of a coordinate system.

Plane analytic geometry includes the study of points, lines, curves, angles, and areas in a plane, and solid analytic geometry is made up of the study of points, lines, planes, curves, and surfaces in three-dimensional space.

The details of each investigation are carried on by establishing a correspondence between equations or sets of equations and geometric configurations. We shall spend part of our time in learning to construct a curve which corresponds to a given equation and the remainder in forming the equation when the curve, or sufficient conditions to determine it, are given.

1.2. *DIRECTED LINE SEGMENTS*

In the study of plane geometry, no distinction was made between the line segments SU and US because we were interested only in the length of the segment. In the study of analytic geometry, however, it is necessary to consider both length and direction. When we refer to the length of a segment, we shall consider it as a *signless* quantity. When we refer to both length and direction of a line segment, we shall call it a *directed line segment.* By a directed line segment we shall mean a segment on which a positive direction has been chosen. The positive direction is usually indicated by placing an arrow somewhere along the segment.

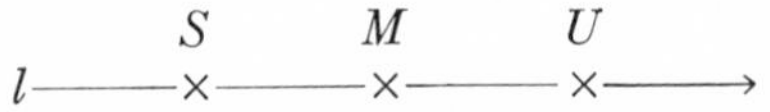

$$S \qquad M \qquad U$$
$$l \text{——×——×—— ×——→}$$

Thus the line l is directed as indicated by the arrow, which means that any length measured from left to right on the line is considered to be in a positive direction. Any length measured from right to left, or opposite to the chosen positive direction on the line, is considered to be in a negative direction. Thus the segment SU is positive, whereas the segment US is negative. The direction of the segment under consideration will be indicated by the order in which the end points of the segment are written. Hence, we have the relation

$$SU = -US$$
$$SU + US = 0.$$

We shall consider the relation of a third point, M on the directed line, to the points S and U.

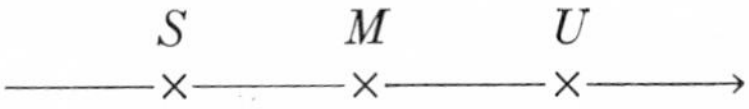

$$S \qquad M \qquad U$$
$$\text{——×——×——×——→}$$

Fig. 1.1a Directed line.

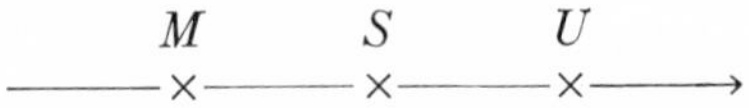

$$M \qquad S \qquad U$$
$$\text{——×——×——×——→}$$

Fig. 1.1b Directed line.

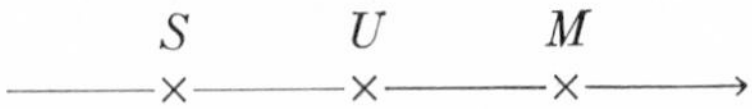

$$S \qquad U \qquad M$$
$$\text{——×——×——×——→}$$

Fig. 1.1c Directed line.

From Fig. 1.1a, we have
$$SU = SM + MU.$$
From Fig. 1.1b, $$SU = -MS + MU$$
$$= SM + MU$$

since $-MS = SM.$

From Fig. 1.1c, $SU = SM - UM,$

                         $= SM + MU$

since $-UM = MU.$

Hence, for the three positions illustrated, the same relation holds between the segments. It may be written in the more convenient form

(1) $SM + MU + US = 0.$

There are only three other relative positions which the three points may have, and these are obtained by interchanging S and U. In each of these cases, equation (1) is also obtained.

1.3. THE CARTESIAN COORDINATE SYSTEM

The framework of the rectangular Cartesian coordinate system consists of a pair of perpendicular directed lines called the coordinate axes. The horizontal line is the X *axis*, the vertical is the Y *axis*, and their intersection is the *origin.*

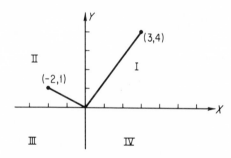

FIG. 1.2 Position of points.

The four parts into which the plane is divided by the coordinate axes are known as the four *quadrants*. The upper right-hand portion of the plane is called the first quadrant and is designated by I; the others are numbered II, III, and IV in a counterclockwise direction, as indicated in Fig. 1.2.

A point is indicated by giving its distance and direction from the coordinate axes. The directed line segment from the Y axis to the point and parallel to the X axis is called the *abscissa* of the point and the directed line segment from the X axis to the point and parallel to the Y axis is known as the *ordinate*. These two quantities are referred to as the *coordinates* of the point. If a point is to the right of the Y axis, its abscissa is positive; if to the left of the Y axis, its abscissa is negative; if the point is above the X axis, its ordinate is positive; if below the X axis, its ordinate is negative. It is customary to represent the point by writing its abscissa and ordinate separated by a comma and enclosed in parentheses, thus (x, y).

ILLUSTRATIVE EXAMPLES

The point that is 3 units to the right of the Y axis and 4 units above the X axis is represented by $(3, 4)$. The positive direction of each segment is indicated by the plus sign that is understood with each coordinate. Furthermore, $(-2, 1)$ represents the point which is 2 units to the left of the Y axis and 1 unit above the X axis. The negative direction from the Y axis is indicated by the minus sign which precedes the 2. These points and the quadrant numbers are shown in Fig. 1.2.

The distance from the origin to a point is called the *radius vector* of the point and is always a positive number. The square of the radius vector of a point is equal to the sum of the squares of the lengths of abscissa and of the ordinate, since the three lengths involved, if not zero, could be used as the sides of a right triangle. That is, $x^2 + y^2 = r^2$, where r is the distance of the point from the origin.

ILLUSTRATIVE EXAMPLES

The radius vector of the point $(3, 4)$ is $\sqrt{3^2 + 4^2} = \sqrt{25} = 5$ and the radius vector of $(-2, 1)$ is $\sqrt{(-2)^2 + 1^2} = \sqrt{5}$. See Fig. 1.2.

It may be desirable at times to use a decimal approximation instead of the indicated square root. This approximation can be found by use of logarithms or a table of square roots.

1.4. THE DISTANCE BETWEEN TWO POINTS

We shall need to know the distance between two given points on many occasions and shall now develop a formula for that quantity. Let the two points be designated by $P_1(x_1, y_1)$ and $P_2(x_2, y_2)$ as indicated in Fig. 1.3. The point $P_3(x_1, y_2)$ is determined by the intersection of a line through P_1 parallel to the Y axis and one through

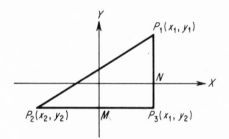

FIG. 1.3 Distance between points.

P_2 parallel to the X axis; hence, its coordinates are x_1 and y_2. Now

$$P_2P_3 = P_2M + MP_3 = MP_3 - MP_2 = x_1 - x_2 \quad \text{and}$$
$$P_3P_1 = P_3N + NP_1 = NP_1 - NP_3 = y_1 - y_2.$$

Consequently, by the Pythagorean theorem,

$$(P_1P_2)^2 = (P_2P_3)^2 + (P_3P_1)^2$$
$$= (x_1 - x_2)^2 + (y_1 - y_2)^2.$$

Hence $$P_1P_2 = \sqrt{(x_1 - x_2)^2 + (y_1 - y_2)^2}.$$

If P_1 had been chosen to the left of P_2, we would have obtained $P_3P_2 = x_2 - x_1$. If P_1 had been chosen below P_2, then it would have been found that $P_1P_3 = y_2 - y_1$ by Article 1.2. The choice of relative position of P_1 and P_2 is immaterial since $(x_2 - x_1)^2 = (x_1 - x_2)^2$ and $(y_2 - y_1)^2 = (y_1 - y_2)^2$.

Hence the following theorem may be stated:

THEOREM. *The length of the line segment which joins* (x_1, y_1) *and* (x_2, y_2) *is*

$$P_1P_2 = \sqrt{(x_1 - x_2)^2 + (y_1 - y_2)^2}.$$

There is no sign given with the radical since we are interested in the numerical value of the distance and not its direction.

EXAMPLE

What is the length of the line segment that joins $(3, 4)$ and $(-2, 1)$?

Solution: It is immaterial whether we select $(3, 4)$ or $(-2, 1)$ as $P_1(x_1, y_1)$ since the choice affects only the sign of $x_1 - x_2$ and of $y_1 - y_2$ and each is squared in the distance formula. If we use $(3, 4)$ as P_1, then

$$\begin{aligned} P_1P_2 &= \sqrt{(x_1 - x_2)^2 + (y_1 - y_2)^2} \\ &= \sqrt{[3 - (-2)]^2 + (4 - 1)^2} \\ &= \sqrt{(3 + 2)^2 + (4 - 1)^2} \\ &= \sqrt{5^2 + 3^2} = \sqrt{34}. \end{aligned}$$

This is the exact length of the segment. An approximate value, correct to four significant figures, is 5.831.

EXERCISE 1.1

1. If $S(-2, 0)$, $U(1, 0)$ and $M(4, 0)$, show by numerical substitution that $SU + UM = SM$, $SM + MU = SU$ and $MS + SU = MU$.

2. If $M(-3, 2)$, $B(2, 2)$ and $R(6, 2)$, show by numerical substitution that $MR = MB + BR$, $BR = MR + BM$, $MB = MR - BR$.

3. If the points M, A, T and H occur along a line in the order named, express each of the following sums and differences of segments as a single segment: $MA + AH, MH - TH, MT + AM, MA - TA$.

4. If the points H, E, L and P occur along a line in the order named, express each of the following sums and differences of segments as a single segment: $HL + LE, HL + LP, -PH + PL, EP + LE$.

Locate each of the following pairs of points, find the radius vector of each point, and the distance between each pair.

5. $(3, 4), (5, -1)$ 6. $(-2, 3), (5, -12)$

7. $(-1, -3), (3, 2)$ 8. $(5, 0), (8, 15)$

Prove that each of the following triples of points lie on a line by use of the distance formula.

9. $(-3, 1), (0, 2), (6, 4)$ 10. $(-5, -2), (-1, 0), (1, 1)$

11. $(7, 0), (5, 3), (1, 9)$ 12. $(8, -3), (5, -1), (-1, 3)$

Prove that each of the following four triples of points can be used as the vertices of a right triangle by use of the distance formula.

13. $(1, -3), (4, 1), (4, -3)$ **14.** $(2, -1), (5, 3), (5, -1)$

15. $(3, 5), (-1, -1), (4, 4)$ **16.** $(-2, 4), (6, 2), (3, -1)$

17. Show that $(1, -2), (3, 2)$ and $(-1, 0)$ can be used as the vertices of an isosceles triangle.

18. Prove that $(-3, 5), (0, 0)$ and $(2, 8)$ can be used as the vertices of an isoceles triangle.

19. Determine y so that $P_1P_2 = P_2P_3$ where $P_1(-1, 6)$, $P_2(3, 1)$ and $P_3(8, y)$.

20. If $P_1(0, 6)$, $P_2(-1, 2)$ and $P_3(x, 3)$, determine x so that P_1P_2 and P_2P_3 are equal.

21. Find the point on the X axis which is equidistant from $(5, 1)$ and $(3, 3)$.

22. What point on the Y axis is equidistant from $(3, -2)$ and $(5, 6)$?

23. By means of an equation, state that (x, y) is 4 units from $(2, -1)$.

24. State, in equation form, that (x, y) is equidistant from $(2, 3)$ and $(6, -1)$.

1.5. DIVISION OF A LINE SEGMENT IN A GIVEN RATIO

We shall let $P(x, y)$ be any point on the line through $P_1(x_1, y_1)$ and $P_2(x_2, y_2)$ and determine x and y so that

(1) $$\frac{P_1P}{PP_2} = \frac{r_1}{r_2}.$$

In order to determine x, we shall draw a line segment through P_1 and P_2. Let $P(x, y)$ be any point on it, drop perpendiculars from P_1, P and P_2 to the X axis and call the feet of these perpendiculars Q_1, Q, and Q_2 respectively. Then

(2) $$\frac{r_1}{r_2} = \frac{P_1P}{PP_2} = \frac{Q_1Q}{QQ_2}.$$

since when three parallels are cut by transversals, the segments into which the transversals are divided are proportional. Now Q_1Q and

QQ_2 are parallel to the X axis; hence $Q_1Q = x - x_1$, and $QQ_2 = x_2 - x$. Therefore,

$$\frac{Q_1Q}{QQ_2} = \frac{x - x_1}{x_2 - x}$$

and, by (2),

$$\frac{r_1}{r_2} = \frac{x - x_1}{x_2 - x}.$$

Solving this equation for x gives

$$x = \frac{r_2x_1 + r_1x_2}{r + r_2}, \quad r_1 + r_2 \neq 0.$$

We can show in a similar manner that

$$y = \frac{r_2y_1 + r_1y_2}{r_1 + r_2}, \quad r_1 + r_2 \neq 0.$$

Figure 1.4 was drawn with P between P_1 and P_2, but the same formulas for x and y would have been obtained had P_1 or P_2 been

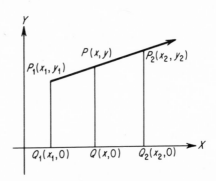

FIGURE 1.4

between P and the other. If P is between P_1 and P_2, then P_1P and PP_2, consequently r_1 and r_2, are of the same sign since they are measured in the same direction. If P is not between P_1 and P_2, then P_1P and PP_2 and hence r_1 and r_2 are of opposite signs since they are measured in opposite directions.

The special case of the point of division formula in which $r_2 = r_1$

is known as the *midpoint formula.* We have

$$x = \frac{r_2 x_1 + r_1 x_2}{r_1 + r_2}$$

$$= \frac{r_1(x_1 + x_2)}{2r_1} \quad \text{if} \quad r_2 = r_1$$

$$= \frac{x_1 + x_2}{2}.$$

Similarly,

$$y = \frac{y_1 + y_2}{2}.$$

Hence, *the midpoint of $P_1 P_2$ is*

$$x = \frac{x_1 + x_2}{2} \quad and \quad y = \frac{y_1 + y_2}{2}.$$

EXAMPLE 1

Determine the coordinates of the point $P(x, y)$ that divides the segment from $(2, 0)$ to $(7, 10)$ in the ratio 4 to 1.

Solution: Since it is required to divide the segment from $(2, 0)$ to $(7, 10)$ we must use the former as P_1. We have $r_1 = 4$ and $r_2 = 1$; hence

$$x = \frac{r_1 x_2 + r_2 x_1}{r_1 + r_2}$$

becomes

$$= \frac{4(7) + 1(2)}{4 + 1} = 6$$

and

$$y = \frac{4(10) + 1(0)}{4 + 1} = 8.$$

Consequently, $(6, 8)$ divides the segment from $(2, 0)$ to $(7, 10)$ in the ratio 4 to 1. The reader should realize that $(6, 8)$ is $\frac{4}{5}$ of the way from $(2, 0)$ to $(7, 10)$.

EXAMPLE 2

Determine the coordinates of the point that divides the segment from $(2, 0)$ to $(7, 10)$ in the ratio 4 to -1.

Solution: The point of division is external to the segment since r_1 and r_2 are of opposite sign. Furthermore, P_1 is $(2, 0)$, P_2 is $(7, 10)$,

$r_1 = 4, r_2 = -1$ and we have

$$x = \frac{r_1 x_2 + r_2 x_1}{r_1 + r_2} = \frac{4(7) + (-1)2}{4 + (-1)} = \frac{26}{3}$$

and

$$y = \frac{r_1 y_2 + r_2 y_1}{r_1 + r_2} = \frac{4(10) + (-1)0}{4 + (-1)} = \frac{40}{3}.$$

Consequently, $(\frac{26}{3}, \frac{40}{3})$ divides the segment from $(2, 0)$ to $(7, 10)$ in the ratio 4 to -1.

EXERCISE 1.2

1. What are the coordinates of the point that divides the segment from $P_1(-1, 8)$ to $P_2(5, 2)$ into the ratio 2 to 1?

2. Find the coordinates of the point that divides the segment from $P_1(1, 2)$ to $P_2(6, -8)$ into the ratio 3 to 2.

3. Find the coordinates of the point that is $\frac{1}{2}$ of the way from $P_1(2, 5)$ to $P_2(6, 0)$.

4. What are the coordinates of the point that is $\frac{2}{5}$ of the way from $P_1(-3, 4)$ to $P_2(2, -6)$?

Find the coordinates of the point that divides the segment from P_1 to P_2 into the given ratio in Problems 5 to 8.

5. $P_1(3, -3), P_2(6, 0)$, 3 to -2

6. $P_1(5, 4), P_2(2, -2), -3$ to 2

7. $P_1(-7, 2), P_2(-1, -1)$, 4 to -1

8. $P_1(4, 3), P_2(1, 6), -5$ to 2

9. Find the midpoint of the segment between $P_1(7, -6)$ and $P_2(1, 2)$.

10. What are the coordinates of the point that is midway between $P_1(3, -8)$ and $P_2(9, 2)$?

11. Find the center of a circle that has $P_1(3, -4)$ and $P_2(8, -1)$ as ends of a diameter.

12. What are the coordinates of the point which divides the segment from $P_1(5, 2)$ to $P_2(-1, 4)$ into the ratio 1 to 1?

13. Show that the diagonals of the quadrilateral with vertices at $(4, 5), (9, 7), (7, 3)$ and $(2, 1)$ bisect one another.

14. Do the diagonals of the quadralateral with vertices at $(6, 2)$, $(8, 3)$, $(6, 10)$ and $(4, 5)$ bisect one another?

15. The vertices of a triangle are at $P_1(8, 2)$, $P_2(-1, 0)$ and $P_3(5, -2)$. Find the point of intersection of the medians.

16. Where do the medians of a triangle meet if the vertices are at $P_1(-8, 1)$, $P_2(0, 5)$ and $P_3(2, 6)$?

17. The midpoints of the sides of a triangle are at $(2, -1)$, $(0, 3)$ and $(-1, -2)$. Find the vertices.

18. Find the vertices of a triangle if the midpoints of the sides are at $(-2, -1)$, $(6, -3)$ and $(4, 5)$.

19. If two vertices of a triangle are at $(3, 6)$ and $(5, -2)$, find the third vertex provided the medians meet at $(2, 0)$.

20. Two vertices of a triangle are at $(5, 9)$ and $(-4, 1)$. Find the third vertex if the medians meet at $(1, 1)$.

1.6. INCLINATION AND SLOPE

The **angle of inclination** *or* **inclination** *of an undirected line is the smallest positive angle from the positive X axis to the line provided*

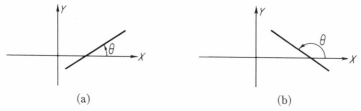

(a)   (b)

FIGURE 1.5

the line is not parallel to the X axis. The inclination is marked θ in Figs. 1.5a and 1.5b. If the line is parallel to the X axis the inclination is defined to be zero. Hence the inclination of an undirected line is always less than $180°$.

The **slope** *of a line is the tangent of the angle of inclination.* The slope is often denoted by m and we write

$$m = \tan \theta$$

as a symbolic statement of the definition of slope.

EXAMPLE

If the inclination of a line is 45° as shown in Fig. 1.6, then the slope is $m = \tan 45° = 1$.

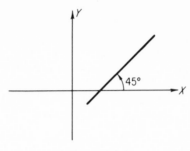

FIGURE 1.6

Since there is no number to represent tan 90°, we exclude lines with an inclination of 90° (lines parallel to the Y axis) in all discussions which involve slope.

If we know the coordinates of two points on a line, we can find the slope in terms of the coordinates of the points. We shall let the points be P_1 and P_2 and let M be the intersection of a horizontal through P_1

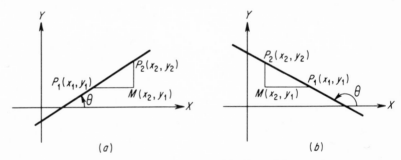

FIG. 1.7 (a) Line with $m > 0$; (b) Line with $m < 0$.

and a vertical through P_2; hence, it has the coordinates as shown. Furthermore, in Fig. 1.7a angle MP_1P_2 is equal to θ; consequently,

$$\tan \theta = \tan MP_1P_2 = \frac{MP_2}{P_1M} = \frac{y_2 - y_1}{x_2 - x_1}.$$

Furthermore, the inclination of the line in Fig. 1.7b is the obtuse angle θ and since θ and MP_1P_2 are supplements, it follows that

$$\tan \theta = -\tan (MP_1P_2)$$

$$= -\frac{MP_2}{MP_1} = -\frac{y_2 - y_1}{x_1 - x_2} = \frac{y_2 - y_1}{x_2 - x_1}.$$

Consequently, we see that *the slope of a line through P_1 and P_2 is*

$$m = \frac{y_2 - y_1}{x_2 - x_1}.$$

1.7. PARALLEL AND PERPENDICULAR LINES

We shall consider two lines L_1 and L_2, neither of which is parallel to the Y axis. If the lines are parallel as shown in Fig. 1.8, their

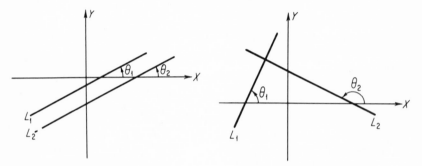

FIG. 1.8 Parallel lines.   FIG. 1.9 Perpendicular lines.

angles of inclination θ_1 and θ_2 are equal; consequently, $\tan \theta_1 = \tan \theta_2$. Conversely, if the slopes of the lines are equal, then $\theta_1 = \theta_2$ and the lines are parallel. Thus we see that *two nonvertical lines are parallel if their slopes are equal and conversely.*

If the lines L_1 and L_2 are perpendicular, then θ_1 and θ_2 differ by $90°$. In Fig. 1.9, $\theta_2 = \theta_1 + 90$. Hence,

$$\tan \theta_2 = \tan (\theta_1 + 90°) = -\cot \theta_1 = -\frac{1}{\tan \theta_1}.$$

Since $\tan \theta_2 = m_2$ and $\tan \theta_1 = m_1$, we have

$$m_2 = -\frac{1}{m_1} \quad \text{or} \quad m_1m_2 = -1.$$

Conversely, if $m_2 = -1/m_1$, then $\tan \theta_2 = -\cot \theta_1$ and $\theta_2 = \theta_1 + 90°$. Consequently, the lines are perpendicular. Thus we have shown that *two lines, neither being vertical, are perpendicular if their slopes are negative reciprocals and conversely.*

EXAMPLE 1

Show that the line through $(-1, 3)$ and $(2, 4)$ is parallel to the one through $(4, 6)$ and $(10, 8)$.

Solution: The slope of the first line is

$$\frac{y_2 - y_1}{x_2 - x_1} = \frac{4 - 3}{2 - (-1)} = \frac{1}{3}.$$

That of the second is

$$\frac{8 - 6}{10 - 4} = \frac{1}{3}.$$

Hence the slopes are equal and the lines are parallel.

EXAMPLE 2

Prove that the line L_1 through $(-1, 3)$ and $(2, 4)$ is perpendicular to the line L_2 through $(4, 6)$ and $(2, 12)$.

Solution: We have

$$m_1 = \frac{3 - 4}{-1 - 2} = \frac{1}{3} \quad \text{and} \quad m_2 = \frac{12 - 6}{2 - 4} = -3.$$

Hence the slopes are negative reciprocals and the lines are perpendicular.

1.8. FORMULA FOR THE POSITIVE ANGLE FROM ONE LINE TO ANOTHER

We shall consider any two non-perpendicular lines L_1 and L_2, neither of which is parallel to the Y axis, and derive a formula for the angle from L_1 to L_2 in terms of their slopes.

A case in which the angle from L_1 to L_2 is acute is pictured in Fig. 1.10a, and one in which it is obtuse is shown in Fig. 1.10b.

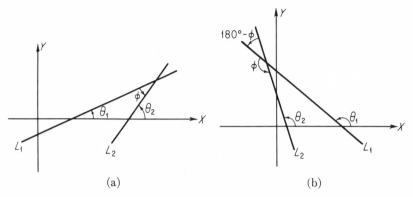

Fig. 1.10 (a & b) Angle from one line to another.

From Fig. 1.10a we see that

$$\theta_2 = \theta_1 + \phi,$$

since θ_2 is an exterior angle of a triangle with θ_1 and ϕ the opposite interior angles. Therefore,

$$\phi = \theta_2 - \theta_1$$

and

$$\tan \phi = \tan (\theta_2 - \theta_1)$$

$$= \frac{\tan \theta_2 - \tan \theta_1}{1 + \tan \theta_2 \tan \theta_1}.$$

If we designate $\tan \theta_2$ and $\tan \theta_1$ by m_2 and m_1, respectively, we have

$$\tan \phi = \frac{m_2 - m_1}{1 + m_2 m_1}.$$

From Fig. 1.10b we see that

$$\theta_1 = \theta_2 + (180° - \phi),$$

since $180° - \phi$ and θ_2 are interior angles of a triangle with θ_1 as the opposite exterior angle. Therefore,

$$\phi = \theta_2 - \theta_1 + 180°$$

and

$$\tan \phi = \tan (\theta_2 - \theta_1 + 180°)$$

$$= \tan (\theta_2 - \theta_1)$$

$$= \frac{\tan \theta_2 - \tan \theta_1}{1 + \tan \theta_2 \tan \theta_1}.$$

Therefore,

$$\tan \phi = \frac{m_2 - m_1}{1 + m_2 m_1}$$

and we see that *the positive angle ϕ from the line L_1 to the line L_2 is determined by the equation*

$$\tan \phi = \frac{m_2 - m_1}{1 + m_2 m_1}$$

if $\tan \phi$, m_1, and m_2 are all defined.

This formula gives the tangent of the desired angle and the value of the angle can be determined from a table of natural trigonometric functions.

There are two special cases in which this formula cannot be used:

(1) If the two lines are perpendicular to each other, then $1 + m_1 m_2 = 1 - 1 = 0$ and division by zero is not permissible. The theorem is not needed in this case, however, since two lines may be shown to be perpendicular to each other by use of the test given in the second theorem of Article 1.7.

(2) If L_1 or L_2 is parallel to the Y axis, then $\tan \theta_1$ or $\tan \theta_2$ is not defined. The reader can readily verify the fact that $\tan \phi = 1/\tan \theta_1$ if L_2 is parallel to the Y axis and $\tan \phi = -1/\tan \theta_2$ if L_1 is parallel to the Y axis.

EXAMPLE

Determine the angle B of the triangle with vertices at $A(2, -3)$, $B(-5, 1)$, and $C(4, 3)$.

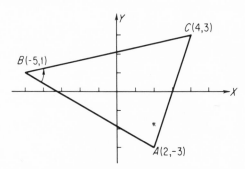

FIGURE 1.11

Solution: The slope of BC is $(3 - 1)/[4 - (-5)] = \frac{2}{9}$ and that of AB is $[1 - (-3)]/(-5 - 2) = -\frac{4}{7}$. Furthermore, the angle B of the triangle is the positive angle from AB to BC as seen from Fig. 1.11; hence

$$\tan B = \frac{m_2 - m_1}{1 + m_2 m_1} = \frac{\frac{2}{9} - (-\frac{4}{7})}{1 + \frac{2}{9}(-\frac{4}{7})} = \frac{10}{11} = .9091.$$

Therefore, $B = 42° \ 16'.$

EXERCISE 1.3

Find the slope of the line through the pair of points in each of Problems 1 to 8.

1. $(2, 5)$ and $(4, 9)$ **2.** $(3, -1)$ and $(2, 4)$

3. $(7, 0)$ and $(5, -3)$ **4.** $(6, 1)$ and $(8, 1)$

5. $(1, 8)$ and $(8, 1)$ **6.** $(3, 2)$ and $(4, 6)$

7. $(2, 6)$ and $(-1, 3)$ **8.** $(-5, 4)$ and $(2, -7)$

Classify the pairs of lines in Problems 9 to 16 as parallel, perpendicular, or neither.

9. Through $(2, 1)$ and $(3, 3)$, through $(5, -2)$ and $(7, 2)$

10. Through $(2, 7)$ and $(5, 1)$, through $(4, 3)$ and $(0, 5)$

11. Through $(2, 7)$ and $(5, 1)$, through $(4, 7)$ and $(0, 5)$

12. Through $(4, 6)$ and $(6, 4)$, through $(-3, 1)$ and $(3, 8)$

13. Through $(3, 2)$ and $(1, 6)$, through $(8, 6)$ and $(6, 2)$

14. Through $(8, 7)$ and $(4, 1)$, through $(2, 3)$ and $(-1, 5)$

15. Through $(-5, -1)$ and $(-2, 3)$, through $(9, 5)$ and $(5, 2)$

16. Through $(6, -3)$ and $(7, 2)$, through $(-2, -4)$ and $(0, 6)$

17. Determine x so that the slope of the line through $(2, 1)$ and $(x, 7)$ is 3.

18. Find the value of x for which the slope of the line through $(x, -1)$ and $(3, -5)$ is 4.

19. For what value of y is the line through $(3, y)$ and $(2, 7)$ parallel to the one through $(-1, 4)$ and $(0, 6)$?

20. For what value of y is the line through $(-1, y)$ and $(3, 8)$ perpendicular to the one through $(4, 5)$ and $(2, 4)$.

21. Prove that $(-2, 5)$, $(-3, -3)$ and $(5, 1)$ can be used as the vertices of an isosceles triangle by showing that two of the angles are equal.

22. Prove that $(-1, 2)$, $(3, -2)$, and $(6, 5)$ can be used as the vertices of an isosceles triangle by showing that two of the angles are equal.

23. Show without use of the Pythagorean theorem that $(1, 0)$, $(5, -2)$, and $(3, 4)$ can be used as the vertices of a right triangle.

24. Show that $(-3, 1)$, $(5, -3)$, and $(3, 3)$ can be used as the vertices of a right isosceles triangle.

Find $\tan \phi$ if m_1 and m_2 are as given in Problems 25 to 28.

25. $m_1 = \frac{1}{2}$, $m_2 = \frac{3}{4}$ $\qquad$ **26.** $m_1 = \frac{3}{5}$, $m_2 = -\frac{2}{3}$

27. $m_1 = -3$, $m_2 = \frac{2}{7}$ $\qquad$ **28.** $m_1 = -\frac{3}{8}$, $m_2 = \frac{1}{7}$

Find the one of m_1 and m_2 that is not given in Problems 29 to 32.

29. $m_1 = \frac{2}{5}$, $\phi = 45°$ $\qquad$ **30.** $m_2 = -\sqrt{3}$, $\phi = 60°$

31. $m_2 = \sqrt{3}$, $\phi = 120°$ $\qquad$ **32.** $m_1 = -2$, $\phi = 135°$

1.9. THE AREA OF A TRIANGLE

We shall now develop a formula for the area of a triangle in terms of the coordinates of its vertices. Consider any triangle with vertices at $P_1(x_1, y_1)$, $P_2(x_2, y_2)$, and $P_3(x_3, y_3)$ and embed it in a

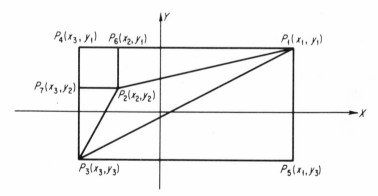

FIG. 1.12 Area of a triangle.

rectangle by drawing lines parallel to the X axis through the highest and lowest vertices and parallel to the Y axis through the vertices that are farthest to the right and to the left. Thus we have the rectangle $P_1P_4P_3P_5$. Then, the area A of the triangle is equal to the area of the rectangle $P_1P_4P_3P_5$ minus the sum of the areas of the rectangle $P_6P_4P_7P_2$ and the right triangles $P_1P_6P_2$, $P_2P_7P_3$, and $P_1P_3P_5$. The area of a rectangle is equal to the length times the width, and the area of a triangle is one-half the base times the altitude. Consequently, if we designate the area of $P_1P_2P_3$ by $A(P_1P_2P_3)$ and the other areas similarly, it follows that (See Fig. 1.12)

$$A(P_1P_2P_3) = A(P_1P_4P_3P_5) - A(P_6P_4P_7P_2) - A(P_1P_6P_2)$$
$$- A(P_2P_7P_3) - A(P_1P_3P_5) = (x_1 - x_3)(y_1 - y_3) -$$
$$(x_2 - x_3)(y_1 - y_2) - \tfrac{1}{2}[(x_1 - x_2)(y_1 - y_2) + (x_2 - x_3)(y_2 - y_3)$$
$$+ (x_1 - x_3)(y_1 - y_3)].$$

Expanding and collecting terms, we get

$$A(P_1P_2P_3) = \tfrac{1}{2}(x_1y_2 + x_2y_3 + x_3y_1 - x_1y_3 - x_2y_1 - x_3y_2).$$

This expression for the area can be more readily recalled if it is written as a determinant. Thus,

$$A(P_1P_2P_3) = \frac{1}{2}\begin{vmatrix} x_1 & y_1 & 1 \\ x_2 & y_2 & 1 \\ x_3 & y_3 & 1 \end{vmatrix}$$

is the area of the triangle with vertices at $P_1(x_1, y_1)$, $P_2(x_2, y_2)$, *and* $P_3(x_3, y_3)$ *or the negative of it.*

A similar figure can be drawn if the original triangle contains only acute angles or if a side is parallel to a coordinate axis. The same formula for the area is obtained in all cases.

NOTE. If the vertices are numbered in a counterclockwise direction, this formula gives the area. If not numbered in this way, we get the negative of the area. This, however, is immaterial since we are interested only in the numerical value of the area.

EXAMPLE 1

Find the area of the triangle with vertices at $(2, 3)$, $(-4, -1)$, and $(6, -5)$.

Solution: The vertices are numbered in a counterclockwise direction if we call them P_1, P_2, and P_3, respectively, in the order in which they occur in the problem. Hence the area A is given by

$$A = \frac{1}{2}\begin{vmatrix} 2 & 3 & 1 \\ -4 & -1 & 1 \\ 6 & -5 & 1 \end{vmatrix}$$

$$= \frac{1}{2}(-2 + 18 + 20 + 6 + 10 + 12) = 32.$$

EXAMPLE 2

Show by use of the formula for the area of a triangle that $(2, 4)$, $(-3, -2)$, and $(12, 16)$ lie on a line.

Solution: The area of the triangle with the given points as vertices is either A or $-A$ where

$$A = \frac{1}{2}\begin{vmatrix} 2 & 4 & 1 \\ -3 & -2 & 1 \\ 12 & 16 & 1 \end{vmatrix}$$

$$= \frac{1}{2}(-4 + 48 - 48 + 24 - 32 + 12) = 0.$$

Hence the points are on a line, since the area of the triangle with them as vertices is zero.

1.10. ANALYTIC PROOFS

Many theorems of plane geometry can be demonstrated readily by making use of the concepts given and the formulas derived in this chapter. A proof is said to be an analytic proof if a coordinate system is used in the demonstration. We shall now solve an example and at the same time point out some general principles to be followed in all analytic proofs.

EXAMPLE

Prove that in any triangle the line segment which connects the midpoints of two sides is parallel to, and one-half as long as, the third side.

Solution: We must be certain that the proof is for a general rather than a specialized triangle. Furthermore, the work will be somewhat simpler if a wise choice is made for the position of the coordinate axes. We can place the axes so that the origin is at one vertex of the triangle and a coordinate axis is along one side as shown in Fig. 1.13. One vertex is at $O(0, 0)$ and another is at a point, say $A(a, 0)$, on the X axis. We shall choose the third vertex at $B(b, c)$ where b and c may be positive as in Fig. 1.13 or negative. Then the midpoints of the sides

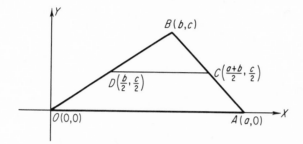

FIGURE 1.13

opposite O and A are $C[(a + b)/2, (c/2)]$ and $D(b/2, c/2)$. The slope of the segment between these midpoints is

$$\frac{c/2 - c/2}{(a + b)/2 - b/2} = 0.$$

Hence the segment is parallel to the third side, since that side has slope zero. Furthermore, the length of CD is

$$\sqrt{\left(\frac{a + b}{2} - \frac{b}{2}\right)^2 + \left(\frac{c}{2} - \frac{c}{2}\right)^2} = \frac{a}{2}.$$

This is one-half of the third side since that side is a.

The reader must be certain that he is using a sufficiently but not unnecessarily general figure and should choose the position of the coordinate axes so as to have as simple coordinates for points as is consistent with the use of a general figure. It is often desirable to choose the origin at one vertex of the figure and one of the coordinate axes along a side of it. The axes should be put in after the figure is drawn.

EXERCISE 1.4

Find the areas of the triangles with vertices at the points given in Problems 1 to 4.

1. $(2, 5)$, $(-3, 1)$, $(4, -2)$ **2.** $(-3, -4)$, $(2, -5)$, $(6, 1)$

3. $(0, 7)$, $(2, 5)$, $(-3, 4)$ **4.** $(2, -1)$, $(5, 0)$, $(-3, 4)$

5. Show in three ways that $(2, 3)$, $(4, 0)$, and $(8, -6)$ lie on a line.

6. Show in three ways that $(6, -7)$, $(4, -4)$, and $(0, 2)$ lie on a line.

7. Show in three ways that $(1, b)$, $\left(\dfrac{1}{b}, \dfrac{b}{a}\right)$, and $\left(\dfrac{2b - 1}{b}, \dfrac{2ab - b}{a}\right)$ lie on a line.

8. Determine x so that $(3, 8)$, $(2, 6)$, and $(-1, y)$ lie on a line.

9. Determine x so that the triangle with vertices at $(3, 1)$, $(2, -2)$, and $(2x, x)$ shall have an area of 3.5.

10. What is the value of x if a triangle with vertices at $(x, 1)$, $(5, -2)$, and $(-1, 3)$ has an area of 1.5?

11. Find the value of x if the area of a triangle with vertices at $(3, x)$, $(x, -5)$, and $(-1, 2)$ is 14.

12. Find a relation between x and y so that the area of the triangle with vertices at $(x, 2)$, $(1, 3)$, and $(-5, y)$ is 4.

13. Find the distance between $(3, 4)$ and the segment from $(4, -1)$ to $(1, 3)$.

14. What is the distance between $(2, -5)$ and the segment that connects $(-1, 8)$ and $(4, -4)$?

15. If $(2, -1)$, $(1, -2)$, and $(5, -3)$ in the order given are three consecutive vertices of a parallelogram, find the fourth vertex and the area of the parallelogram.

16. In the given order, $(-3, 4)$, $(3, 2)$, and $(1, -1)$ are consecutive vertices of a parallelogram. Find its area and the fourth vertex.

Prove each of the following theorems analytically.

17. The diagonals of an isosceles trapezoid are equal.

18. Two medians of an isosceles triangle are equal length.

19. The diagonals of a rectangle are equal.

20. The diagonals of a rhombus are perpendicular.

21. The segments which connect the midpoints of the sides of a quadrilateral if taken in order form a parallelogram.

22. The segments which connect the midpoints of opposite sides of a quadrilateral bisect each other.

23. The segments which connect the midpoints of the sides of a rhombus if taken in order form a rectangle.

24. The segments which connect the midpoints of the successive sides of a rectangle if taken in order form a rhombus.

25. The segments which join the midpoints of consecutive sides of a square form a square with one half of the area of the original one.

26. In any triangle, four times the sum of the squares of the medians is equal to three times the sum of the squares of the sides.

27. In any triangle, the sum of the squares of two sides is equal to twice the square of one-half the third side plus twice the square of the median drawn to that side.

28. The segment which joins the vertex of the right angle of a right triangle and the midpoint of the hypotenuse is half as long as the hypotenuse.

29. If the diagonals of a parallelogram are equal, the figure is a rectangle.

30. If the diagonals of a rectangle are perpendicular, the figure is a square.

31. If the diagonals of a parallelogram are perpendicular, the figure is a rhombus.

32. If the diagonals of a trapezoid are equal, the figure is an isosceles trapezoid.

2 *THE STRAIGHT LINE*

2.1. *THE EQUATION OF A SET OF POINTS*

Two important types of problems studied in analytic geometry are:

> I. *Given sufficient geometrical data to determine a set of points, to find the equation of the set.*
> II. *Given the equation of a set of points, to sketch its graph.*

The two types of problems will be illustrated by means of examples, and the concepts involved in them will be introduced from time to time during the development of this course.

EXAMPLE 1

Find the equation of the set of points in a plane so situated that each is 5 units from the origin. (The reader should recognize this from plane geometry as a circle of radius 5 with center at the origin.)

Solution: Let $P(x, y)$ represent a typical point of the set; then, by use of the distance formula, $(OP)^2 = 5^2$ or

$$(x - 0)^2 + (y - 0)^2 = 5^2,$$
$$x^2 + y^2 = 25.$$

The graph of this equation is shown in Fig. 2.1.

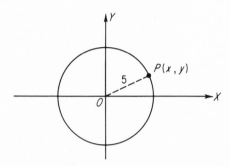

FIGURE 2.1

The method of procedure illustrated in Example 1 is very similar to that followed in solving word problems in algebra. The steps in the process are:

(1) *let* $P(x, y)$ *represent a typical point in the set which determines the curve;*

(2) *write a description of the curve in terms of geometrical quantities and symbols by use of an equation;*

(3) *translate this symbolic geometrical description into an algebraic equation by use of the various formulas with which the reader is familiar.*

The equation obtained by following these steps is called the equation of the curve and is satisfied by points on the curve and only by them. The point $P(x, y)$ may be thought of as a point on the curve and the curve made up of those and only those points which satisfy the given condition, or it may be thought of as a single point which moves in such a way that it traces out the curve.

The reader may be able to better visualize the situation if he draws a figure.

EXAMPLE 2

Find the equation of the set of points so located that the slope of the segment connecting each of them to $(1, -1)$ is $\frac{2}{3}$.

Solution: If $P(x, y)$ represents a typical member of the set, we know from the statement of the problem that the slope of the segment PP_1 is $m = \frac{2}{3}$. Furthermore, by use of the slope formula, we get

$$m = \frac{y - (-1)}{x - 1}$$

Now, equating these two expressions for m, we have

$$\frac{y + 1}{x - 1} = \frac{2}{3}$$

as the desired equation. The graph is in Fig. 2.2.

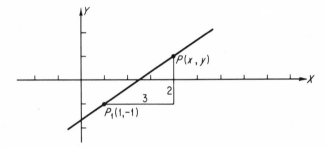

FIGURE 2.2

We can change the form of the equation by multiplying both members by the common denominator, $3(x - 1)$, and then having

$$3(y + 1) = 2(x - 1).$$

This can be put in the form

$$2x - 3y = 5.$$

2.2. INTRODUCTION TO THE STRAIGHT LINE

We shall restrict the remainder of this chapter to a study of the straight line, and consider in later chapters problems on sets of points that lead to equations of degree two or more.

If a line is parallel to a coordinate axis, its equation is relatively simple; furthermore, the equation cannot be put in all the forms that will be given in this chapter. Hence we shall give a discussion of lines that are parallel to a coordinate axis at this time.

If the line is parallel to the Y axis, its abscissa is a constant and the equation is of the form $x = x_1$ where x_1 gives the distance and the direction from the Y axis. If the line is parallel to the X axis, its ordinate is a constant and its equation is $y = y_1$. The equations of the X axis and the Y axis are, respectively, $y = 0$ and $x = 0$.

ILLUSTRATIVE EXAMPLES

The equation of the line that is parallel to, and 3 units to the right of, the Y axis is $x = 3$. The equation of the line that is parallel to, and 5 units below, the X axis is $y = -5$.

2.3. THE POINT-SLOPE FORM OF THE EQUATION

We shall now derive the equation of the line through a given point $P_1(x_1, y_1)$ and with a given slope m. If a typical point on the line is represented by $P(x, y)$, then $(y - y_1)/(x - x_1)$ is the slope of the line through P_1 and P but this is given as m. Hence

$$\frac{y - y_1}{x - x_1} = m, \quad \text{or}$$

(1) $$y - y_1 = m(x - x_1)$$

is the equation of the line of slope m and passing through $P_1(x_1, y_1)$ and it is satisfied by all points $P(x, y)$ on the line and not by other points.

Equation (1) is known as the *point-slope form* of the equation of a straight line since it is in terms of a point and the slope. It can be used readily to find the equation of a line with a given slope and passing through a given point.

EXAMPLE

What is the equation of the line through $(4, -2)$ and with slope $-\frac{3}{5}$?

Solution: If we put the given values of x_1, y_1, and m in the point-slope form of the equation, we get

$$y - (-2) = -\tfrac{3}{5}(x - 4)$$

The form of the equation can be changed by removing the parentheses, multiplying through by the common denominator and putting the constant on the right. Thus, we get $3x + 5y = 2$.

2.4. THE SLOPE-Y-INTERCEPT FORM OF THE EQUATION

This form of the equation of a line is a special case of the point-slope form but is of sufficient use to warrant a separate name. The intersection of the line and the Y axis is the point used.

DEFINITION. *The ordinate of each point of intersection of a curve and the Y axis is called a **y-intercept** of the curve.*

The abscissa of each such point is zero; and we shall use b as the symbol for its ordinate in the case of a straight line. Hence we shall find the equation of the line through $(0, b)$ and with slope m. If we substitute $(0, b)$ for (x_1, y_1) in the point-slope form we get $y - b = m(x - 0)$. Solving for y, we see that

$$y = mx + b$$

*is the equation of the line with slope **m** and **y-intercept b**.*

This equation is known as the *slope-y-intercept* form of the equation since it is in terms of the slope m and the y-intercept b. It is very useful since it gives the slope and the y-intercept if the equation is solved for y. It is satisfied by points (x, y) on the line and only by them. It cannot be used if the line is parallel to the Y axis since such a line does not have a y-intercept. We know, however, that $x = x_1$ is the equation of such a line.

EXAMPLE 1

What is the equation of the line with slope 2 and y-intercept equal to 3?

Solution: If we substitute the given values of m and b in the slope y-intercept form of the equation we get

$$y = 2x + 3$$

as the desired equation.

EXAMPLE 2

What are the slope and y-intercept of the line whose equation is $2x + 3y = 7$?

Solution: Solving for y, we have

$$y = \frac{-2x}{3} + \frac{7}{3}.$$

Therefore, $\qquad m = -\tfrac{2}{3} \quad\text{and}\quad b = \tfrac{7}{3}.$

2.5. THE TWO-POINT FORM OF THE EQUATION

We shall now derive the equation of the line through two given points $P_1(x_1, y_1)$ and $P_2(x_2, y_2)$. If a typical point on the line is represented by $P(x, y)$, then $(y - y_1)/(x - x_1)$ and $(y_1 - y_2)/(x_1 - x_2)$ are two expressions for the slope. Hence, by use of (1) of Art. 2.3,

$$y - y_1 = \frac{y_1 - y_2}{x_1 - x_2}(x - x_1)$$

is the equation of the line through $P_1(x_1, y_1)$ *and* $P_2(x_2, y_2)$. It is called the *two-point form* of the equation of a straight line and is satisfied by all points (x, y) on the line and not by any others. This form cannot be used if the abscissas of the two fixed points are equal since $x_1 - x_2$ is then zero and we cannot divide by zero. In that case, however, the two points are at a distance x_1 from the Y axis and the equation of the line is $x = x_1$.

EXAMPLE

What is the equation of the line through $(4, 3)$ and $(1, -2)$?

Solution: It is immaterial which point is used as P_1, since the slope is the same in either case. If we use $(4, 3)$ as P_1, let $P(x, y)$ be any point on the line and equate two expressions for the slope, we get

$$\frac{y - 3}{x - 4} = \frac{3 - (-2)}{4 - 1} = \frac{5}{3}.$$

This becomes

$$5x - 3y = 11.$$

2.6. THE TWO-INTERCEPT FORM OF THE EQUATION

The two-intercept form of the equation of a line is a special case of the two-point form in which the points are the intersections of the line and the coordinate axes. These points have names as given in the following definition.

> DEFINITION. *The abscissa of each point of intersection of a curve and the X axis is called an x-intercept of the curve. The ordinate of each point of intersection of a curve and the Y axis is called a y-intercept of the curve as stated in Article 2.4.*

If a curve or a line intersects the axes at $(a, 0)$ and $(0, b)$, then a is the x-intercept and b is the y-intercept. Now, if we use these two points as the points in the two-point form, it becomes

$$y - 0 = \frac{0 - b}{a - 0}(x - a) = \frac{-b}{a}(x - a)$$

Hence, clearing of fractions, we have $ay = -bx + ab$ or $bx + ay = ab$. Finally, dividing by ab, we see that

$$\frac{x}{a} + \frac{y}{b} = 1$$

is the equation of the line with a and b as x- and y-intercepts. It is called the *two-intercept form.* If the line fails to intersect one of the axes, this form cannot be used, but the line is then parallel to one of the axes and its equation is $x = k$ or $y = k$. Furthermore, if the line passes through the origin, both intercepts are zero and we cannot use the two-intercept form, but in that case we can use the point-slope form with $(0, 0)$ as the point.

EXAMPLE

The equation of the line with x-intercept equal to two and passing through $(0, -3)$ is

$$\frac{x}{2} + \frac{y}{-3} = 1$$

since the x-intercept is 2 and the y-intercept is -3.

EXERCISE 2.1

Find the equations of the lines in Problems 1 to 8.

1. Through $(2, 1)$ with slope 3; through $(3, 2)$ with slope 5.

2. Through $(3, -1)$ with slope 2; through $(-4, 0)$ with slope 4.

3. Through $(-2, 0)$ with slope -4; through $(5, -3)$ with slope -2.

4. Through $(-2, -1)$ with slope 3; through $(-4, -1)$ with slope -3.

5. Through $(2, 3)$ and $(4, 6)$; through $(3, 1)$ and $(5, 1)$.

6. Through $(4, -3)$ and $(5, -1)$; through $(2, 0)$ and $(2, 6)$.

7. Through $(-5, -1)$ and $(-8, 2)$; through $(7, 4)$ and $(7, 1)$.

8. Through $(6, -5)$ and $(-6, 5)$; through $(3, 2)$ and $(-4, 2)$.

Find the equation of each line in Problems 9 to 12.

9. Through $(2, 0)$ and $(0, 3)$

10. Through $(3, 0)$ and $(0, -5)$

11. With $a = -6$ and $b = 4$

12. With $a = -5$ and $b = -7$

Put the line in each of Problems 13 to 17 in two-intercept form.

13. $2x + 3y = 6$ **14.** $5x + 4y = 20$

15. $3x - 4y = 12$ **16.** $2x + 7y = -14$

17. Find the equation of the line through $(4, 2)$ and parallel to the segment through $(1, 5)$ and $(3, 8)$.

18. Find the equation of the line through $(5, -2)$ and parallel to $2x - y = 5$.

19. What is the equation of the line through $(1, 3)$ and perpendicular to the segment through $(2, 5)$ and $(4, 9)$?

20. What is the equation of the line through $(5, -4)$ and perpendicular to $x + 3y = 7$?

21. Find the equation of the line through the midpoint of the segment that connects $(4, -3)$ and $(8, 1)$ and parallel to $3x - 2y = 4$.

22. Find the equation of the line that passes through the point that divides the segment from $(-3, -4)$ to $(7, 1)$ into the ratio 3 to 2 and is perpendicular to that segment.

23. What is the equation of the line that passes through the midpoint of the segment between $(7, -4)$ and $(1, 2)$ and makes an angle of $45°$ with that segment?

24. Find the equation of the perpendicular bisector of the segment that connects $(2, 8)$ and $(4, -2)$.

Find the slope and y-intercept of each line in Problems 25 to 28.

25. $2x - y = 5;\ 3x + y = 4$

26. $5x - y = 8;\ 3x + y = -2$

27. $2x + 3y = 9;\ 5x + 2y = 7$

28. $3x - 5y = 15;\ 6x - 7y = 10$

Find the angle from the first line to the second in each of Problems 29 and 30.

29. $3x - y = 4,\ 4x + y = 7$

30. $2x + y = 9,\ 5x - y = 12$

If the equation of the sides of a triangle are as given in Problems 23 and 24, find the angles without finding the vertices.

31. $x - y = 3,\ 2x - y = 2,\ 3x + y = 3$

32. $x - y = 2,\ 2x + 3y = 7,\ 5x - 2y = 10$

33. Find the equation of the set of points such that the distance of each from $(2, 5)$ is equal to its distance from $(7, -4)$.

34. Find the equation of the set of points such that the distance of each from $(-3, 4)$ is equal to its distance from $(5, -2)$.

35. Find the equation of the set of points such that the difference of the squares of the distances of each from $(3, 5)$ and $(7, -1)$ is 4.

36. What is the equation of the set of points such that the differences of the squares of the distances of each from $(-4, 9)$ and $(1, -2)$ is 6?

2.7. THE STRAIGHT LINE AND $Ax + By + C = 0$

We shall now prove two theorems concerning a straight line.

THEOREM 1. *The equation $Ax + By + C = 0$ always represents a straight line provided A and B are not both zero.*

Proof. If $B = 0$ the equation becomes $Ax = -C$ or $x = -C/A$ and is satisfied by points on the line that is $-C/A$ units from the Y axis and no others. If $B \neq 0$, we can solve the equation for y and obtain

$$y = \frac{-Ax}{B} + \frac{-C}{B}.$$

This represents the line with slope $-A/B$ and y-intercept equal to $-C/B$.

THEOREM 2. *Every straight line has an equation of the form* $Ax + By + C = 0$ *where* A, B, *and* C *are constants.*

Proof. If we are given any straight line, it cuts the Y axis, is parallel to it, or is coincident with it. It was shown in Article 2.4 that the equation of a line which cuts the Y axis can be put in the form $y = mx + b$; furthermore, if the line is parallel to or coincident with the Y axis, its equation is of the form $x = x_1$, where $x_1 = 0$ in the case of coincidence. Both of these equations are of the form given in the theorem; hence; the proof is complete.

2.8. COINCIDENT, PARALLEL, AND INTERSECTING LINES

We shall consider any two straight lines, represent them by $A_1x + B_1y + C_1 = 0$ and $A_2x + B_2y + C_2 = 0$, and determine conditions under which they are (1) coincident, (2) parallel, and (3) intersecting lines.

We are primarily interested in the case in which neither B_1 nor B_2 is zero but shall first dispose of the case in which $B_1 = B_2 = 0$ and the case in which only one of them is zero. If both are zero, the equations become $A_1x = -C_1$ and $A_2x = -C_2$. Hence we have a pair of lines parallel to the Y axis and, consequently, parallel to one another, or coincident. If either $B_1 = 0$ or $B_2 = 0$ and the other is not, only one of the lines is parallel to the Y axis and they intersect.

If neither B_1 nor B_2 is zero, each equation can be put in the slope-y-intercept form and we have

$$y = \frac{-A_1}{B_1}x - \frac{C_1}{B_1} \quad \text{and} \quad y = \frac{-A_2}{B_2}x - \frac{C_2}{B_2}.$$

The lines are coincident if they have the same slope and same y-intercept; hence the lines are coincident if

$$\frac{-A_1}{B_1} = \frac{-A_2}{B_2} \quad \text{and} \quad \frac{-C_1}{B_1} = \frac{-C_2}{B_2}.$$

If these two equations are solved for B_1/B_2, we have

$$\frac{B_1}{B_2} = \frac{A_1}{A_2} \quad \text{and} \quad \frac{B_1}{B_2} = \frac{C_1}{C_2}, \quad A_2 \neq 0, B_2 \neq 0, C_2 \neq 0.$$

Therefore, if

$$\frac{A_1}{A_2} = \frac{B_1}{B_2} = \frac{C_1}{C_2}$$

the two lines are coincident.

The two lines are parallel, but not coincident, if they have equal slopes and unequal y-intercepts; hence the two lines are parallel if

$$\frac{-A_1}{B_1} = \frac{-A_2}{B_2} \quad \text{and} \quad \frac{-C_1}{B_1} \neq \frac{-C_2}{B_2}.$$

Solving for B_1/B_2, we see that *if*

$$\frac{A_1}{A_2} = \frac{B_1}{B_2} \neq \frac{C_1}{C_2}, \quad A_2 \neq 0, B_2 \neq 0, C_2 \neq 0$$

the two lines are parallel.

The two lines are not parallel if their slopes, $-A_1/B_1$ and $-A_2/B_2$, are unequal. Hence *we have intersecting lines if*

$$\frac{A_1}{A_2} \neq \frac{B_1}{B_2}, \quad A_2 \neq 0, B_2 \neq 0.$$

ILLUSTRATIVE EXAMPLES

The lines represented by $3x + 7y - 8 = 0$ and $6x + 14y - 16 = 0$ are coincident since $\frac{3}{6} = \frac{7}{14} = (-8)/(-16)$.

The lines represented by $3x + 7y - 8 = 0$ and $6x + 14y - 4 = 0$ are parallel, but not coincident, since $\frac{3}{6} = \frac{7}{14} \neq -8/(-4)$.

The lines represented by $3x + 7y - 8 = 0$ and $6x + 5y - 8 = 0$ intersect since $\frac{3}{6} \neq \frac{7}{5}$.

2.9. THE NORMAL FORM OF THE EQUATION

We shall now derive the equation of a line in terms of the directed distance p from the origin to the line and the angle of inclination ω of this directed segment. We shall consider the positive direction to be from the origin to the line. Furthermore, we shall allow ω to be in the range 0 to 360° since by the inclination of a directed line we shall mean the smallest positive angle through which the positive X axis can be rotated to bring it parallel to and directed as the line.

We shall derive the equation by evaluating the slope of the line and the coordinates (x_1, y_1) of the point P_1 on the line in terms of p and ω and substituting them in the point-slope form.

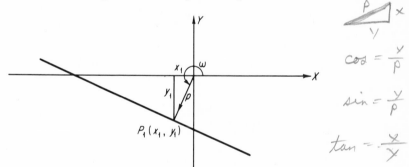

FIG. 2.3 For normal form.

In all cases, except those in which the line passes through the origin, we have, as seen from Fig. 2.3,

(1)
$$\begin{cases} \cos \omega = \dfrac{x_1}{p} \quad \text{or} \quad x_1 = p \cos \omega, \\[2mm] \sin \omega = \dfrac{y_1}{p} \quad \text{or} \quad y_1 = p \sin \omega. \end{cases}$$

Since the line is perpendicular to its normal,* its slope is the

---

* Normal, as used here, is a synonym of perpendicular.

negative reciprocal of the slope of the normal; that is

$$(2) \qquad m = -\frac{1}{\tan \omega} = -\cot \omega = -\frac{\cos \omega}{\sin \omega}.$$

Substituting the values of x_1, y_1, and m as given by (1) and (2) in the point-slope form of the equation of a line, we have $y = mx + b$

$$y - p \sin \omega = -\frac{\cos \omega}{\sin \omega} (x - p \cos \omega).$$

Now, multiplying each member of this equation by $\sin \omega$ and transposing, gives

$$x \cos \omega + y \sin \omega - p(\sin^2 \omega + \cos^2 \omega) = 0.$$

Since $\sin^2 \omega + \cos^2 \omega = 1$, we have

$$(3) \qquad x \cos \omega + y \sin \omega - p = 0.$$

Equation (3) is known as the *normal form* of the equation of a line. This is the equation of the line in terms of the normal and not the equation of the normal.

In deriving Eq. (3), we assumed that $\sin \omega$, $\cos \omega$, and p are not zero; however, it can be shown that (3) holds in all cases.

If the line passes through the origin, we will choose the direction of the normal so that ω will be less than 180°. If $p = 0$, the line passes through the origin and has slope equal to the negative reciprocal of the slope of the normal; hence the slope is $-\cos \omega / \sin \omega$. Now, using the origin as the point in the point-slope form, we have

$$\frac{y}{x} = -\frac{\cos \omega}{\sin \omega},$$

$$x \cos \omega + y \sin \omega = 0.$$

EXAMPLE

What is the equation of the line 4 units from the origin if its normal has an angle of inclination of 150°?

Solution: Since the inclination of the normal is 150°, it follows immediately that $\omega = 150°$. Consequently, the normal form of the equation of the line is

$$x \cos 150° + y \sin 150° - 4 = 0.$$

This can be written in the form

$$\frac{-\sqrt{3}}{2}x + \frac{1}{2}y - 4 = 0,$$

or $-\sqrt{3}\,x + y - 8 = 0$ since $\sin 150° = \frac{1}{2}$ and $\cos 150° = -\sqrt{3}/2$. The line is shown in Fig. 2.4.

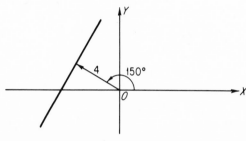

FIGURE 2.4

2.10. REDUCTION TO NORMAL FORM

We shall now consider the problem of reducing $Ax + By + C = 0$ to normal form. If this equation and $x \cos \omega + y \sin \omega - p = 0$ represent the same line, we must have

$$\frac{\cos \omega}{A} = \frac{\sin \omega}{B} = \frac{-p}{C}$$

since this is the condition for coincident lines. If we represent the common value of these ratios by k, we then have

$$\cos \omega = kA, \quad \sin \omega = kB, \quad -p = kC.$$

Squaring each member of the first two of these equations and adding corresponding members of the resulting equations gives

$$k^2(A^2 + B^2) = \cos^2 \omega + \sin^2 \omega = 1.$$

Consequently, $$k = \frac{1}{\pm \sqrt{A^2 + B^2}}.$$

If we multiply each member of the given equation by this value of k, we get

$$\frac{A}{\pm \sqrt{A^2 + B^2}} x + \frac{B}{\pm \sqrt{A^2 + B^2}} y + \frac{C}{\pm \sqrt{A^2 + B^2}} = 0.$$

Since the quantity p in the normal form is a non-negative number and $-p$ enters in the left member of the equation, it follows that we must choose the sign of the radical so as to make the new constant term non-positive when on the left; consequently, *the sign of the radical must be chosen opposite to that of* **C,** *if* **C** $\neq$ **0.**

If $C = 0$, the line passes through the origin and the normal through the origin makes two non-negative angles less than $360°$ with the positive X axis. We shall choose ω to be the one which is less than $180°$ as was done in Article 2.9. Hence, if $C = 0$ and $B \neq 0$, then ω is less than $180°$ and sin ω is positive. Consequently, *the radical must have the same sign as that of* **B** *if* **C** $= 0$ *and* **B** $\neq$ **0.**

If $B = C = 0$, then sin $\omega = 0$; hence, $\omega = 0$ or $180°$. We choose $\omega = 0$ and have cos $\omega = 1$; hence, *the radical must have the same sign as that of* **A,** *if* **B** $=$ **C** $=$ **0.**

EXAMPLE 1

Reduce $3x - 4y = 10$ to the normal form and draw the line.

Solution: The general form of the equation used in determining how to change an equation to normal form contains the constant on the left. Therefore, the given equation should be written in the form $3x - 4y - 10 = 0$ before proceeding further. We now divide by $+ \sqrt{3^2 + 4^2} = 5$, the positive sign being used with the radical in

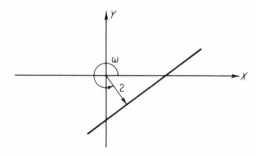

FIGURE 2.5

order to have a negative constant on the left. Thus, we obtain

$$\frac{3x}{5} - \frac{4y}{5} - \frac{10}{5} = 0 \quad \text{or}$$

$$\frac{3x}{5} - \frac{4y}{5} - 2 = 0.$$

Therefore, the given line is 2 units from the origin, $\cos \omega = \frac{3}{5}$ and $\sin \omega = -\frac{4}{5}$. Hence ω is an angle in quadrant four. The line is shown in Fig. 2.5.

EXAMPLE 2

Reduce $3x - 4y = 0$ to the normal form.

Solution: Since $C = 0$ and $B \neq 0$, we must choose the sign of the radical the same as that of B.

Hence we divide by $-\sqrt{A^2 + B^2} = -\sqrt{9 + 16} = -5$ and obtain

$$\frac{-3}{5} x + \frac{4}{5} y = 0.$$

EXAMPLE 3

Reduce $5x = 0$ to the normal form.

Solution: Since $B = C = 0$, we must choose the sign of the radical the same as that of A.

Hence we divide by $+\sqrt{A^2 + B^2} = +\sqrt{25 + 0} = +5$ and obtain

$$\frac{5x}{5} = 0, \quad x = 0.$$

EXAMPLE 4

Find the equation of the line or lines parallel to $3x - 4y - 15 = 0$ and 4 units from it.

Solution: The normal form of the given line, L, is

$$\frac{3x - 4y - 15}{5} = 0 \quad \text{or} \quad \frac{3x}{5} - \frac{4y}{5} - 3 = 0.$$

Hence it is $p = 3$ units from the origin. Consequently, we want lines that are $3 \pm 4 = 7, -1$ units from the origin. The desired line L_1 that is 7 units from the origin is the same direction from the origin as is L; hence, ω is the same for it as for L. Therefore, the equation of L_1, is

$$\tfrac{3}{5}x - \tfrac{4}{5}y - 7 = 0.$$

The desired line L_2 that is -1^* units from the origin and L are in opposite directions from the origin; hence, ω and ω_2 differ by 180° and

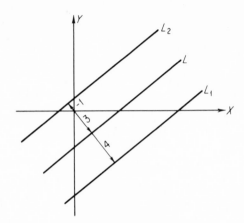

FIGURE 2.6

$\omega_2 = \omega - 180°$. Therefore, $\sin \omega_2 = -\sin \omega = \tfrac{4}{5}$ and $\cos \omega_2 = -\cos \omega = -\tfrac{3}{5}$. Finally, the equation of L_2 is

$$-\tfrac{3}{5}x + \tfrac{4}{5}y - 1 = 0.$$

Both lines are shown in Fig. 2.6.

EXERCISE 2.2

Classify the pairs of lines in Problems 1 to 8 as coincident, parallel, intersecting, or intersecting and perpendicular.

1. $2x - 3y = 7, 6x - 9y = 21$
2. $5x - 2y = 3, 10x - 4y = 5$
3. $3x + 4y = 9, 2x + 3y = 7$
4. $3x + 4y = 6, 4x - 3y = 16$
5. $5x + 8y = 13, 10x + 17y = 26$

---

* If we use the positive direction as determined by L.

Sec. 2.10 THE STRAIGHT LINE 41

6. $4x - 5y = 8, 5x + 4y = 10$

7. $2x - 7y = -3, -4x + 14y = 16$

8. $8x + 2y = 4, 4x + y = 2$

Find the equations of the lines that satisfy the conditions given in Problems 9 to 12.

9. $p = 3, \omega = 45°; p = 7, \omega = 150°; p = 2, \omega = 300°$

10. $p = 4, \omega = 120°; p = 5, \omega = 225°; p = 3, \omega = 30°$

11. $p = 7, \omega = 210°; p = 4, \omega = 300°; p = 8, \omega = 135°$

12. $p = 5, \omega = 330°; p = 2, \omega = 45°; p = 5, \omega = 210°$

Change each equation in Problems 13 to 16 to normal form.

13. $5x - 12y + 39 = 0, 3x + 4y - 20 = 0$

14. $7x + 24y - 100 = 0, -8x + 15y + 85 = 0$

15. $4x - 3y + 10 = 0, 24x - 7y - 150 = 0$

16. $15x + 8y - 68 = 0, 12x - 5y + 91 = 0$

Find the distance between the pair of lines in each of Problems 17 to 21.

17. $3x - 4y - 10 = 0, 3x - 4y - 25 = 0$

18. $5x - 12y - 39 = 0, 5x - 12y + 26 = 0$

19. $7x + 24y - 50 = 0, 7x + 24y + 75 = 0$

20. $15x + 8y - 34 = 0, 15x + 8y = 0$

Find the equations of the lines described in Problems 21 to 28.

21. Parallel to and 3 units from $5x - 12y - 26 = 0$.

22. Parallel to and 2 units from $8x + 15y - 68 = 0$.

23. Parallel to $7x + 24y - 75 = 0$ and 3 units from the origin.

24. Parallel to $4x - 3y - 15 = 0$ and 5 units from the origin.

25. Four units from the origin and perpendicular to $15x - 8y - 2 = 0$.

26. Seven units from the origin and perpendicular to $24x - 7y + 8 = 0$.

27. Perpendicular to $3x + 4y + 7 = 0$ and 4 units from the origin.

28. Perpendicular to $7x - 24y - 9 = 0$ and 3 units from the origin.

29. What is the area of a circle if $8x + 15y + 51 = 0$ and $8x + 15y - 17 = 0$ are tangent to it.

30. Find the area of a square that has two sides along $3x - 4y - 10 = 0$ and $3x - 4y + 15 = 0$.

31. Where can the center of a circle be if $5x - 12y - 39 = 0$ and $5x - 12y + 13 = 0$ are tangent to it?

32. Without finding the vertices, determine the area of the rectangle with sides along $3x - 4y - 5 = 0$, $3x - 4y + 15 = 0$, $4x + 3y + 30 = 0$ and $4x + 3y - 5 = 0$.

2.11. DISTANCE AND DIRECTION FROM A LINE TO A POINT

We shall use the normal form of the equation of a straight line as a basis for developing a formula for the perpendicular distance d from any line AB to any point $P_1(x_1, y_1)$ and for the direction from the line to the point.

If the direction from AB to P_1 is the direction in which p is measured, then d is positive; otherwise d is negative, unless P_1 is on the line AB and then d is zero.

The normal form of the equation of any line AB is $x \cos \omega + y \sin \omega - p = 0$. Now, we shall draw a line through P_1 parallel to AB and use its equation in determining d. We shall consider two relative positions of the origin, AB and the line through P_1 parallel to AB.

Case I. If this line and AB are on the same side of the origin (i.e. if the origin is not between the two lines), the equation of the line through P_1 and parallel to AB is

$$x \cos \omega + y \sin \omega - (p + d) = 0$$

since it is a distance $p + d$ from the origin. The reader should notice that d is positive in Fig. 2.7a but negative in Fig. 2.7b.

Case II. If the origin is between the line AB and the one parallel to it through P_1, then the equation of the latter is

$$x \cos \omega_1 + y \sin \omega_1 - p_1 = 0$$

where p_1 is positive since the positive direction is determined by $\omega_1 = \omega + \pi$. Hence, $x \cos (\omega + \pi) + y \sin (\omega + \pi) + (p + d) = 0$ since p_1 and $p + d$ are the same size but have opposite positive directions. Consequently, $-x \cos \omega - y \sin \omega + (p + d) = 0$ since $\cos (\omega + \pi) = -\cos \omega$ and $\sin (\omega + \pi) = -\sin \omega$. Therefore, multiplying through by -1, we see that

$$x \cos \omega + y \sin \omega - (p + d) = 0$$

is the equation of the line through P_1 parallel to AB as in Case I.

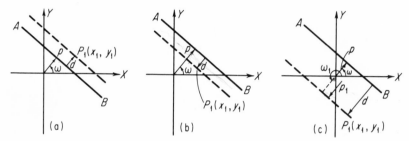

Fig. 2.7 (a, b, and c) Distance and direction from a line to a point.

Since the line is through P_1 its equation is satisfied by $x = x_1$ and $y = y_1$ and in each case we have

$$x_1 \cos \omega + y_1 \sin \omega - (p + d) = 0.$$

Solving this equation for d, we get the following theorem.

THEOREM. *The distance and direction from the line*

$$x \cos \omega + y \sin \omega - p = 0$$

to the point $P_1(x_1, y_1)$ *is given by*

$$d = x_1 \cos \omega + y_1 \sin \omega - p.$$

Thus, *the distance and direction from* $Ax + By + C = 0$ *to* $P_1(x_1, y_1)$ *is found by substituting the coordinates of* P_1 *in the normal form of the equation and is*

$$d = \frac{Ax_1 + By_1 + C}{\pm \sqrt{A^2 + B^2}}$$

where the ambiguous sign is chosen as in Article 2.10. The sign of
d indicates the direction from the line to the point.

EXAMPLE 1

Find the distance and direction from the line whose equation is
$7x + 24y - 75 = 0$ to $(5, -6)$.

Solution: The normal form of the given equation is obtained by
dividing by $+ \sqrt{7^2 + 24^2} = + \sqrt{625} = +25$ and is

$$\frac{7x}{25} + \frac{24y}{25} - 3 = 0.$$

Consequently,

$$d = \frac{7(5)}{25} + \frac{24(-6)}{25} - 3 = \frac{-184}{25}$$

The point is in the negative direction from the line and $\frac{184}{25}$ units
from it. The situation is pictured in Fig. 2.8.

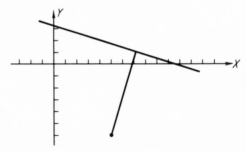

FIGURE 2.8

2.12. *THE BISECTOR OF AN ANGLE*

In order to find the equation of the bisector of an angle, we shall
make use of the distance and direction from a line to a point. The
procedure will be illustrated by a typical example.

EXAMPLE

Find the equation of the bisector of each angle (there are two pairs
of vertical angles, and if an angle is bisected, so is its vertical angle)
between the lines L_1 and L_2 if their equations are $7x - 24y + 42 = 0$
and $3x + 4y - 12 = 0$.

Solution: A point on the bisector of an angle is equidistant from the lines that form the angle; hence we shall put each equation in normal form since that is a necessary step in finding the distance and direction from a line to a point. The normal forms are

$$L_1: \quad \frac{7x - 24y + 42}{-25} = 0 \quad \text{and}$$

$$L_2: \quad \frac{3x + 4y - 12}{5} = 0.$$

If $P'(x', y')$ is any point on the bisector of the angle from L_1 to L_2 (see Fig. 2.9), then d'_1 and d'_2 are of the same sign since both are meas-

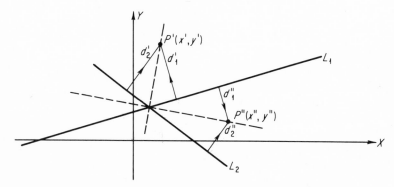

FIG. 2.9 Bisectors.

ured in positive directions or both in negative. Both are positive in Fig. 2.9. Substituting the coordinates of P' in the normal forms of the equations, we have

$$d'_1 = \frac{7x' + 24y' + 42}{-25} \quad \text{and} \quad d'_2 = \frac{3x' + 4y' - 12}{5}.$$

Since P' is on the bisector of the angle, d'_1 and d'_2 are equal. Hence

$$\frac{7x' - 24y' + 42}{-25} = \frac{3x' + 4y' - 12}{5}$$

is the equation of the bisector of the angle from L_1 to L_2. The form of the equation can be changed by dropping the primes, multiplying through by the common denominator, and collecting coefficients of like terms. Thus, we have $11x - 2y = 9$.

The equation of the bisector of the angle from L_2 to L_1 can be found in a similar manner. We must use the fact that d''_1 and d''_2 are the same length but of opposite sign. Why? Their values can be found from the normal forms of the equations; then $d''_1 = -d''_2$ becomes

$$\frac{7x'' - 24y'' + 42}{-25} = -\frac{3x'' + 4y'' - 12}{5}.$$

Hence, after simplifying and dropping the primes,

$$4x + 22y = 51$$

is seen to be the desired equation.

EXERCISE 2.3

Find the distance and direction from the line to the point in each of Problems 1 to 6.

1. $5x - 12y + 62 = 0$, $(3, 1)$ **2.** $8x + 15y - 54 = 0$, $(2, -2)$

3. $-7x + 24y + 2 = 0$, $(4, -1)$ **4.** $3x - 4y - 36 = 0$, $(4, -1)$

5. $15x - 8y = 12$, $(3, 2)$ **6.** $24x - 7y = 75$, $(7, 24)$

7. Find the area of a rectangle that has sides along $3x - 4y = 10$ and $4x + 3y + 7 = 0$ and a vertex at $(3, 2)$.

8. Find the area of a rhombus that has a side along $15x - 8y - 72 = 0$ and the opposite one through $(6, -2)$.

9. What is the radius of a circle with center at $(3, -2)$ if $5x + 12y - 17 = 0$ is tangent to the circle?

10. If $(4, 5)$ and the point of tangency of $3x - 4y = 12$ are on opposite ends of a diameter of a circle, what is the radius?

11. If the center of a circle is at $(5, -1)$ and $8x + 15y = 8$ is tangent to the circle, find the radius.

12. If $(-3, 2)$ is on a circle and the line $7x - 24y = 106$ is tangent to it at the farthest possible point from $(-3, 2)$, find the radius of the circle.

Find the areas of the triangles with vertices as given in Problems 13 to 16 by multiplying the base by half the altitude.

13. $(2, 3)$, $(-1, -1)$, $(-2, 1)$ **14.** $(4, 7)$, $(0, 4)$, $(-3, 0)$

15. $(-5, 2)$, $(3, -13)$, $(5, 1)$ **16.** $(-3, -6)$, $(5, 9)$, $(9, 6)$

17. Show that $(3, -1)$ and $(5, 2)$ are on the same side of $x - y = 2$.

18. Show that $(4, 1)$ and $(1, 6)$ are on the same side of $2x + y - 7 = 0$.

19. Show that $(2, 1)$ and $(3, -2)$ are on opposite sides of $3x - 4y - 8 = 0$.

20. Show that $(3, -1)$ and $(1, -3)$ are on opposite sides of $5x + 8y + 9 = 0$.

21. Find the distance between $3x + 5y = 11$ and $3x + 5y = -23$.

22. How far apart are $2x - 3y = 5$ and $2x - 3y = 18$?

23. What is the distance between $5x - 2y = 10$ and $5x - 2y = -19$?

24. Find the distance between $3x - 5y = 13$ and $-3x + 5y = 21$.

25. Find the equations of the bisectors of the interior angles of the triangles with the lines $3x - 4y = 10$, $5x + 12y = 13$, and $8x - 15y = 51$ as sides.

26. The sides of a triangle lie along $4x + 3y = 25$, $15x - 8y = 68$, and $5x - 12y = 52$. Find the equations of the bisectors of the interior angles.

27. Find the equation of the bisector of the smaller angle between $7x - 24y = 125$ and $12x + 5y = 39$.

28. Find the equation of the bisector of the larger angle between $8x + 15y = 85$ and $3x - 4y = 30$.

29. Find the equation satisfied by a set of points if each is equidistant from $3x + y - 7 = 0$ and $(2, -1)$.

30. Each point of a set is equidistant from $(1, 2)$ and $3x + 4y + 12 = 0$. Find the equation satisfied by the set.

31. Find the equation that is satisfied by the coordinates of the centers of a set of circles that are tangent to $5x + 12y - 39 = 0$ and to $12x - 5y - 13 = 0$.

32. A set of circles is tangent to both $2x - 3y - 5 = 0$ and $6x + 4y - 8 = 0$. Find the equation that is satisfied by the coordinates of the centers.

2.13. FAMILIES OF LINES

In Article 2.7 it was proved that the equation of any line can be put in the form $Ax + By + C = 0$, with not both A and B zero, and that this equation always represents a straight line. There are obviously three constants in this equation. A and B cannot be zero simultaneously since then we would not have a line. Why? We can divide by the one of A and B that is not zero and then have only two constants (each a quotient) in the equation. Since the number of constants cannot be further decreased, we say that there are two essential constants in the equation of a straight line.

If we impose one condition on the line, we can get one equation in the two essential constants, and if we impose another condition we have two linear equations in two unknowns. Since two linear equations in two unknowns can be solved simultaneously unless they represent parallel lines, we see that we must put two conditions on $Ax + By + C = 0$ in order to have a definite line.

We get a definite line if we impose two independent and consistent conditions. If only one is imposed, there is another that can be imposed in any way that does not contradict the first one. Since there are infinitely many ways in which the second condition can be imposed, we are led to the conclusion that *there are infinitely many lines satisfying one condition.* Such a system of lines is called a *one-parameter family* of lines and the undetermined constant is called the *parameter.*

EXAMPLE 1

What is the equation of the family of lines with slope equal to 2?

Solution: Since the slope is given and the slope and y-intercept determine a line, we put $m = 2$ in the slope-y-intercept form and obtain $y = 2x + b$ as the equation of the family of lines. There is a line for each value assigned to the parameter b. The lines for $b = -3, -2, -1, 0, 1, 2, 3$ are shown in Fig. 2.10 on page 49.

EXAMPLE 2

Find the equation of the family of lines with x-intercept equal to 3. Select the member with slope 2.

Solution: Since we know the x-intercept, we shall write the equation of the family in the two-intercept form. Thus $x/3 + y/b = 1$ represents the family. Solving for y we get $y = (-b/3)x + b$ and see that

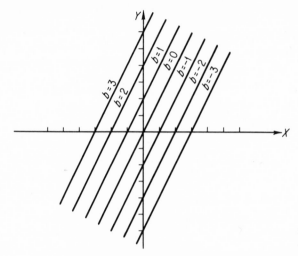

FIG. 2.10 Family of lines.

the slope of each member is $-b/3$. We want the member with slope 2; hence, we put $-b/3 = 2$ or $b = -6$ in the equation of the family. Therefore, $x/3 + y/(-6) = 1$ is the desired member.

EXAMPLE 3

Find the equation of the family of lines with $b = 5$ and select the member or members with $p = 4$.

Solution: The equation of the family with y-intercept equal to 5 is

(1) $$y = mx + 5.$$

In order to impose the condition that $p = 4$, we must put the equation in normal form. Thus, we have

$$\frac{mx - y + 5}{-\sqrt{1 + m^2}} = 0.$$

Hence, we must determine m so that

$$p = \frac{5}{\sqrt{1 + m^2}} = 4.$$

Solving this equation for m, we obtain $m = \pm\frac{3}{4}$. Substituting in (1), we find the desired members are

$$y = \pm\tfrac{3}{4}x + 5.$$

2.14. *THE FAMILY OF LINES THROUGH THE INTERSECTION OF TWO LINES*

If we are given two intersecting lines, we can solve their equations simultaneously and obtain the coordinates x_1 and y_1 of their point of intersection. It is then possible to use the point-slope form and write the equation of the line through the definite point (x_1, y_1) and with any desired slope m. The system of lines containing the parameter m together with (x_1, y_1) is called the family of lines through (x_1, y_1).

This method for obtaining the equation of the family of lines through the intersection of two lines is not difficult to use but is unnecessarily long.

If the equations of the two lines are $a_1x + b_1y + c_1 = 0$ and $a_2x + b_2y + c_2 = 0$, then their point of intersection satisfies

$$(1) \qquad k_1(a_1x + b_1y + c_1) + k_2(a_2x + b_2y + c_2) = 0.$$

since the quantity in each pair of parentheses is zero for this point. This equation is of the form $Ax + By + C = 0$; hence unless $A = B = 0$, it represents a straight line by Article 2.7. If $k_1 = 0$, (1) reduces to $a_2x + b_2y + c_2 = 0$; and if $k_2 = 0$, it reduces to $a_1x + b_1y + c_1 = 0$. If we are willing to leave out one member of the family, we can simplify (1) by replacing k_1 or k_2 by 1 and the other by k. If $k_1 = 1$ and $k_2 = k$, we have

$$(2) \qquad a_1x + b_1y + c_1 + k(a_2x + b_2y + c_2) = 0.$$

This is essentially dividing each member of (1) by k_1 and replacing k_2/k_1 by k. We must realize that the member $a_2x + b_2y + c_2 = 0$ of the family of lines through the intersection of the two lines is left out in (2) since it is impossible to assign a value to k to get that equation.

EXAMPLE

Find the equation of the family of lines through the intersection of $2x - 3y - 3 = 0$ and $x + 4y + 7 = 0$. Select the member of the family with $m = 1$.

Solution: The equation of the family of lines is, by use of (2),

$(2x - 3y - 3) + k(x + 4y + 7)$
$$= (2 + k)x + (-3 + 4k)y - 3 + 7k = 0.$$

The slope of each member of the family is $(2 + k)/(3 - 4k)$. Hence, in order to select the member of the family with slope 1, we put

$$\frac{2 + k}{3 - 4k} = 1$$

and solve for k, thus obtaining $k = \frac{1}{5}$. Therefore, the equation of the desired member is

$$(2x - 3y - 3) + \tfrac{1}{5}(x + 4y + 7) = 0, \text{ or}$$
$$11x - 11y = 8.$$

EXERCISE 2.4

Write the equation of each family of lines described in Problems 1 to 8.

1. Through $(3, -1)$ **2.** With slope 2

3. With $b = 6$ and with m as the parameter

4. With $b = 2$ and with a as the parameter

5. With $a = 5$ **6.** With $\omega = 60°$

7. With $p = 4$

8. Through the intersection of $3x - 5y = 8$ and $2x + 7y = 4$.

Draw two members of each family in Problems 9 to 12.

9. $y = 2x + b$ **10.** $y = mx - 3$

11. $x \cos \omega + y \sin \omega = 2$ **12.** $y - 5 = m(x + 2)$

Determine the value of k so that the stated condition is satisfied in Problems 13 to 20.

13. $2x - 3y - k = 0$ passes through $(2, -1)$

14. $5x + 2y + k = 0$ passes through $(-3, 2)$

15. $kx + 5y + 7 = 0$ has slope 2

16. $3x - 8y + k = 0$ has a y-intercept of $\frac{1}{2}$

17. $5x + ky + 26 = 0$ is 2 units from the origin

18. $4x + ky + 2k = 0$ has slope $\frac{1}{3}$

19. $kx + y + 6 = 0$ has an x-intercept of 3

20. $kx - 3y + 15 = 0$ is 3 units from the origin

Find the equation of the family of lines described in each of Problems 21 to 48. Evaluate the parameter so as to determine the specified member of the family.

21. Family through $(2, 5)$, member with $m = 3$

22. Family through $(-1, 4)$, member with $b = 2$

23. Family with $m = 5$, member with $b = 4$

24. Family with $m = -2$, member with $a = -1$

25. Family with $b = 7$, member with $m = 5$

26. Family with $b = -2$, member with $a = 4$

27. Family with $a = 7$, member with $b = 6$

28. Family with $a = -3$, member with $m = 3$

29. Family with $\omega = 45°$, member with $p = 5\sqrt{2}$

30. Family with $\omega = 60°$, member with $b = 4$

31. Family with $p = 6$, member with $\omega = 30°$

32. Family with $p = 4$, member with $m = \sqrt{3}$

33. Family through the intersection of $2x + 3y - 5 = 0$ and $3x - y + 2 = 0$, member with $a = -1$.

34. Family through the intersection of $4x - y = 10$ and $5x + 3y = 10$, member with $b = 5$.

35. Family through the intersection of $10x + 3y = 13$ and $-2x - 7y = 11$, member with $m = 2$.

36. Family through the intersection of $2x + y = 10$ and $3x - 2y = 8$, member with $p = 4$.

37. Find the equation of the family of lines that are 7 units from the origin. Select the member that makes a triangle of area 49 with the positive coordinate axes.

38. Find the equation of all lines with slope 3. Select all that make a triangle of area 6 with the coordinate axes.

39. Find the equation of the family of lines through $(1, 2)$. Select the member or members that make an angle of $45°$ with $y = 3x + 2$.

40. Find the equation of the family of lines 3 units from the origin. Select the members that make an angle of $60°$ with $y = \sqrt{3}\,x - 1$.

3 THE CIRCLE

3.1. THE STANDARD EQUATION OF A CIRCLE

We shall now derive and discuss the equation of a circle, but first we must define the circle in analytic terms.

DEFINITION. *A circle is the set of points in a plane such that the distance of each from a fixed point of the plane is a nonzero constant.*

The fixed point and the given distance are called the *center* and *radius*, respectively.

We shall now derive the equation of a circle with center at $C(h, k)$ and radius equal to r as shown in Fig. 3.1. Let $P(x, y)$ be any point on the circle; then $CP - r = 0$, since each term is an expression for the radius. This is a symbolic statement of the equation. We shall translate it into an equation that involves x, y, and appropriate constants.

If we multiply each member of $CP - r = 0$ by $CP + r$, we get $(CP)^2 - r^2 = 0$. Furthermore, these two equations are satisfied by the same points since $CP + r$ cannot be zero, inasmuch as CP and

r are both undirected segments. Now, using the distance formula, we see that $(CP)^2 = r^2$ becomes

$$(x - h)^2 + (y - k)^2 = r^2.$$

This equation is satisfied by all points (x, y) that are r units from

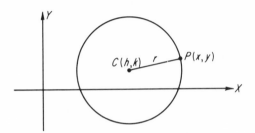

FIG. 3.1 The circle.

the point (h, k) and is not satisfied by any other point. Hence we have the following theorem.

THEOREM. *The equation of the circle with center at* $C(h, k)$ *and radius equal to* r *is*

(1) $(x - h)^2 + (y - k)^2 = r^2.$

COROLLARY. *If the center of the circle with radius* r *is at the origin, the equation of the circle reduces to*

$$x^2 + y^2 = r^2.$$

Equation (1) is called the *standard form* of the equation of a circle. The circle is real if $r^2 > 0$; it is said to be a point circle if $r = 0$; and to be imaginary if $r^2 < 0$.

EXAMPLE

Find the equation of the circle with center at $(2, -1)$ and radius 3.

Solution: Since $h = 2$, $k = -1$, and $r = 3$, the equation of the circle can be obtained immediately by substituting in (1) and is

$$(x - 2)^2 + (y + 1)^2 = 3^2.$$

3.2. *THE GENERAL EQUATION OF THE CIRCLE*

If the parentheses in equation (1) of Article 3.1 are removed, we have

(1) $$x^2 - 2hx + h^2 + y^2 - 2ky + k^2 = r^2.$$

This equation has the same form as

(2) $$x^2 + y^2 + Dx + Ey + F = 0.$$

Equation (2) is called the *general form* of the equation of a circle.

If the general form of the equation of a circle is given, it can be changed to standard form by completing the square of the quadratic expression in x and of the quadratic expression in y. After the square of each quadratic is completed, there will be a constant term as the right member of the equation. The equation represents a real circle, a point circle, or an imaginary circle when this constant is, respectively, positive, zero, or negative.

EXAMPLE 1

Put $3x^2 + 6x + 3y^2 - 8y = 48$ in standard form and give the radius of the circle and the coordinates of its center.

Solution: Dividing each member of the given equation by the coefficient 3 of x^2 and y^2, we get $x^2 + 2x + y^2 - (8y/3) = 16$. If we complete the square of each quadratic expression by adding the square of one-half of the coefficient of the proper first degree term, we obtain

$$x^2 + 2x + 1^2 + y^2 - \frac{8y}{3} + \left(-\frac{4}{3}\right)^2 = 16 + 1 + \frac{16}{9}.$$

Collecting terms and putting the equation in standard form, we have

$$(x + 1)^2 + \left(y - \frac{4}{3}\right)^2 = \left(\frac{13}{3}\right)^2.$$

Hence the radius is $\frac{13}{3}$ and the center is at $(-1, \frac{4}{3})$.

EXAMPLE 2

What type of circle is represented by $x^2 + 2x + y^2 - 4y + 5 = 0$?

Solution: If we complete the squares of the quadratics, we have

$$(x + 1)^2 + (y - 2)^2 = -5 + 1 + 4 = 0;$$

hence the given equation represents a point circle.

EXAMPLE 3

What type of circle is represented by

$$x^2 + 2x + y^2 - 4y + 7 = 0?$$

Solution: If we complete the squares of the quadratics, we get

$$(x + 1)^2 + (y - 2)^2 = -7 + 1 + 4 = -2;$$

hence the given equation represents an imaginary circle.

EXERCISE 3.1

Find the equation of each circle described in Problems 1 to 20.

1. Center at $(3, 2)$, radius 5
2. Center at $(2, -1)$, radius 4
3. Center at $(-5, 4)$, radius 6
4. Center at $(-3, -6)$, radius 2
5. Center at $(2, 1)$, passing through $(5, -4)$
6. Center at $(3, -4)$, passing through $(5, 2)$
7. Center at $(-6, 7)$, passing through $(2, -8)$
8. Center at $(-5, -3)$, passing through $(-1, 0)$
9. Center at $(4, 5)$, tangent to $3x - 4y - 2 = 0$
10. Center at $(7, -2)$, tangent to $5x + 12y + 15 = 0$
11. Center at $(-1, 3)$, tangent to $-8x + 15y + 15 = 0$
12. Center at $(-6, -4)$, tangent to $7x - 24y + 21 = 0$
13. Passing through $(4, -3)$, center at the intersection of $3x - 4y + 1 = 0$ and $2x + y - 3 = 0$.
14. Passing through $(2, 5)$, center at the intersection $2x - 5y + 4 = 0$ and $3x + y - 11 = 0$.
15. Passing through the intersection of $3x + 5y - 1 = 0$ and $x + 5y + 3 = 0$, center at $(-6, 3)$.
16. Passing through the intersection of $4x + 5y + 1 = 0$ and $2x + y + 5 = 0$, center at $(-2, -4)$.
17. With $(2, 3)$ and $(-4, 7)$ as ends of a diameter.
18. Ends of a diameter at $(5, -3)$ and $(1, 7)$.

19. With $(3, -5)$ and the intersection of $2x + y + 1 = 0$ and $5x + 2y + 1 = 0$ as ends of a diameter.

20. Ends of a diameter at $(-2, -3)$ and the intersection of $3x + 2y - 2 = 0$ and $2x + y - 3 = 0$.

21. Prove that $(x - 1)^2 + (y - 3)^2 = 16$ and $(x + 2)^2 + (y + 1)^2 = 4$ are intersecting circles without solving the equations simultaneously.

22. Prove that $(x + 2)^2 + (y - 5)^2 = 3^2$ and $(x - 2)^2 + (y - 2)^2 = 2^2$ are tangent externally.

23. Prove that $(x - 3)^2 + (y - 1)^2 = 13^2$ and $(x - 9)^2 + (y - 9)^2 = 3^2$ are tangent internally.

24. Prove that $(x - 5)^2 + (y + 2)^2 = 2^2$ and $(x + 7)^2 + (y - 3)^2 = 10^2$ do not intersect.

Find the radius and coordinates of the center of each circle given in Problems 25 to 32.

25. $x^2 + y^2 - 2x + 4y = 4$

26. $x^2 + y^2 + 6x - 4y = 3$

27. $x^2 + y^2 - 4x - 10y = -25$

28. $x^2 + y^2 + 2x - 14y = -14$

29. $4x^2 + 4y^2 - 4x - 12y = 6$

30. $9x^2 + 9y^2 - 12x + 24y = -11$

31. $25x^2 + 25y^2 - 20x - 30y = 87$

32. $16x^2 + 16y^2 - 40x + 24y = 110$

Determine the value or set of values of k so that the equation in each of Problems 33 to 36 represents a real circle, a point circle, and an imaginary circle.

33. $x^2 + y^2 - 2x - 6y = k$

34. $x^2 + y^2 - 4x + 8y = -k - 10$

35. $x^2 + y^2 - 7x - 3y = k - 16.5$

36. $x^2 + y^2 - 6x + 4y = 13 - k$

37. Prove that the sum of the squares of the distances of any point on a circle from the ends of a diameter is equal to the square of the diameter.

38. Prove that any two angles inscribed in the same segment of a circle are equal.

39. Find the equation satisfied by the set of points such that each is k times as far from (a, b) as from (c, d).

40. Find the equation satisfied by a set of points if each is the midpoint of a segment from the circle $x^2 + y^2 = 4r^2$ to the point $(2a, 0)$.

3.3. THE CIRCLE AND THREE CONDITIONS

Since the common coefficient of x^2 and y^2 in any form of the equation of the circle is different from zero, we can divide each member of the equation by it and obtain the general form

$$(1) \qquad\qquad x^2 + y^2 + Dx + Ey + F = 0.$$

Consequently, there are three essential constants in the equation of a circle since, in general, it is impossible to reduce the number of constants that appear in (1).

If we substitute the coordinates of any point in (1), we obtain a linear equation in the three unknowns D, E, and F. Hence if we substitute the coordinates of any three points, we get three linear equations in the three unknowns. Consequently, a circle is determined by any three distinct points if the resulting system of linear equations is consistent. It can be shown that the system is consistent except when the three distinct points lie on a straight line. Therefore, we have the following theorem.

THEOREM. *A circle is determined by any three distinct points in the plane that are not on a straight line.*

EXAMPLE 1

Find the equation of the circle that passes through $P_1(1, -2)$, $P_2(3, -4)$, and $P_3(5, 0)$.

Solution 1: If we substitute the coordinates of P_1 in (1) of this article, we obtain

$$1^2 + (-2)^2 + D(1) + E(-2) + F = D - 2E + F + 5 = 0.$$

Similarly, we get

$$3D - 4E + F + 25 = 0 \text{ from } P_2 \quad \text{and}$$
$$5D + F + 25 = 0 \text{ from } P_3.$$

This system may be solved by any one of several methods and, regardless of the method used, we find that

$$D = -\tfrac{20}{3}, \quad E = \tfrac{10}{3}, \quad \text{and} \quad F = \tfrac{25}{3}.$$

If we put these values in (1), we get

$$x^2 - \frac{20x}{3} + y^2 + \frac{10y}{3} + \frac{25}{3} = 0.$$

Hence
$$3x^2 - 20x + 3y^2 + 10y + 25 = 0$$

is the desired equation.

Solution 2: This problem can be solved by a second method which has the advantage of giving the equation of the circle directly in terms of the radius and coordinates of the center.

Since the center is equidistant from the three points, it lies on the perpendicular bisectors of P_1P_2, P_1P_3, and P_2P_3. Consequently, it is at their point of intersection.

We shall get the equations of two of these lines and find their point of intersection as a first step in determining the equation of the circle. The perpendicular bisector of P_1P_2 passes through the midpoint $(2, -3)$ of the segment that joins the points, and its slope is equal to 1 since the slope of the segment is -1. Consequently,

$$\frac{y + 3}{x - 2} = 1 \quad \text{or} \quad x - y = 5$$

is its equation. We can find that $x + 2y = 0$ is the equation of the perpendicular bisector of P_2P_3 in a similar manner. The point of intersection of these lines is readily seen to be $(\tfrac{10}{3}, -\tfrac{5}{3})$. Hence the center of the circle is at this point. The radius is equal to the distance from the center to any one of the three given points and is $5\sqrt{2}/3$ by means of the distance formula. Hence the equation of the circle is

$$\left(x - \frac{10}{3}\right)^2 + \left(y + \frac{5}{3}\right)^2 = \left(\frac{5\sqrt{2}}{3}\right)^2.$$

The reader should expand this and collect terms in order to see that it is the same equation as was obtained in Solution 1.

We have seen that a circle is determined by any three distinct noncolinear points. It is also true that any three independent conditions which lead to a consistent system of equations determine a circle.

EXAMPLE 2

Find the equation of the circle through $P_1(-2, 3)$ and $P_2(1, 4)$ and with center on the line whose equation is $3x + 4y = 5$.

Solution 1: The center of the circle is on the line $3x + 4y = 5$ and the circle passes through P_1 and P_2 as pictured in Fig. 3.2; hence we must find the coordinates of the point on the given line that is equidistant from the given points, since the center is the same distance from all points on the circle. We shall represent the center by (h, k). Then

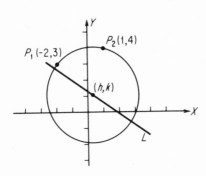

$$(1) \qquad 3h + 4k = 5,$$

since (h, k) is on the given line. Furthermore,

$$(2) \qquad \sqrt{(h + 2)^2 + (k - 3)^2} = \sqrt{(h - 1)^2 + (k - 4)^2}$$

FIGURE 3.2

since the center is equidistant from P_1 and P_2. Squaring each member of (2), collecting terms, and dividing by 2, we have

$$(3) \qquad\qquad\qquad 3h + k = 2.$$

If we solve (1) and (3) for h and k, we find that $h = \frac{1}{3}$ and $k = 1$. Furthermore, the radius is

$$r = \sqrt{\left(\frac{1}{3} - 1\right)^2 + (1 - 4)^2} = \frac{\sqrt{85}}{3}$$

since this is the distance from the center to P_2. Hence the equation of the desired circle is

$$\left(x - \frac{1}{3}\right)^2 + (y - 1)^2 = \frac{85}{9}.$$

Solution 2: Since the circle passes through P_1 and P_2, its center is on the perpendicular bisector of that segment. Hence, using the midpoint formula we see that the perpendicular bisector passes through $(-\frac{1}{2}, \frac{7}{2})$. Furthermore, the slope of the perpendicular bisector is -3, since the slope of P_1P_2 is $\frac{1}{3}$. Therefore, by use of the point-slope equation of a line, we see that the center of the circle is on $y + 3x = 2$. Solving this and the given equation simultaneously, we find that the center is at $(\frac{1}{3}, 1)$. Therefore, $(x - \frac{1}{3})^2 + (y - 1)^2 = \frac{85}{9}$ is the equation of the desired circle, since the distance from the center to P_1 is $\sqrt{\frac{85}{3}}$.

EXERCISE 3.2

Find the equation of each circle described in Problems 1 to 28.

1. Through $(5, 6)$, $(-2, -1)$ and $(4, 7)$
2. Through $(1, 5)$, $(-5, -3)$ and $(2, 4)$
3. Through $(2, -5)$, $(9, 2)$ and $(-15, 12)$
4. Through $(10, -1)$, $(-7, 6)$, $(17, 16)$
5. Through the vertices of a triangle determined by the intersections of $4x - 3y + 10 = 0$, $x - y + 2 = 0$, and $x + y - 8 = 0$
6. Through the intersections of $x + y - 2 = 0$, $3x - 4y - 6 = 0$, and $x - y = 0$
7. Circumscribed about the triangle with vertices at the intersections of $y + 3 = 0$, $x - y - 11 = 0$, and $7x - 17y - 37 = 0$
8. Circumscribed about the triangle with vertices determined by the intersections of $x + y - 7 = 0$, $3x - 4y - 7 = 0$, and $x - y - 1 = 0$
9. Tangent to $3x - 4y = 10$ and concentric with $x^2 + y^2 - 2x - 4y = 11$
10. Concentric with $x^2 + y^2 + 6x - 4y = 3$ and tangent to $5x + 12y + 17 = 0$
11. With the same center as $x^2 + y^2 - 4x + 8y = 1$ and through $(-1, 0)$
12. Through $(4, 6)$ and concentric with $x^2 + y^2 + 6x - 10y = 2$
13. With center on $2x - 5y = 0$ and through $(2, -2)$ and $(1, 5)$
14. With center on $y = 2x + 5$ and through $(4, 15)$ and $(-6, -9)$
15. Through $(5, 3)$ and $(-2, 2)$ and with center on $x + 3y = -1$
16. Through $(-2, -6)$ and $(-9, 1)$ and with center on $4x - 3y + 3 = 0$

17. Through $(0, 1)$ and $(-1, 2)$ and tangent to the X axis

18. Through $(1, 6)$ and $(2, -1)$ and tangent to the Y axis

19. Tangent to $x + y = 3$ at $(2, 1)$ and passing through $(6, 3)$

20. Tangent to $2y - x = 5$ at $(1, 3)$ and passing through $(-1, 5)$

21. Through $(-2, 4)$ and tangent to the lines $-4x + 3y + 30 = 0$ and $3x + 4y = 35$

22. Through $(6, -2)$ and tangent to the lines $3x + 4y = 35$ and $-4x + 3y = 20$

23. Through $(-6, -3)$ and tangent to the lines $5x - 12y - 38 = 0$ and $4x + 3y - 16 = 0$

24. Through $(10, 4)$ and tangent to the lines $3x + 4y - 48 = 0$ and $5x - 12y + 48 = 0$

25. Radius 5, tangent to $3x - 4y - 10 = 0$ and center on $2x + y - 1 = 0$

26. Center on $6x + y - 3 = 0$, radius 17, and tangent to $5x - 12y + 103 = 0$

27. Center on $3x + 4y - 1 = 0$, tangent to $3x - 4y + 8 = 0$ and radius 5

28. Tangent to $5x - 12y + 8 = 0$, radius 5, and center on $2x + 3y - 2 = 0$

Find the equation of each set of points described below.

29. The distance of each point from $(1, 4)$ is twice its distance from $(3, -2)$.

30. The distance of each from $(6, -3)$ is one half of its distance from $(-1, 5)$.

31. The sum of the squares of the distances of each from $(4, 3)$ and $(-2, 5)$ is 8.

32. The sum of the squares of the distances of each from $(2, 6)$ and $(-4, 4)$ is 7.

33. Prove that the equation of the circle through the three noncolinear points $P_1(x_1, y_1)$, $P_2(x_2, y_2)$, and $P_3(x_3, y_3)$ is

$$\begin{vmatrix} x^2 + y^2 & x & y & 1 \\ x_1^2 + y_1^2 & x_1 & y_1 & 1 \\ x_2^2 + y_2^2 & x_2 & y_2 & 1 \\ x_3^2 + y_3^2 & x_3 & y_3 & 1 \end{vmatrix} = 0$$

3.4. *FAMILIES OF CIRCLES*

It has been pointed out that there are three essential constants in the equation of a circle; hence if conditions are given which determine any two of them, the third may be chosen arbitrarily, provided the condition which determines it is independent of and does not contradict the conditions which determine the other two. We have, therefore, a system in which one arbitrary constant appears; consequently, we have a one-parameter family, since a circle corresponds to each value assigned to the arbitrary constant which is at our disposal.

EXAMPLE

What is the equation of the family of circles tangent to $3x - y = 6$ at $(1, -3)$? Select the member or members of the family with radius equal to $2 \sqrt{10}$.

Solution: The circles are tangent to $3x - y = 6$ at $(1, -3)$ as shown in Fig. 3.3; hence their centers are on the perpendicular to the

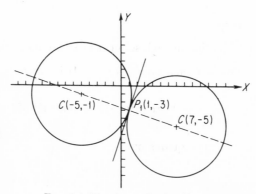

FIG. 3.3 Members of a family.

line at $(1, -3)$ since a radius is perpendicular to a tangent at the point of tangency.

The slope of the perpendicular is $-\frac{1}{3}$ since the slope of the given line is 3. Therefore, $(y + 3)/(x - 1) = -\frac{1}{3}$ or $x + 3y + 8 = 0$ is the equation of the line on which the centers of the circles must lie. If we represent the center of each circle of the family by (h, k), then $h + 3k$

$+ 8 = 0$ or $h = -3k - 8$. Consequently, the center of each is at $(-3k-8, k)$. Furthermore, the radius of each circle is the distance between $C(h, k)$ and $P_1(1, -3)$. Hence

$$
\begin{aligned}
r^2 &= \overline{CP_1}^2 \\
&= (h - 1)^2 + (k + 3)^2 \\
&= (-3k - 8 - 1)^2 + (k + 3)^2 \\
&= 10(k + 3)^2.
\end{aligned}
$$

Therefore, using the standard form, $(x - h)^2 + (y - k)^2 = r^2$, of the equation of a circle, we see that

(1) $(x + 3k + 8)^2 + (y - k)^2 = 10(k + 3)^2$

is the equation of the family of circles.

To select the members with radius equal to $2\sqrt{10}$, we must solve

(2) $10(k + 3)^2 = (2\sqrt{10})^2 = 40$

for k and substitute in the equation of the family. The solutions of the quadratic (2) are readily seen to be $k = -1$ and $k = -5$. If we put $k = -1$ in (1) and collect terms, we find that

$$(x + 5)^2 + (y + 1)^2 = 40$$

is the equation of one of the desired circles. The equation of the other is obtained by putting $k = -5$ in (1) and is

$$(x - 7)^2 + (y + 5)^2 = 40.$$

3.5. THE FAMILY OF CIRCLES THROUGH THE INTERSECTION OF TWO CIRCLES

We shall let

(1) $x^2 + y^2 + D_1 x + E_1 y + F_1 = 0$

and

(2) $x^2 + y^2 + D_2 x + E_2 y + F_2 = 0$

be the equations of any two intersecting circles. If we multiply (2) by any constant k and add the result to (1), we get

(3) $(x^2 + y^2 + D_1 x + E_1 y + F_1) + k(x^2 + y^2 + D_2 x$
$$+ E_2 y + F_2) = 0$$

or

(4) $(1 + k)(x^2 + y^2) + (D_1 + kD_2)x + (E_1 + kE_2)y$
$$+ F_1 + kF_2 = 0.$$

If k is not equal to -1, dividing each term in (4) by $1 + k$ will reduce it to the same form as the general equation of a circle. Furthermore, the circle represented by (3) or (4) passes through both intersections of (1) and (2), since the coordinates of these points make each expression in parentheses in (3) zero.

Since there are infinitely many values that can be assigned to k, there are infinitely many circles through the intersections of two circles and we say that we have a *one-parameter family* of circles. The circle (2) is a member of the family but cannot be found by assigning a value to k. Why? We get a circle for each value assigned to k and can find the value of k in order that the circle satisfy one condition in addition to passing through the intersections of the given circles.

If $k = -1$, (4) becomes

(5) $(D_1 - D_2)x + (E_1 - E_2)y + F_1 - F_2 = 0$

regardless of whether (1) and (2) intersect. If they intersect, (5) is their *common chord;* if they are tangent, (5) is their *common tangent;* and if they do not contact one another, (5) is called their *radical axis.*

EXAMPLE

Find the equation of the family of circles through the intersections of $C_1: x^2 + y^2 - 2x + 4y = 4$ and $C_2: x^2 + y^2 + 4x - 6y = 3$. Pick out the member of the family that passes through $(2, 1)$. Find the equation of the common chord of the given circles.

Solution: The equation of the family is

$x^2 + y^2 - 2x + 4y - 4 + k(x^2 + y^2 + 4x - 6y - 3) = 0,$ or

(1) $(1 + k)(x^2 + y^2) + (-2 + 4k)x + (4 - 6k)y - 4 - 3k = 0.$

We want the member of the family that passes through $(2, 1)$; hence we shall substitute the coordinates of that point in the equation of the

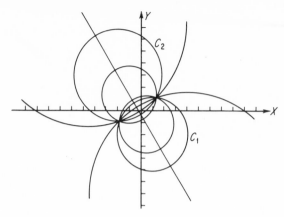

FIG. 3.4 Family of circles.

family in order to find the proper value of k. Thus (1) becomes

$$(1 + k)(2^2 + 1^2) + (-2 + 4k)2 + (4 - 6k)1 - 4 - 3k$$
$$= 4k + 1 = 0.$$

Therefore, $k = -\frac{1}{4}$. Hence putting this value of k in the equation of the family and multiplying by 4, we find that

$$3x^2 + 3y^2 - 12x + 22y - 13 = 0$$

is the equation of the desired circle.

The equation of the common chord is obtained by putting $k = -1$ in (1). If we do this and collect terms, we get

$$-6x + 10y - 1 = 0.$$

EXERCISE 3.3

Find the equation of each family of circles described in Problems 1 to 16 and select the specified member.

1. Center at $(3, 2)$; member with radius 5

2. Center at $(2, -1)$; member with radius 4

3. Center at $(-5, 3)$; member with radius 2

4. Center at $(-4, -5)$; member with radius 3

5. Center at $(6, 3)$; member tangent to $3x - 4y + 9 = 0$

6. Center at $(5, -1)$; member tangent to $5x + 12y + 13 = 0$

7. Center at $(3, -5)$; member through $(0, -1)$

8. Center at $(-2, 4)$; member through $(10, 9)$

9. Center on $2x - y - 5 = 0$, radius 5; member tangent to $3x - 4y - 10 = 0$

10. Center on $x + 3y - 7 = 0$, radius 3; member tangent to $5x + 12y - 5 = 0$

11. Center on $y = 3x + 1$, tangent to $3x + 4y - 4 = 0$; member with radius 6

12. Center on $y = 2x - 3$, tangent to $4x - 3y - 9 = 0$; member with radius 2

13. Tangent to $5x - 12y - 3 = 0$ at $(3, 1)$; member with center at $(2, 3.4)$

14. Tangent to $3x + 4y - 3 = 0$ at $(5, -3)$; member with center at $(2, -7)$

15. Tangent to $8x - 15y - 4 = 0$ at $(8, 4)$; member through $(-8, 34)$

16. Tangent to $2x + 3y - 7 = 0$ at $(5, -1)$; member through $(3 + \sqrt{13}, -4)$

Find the equation of the family of circles through the intersections of each pair of circles in Problems 17 to 20. Find the equation of each common chord or common tangent.

17. $x^2 + y^2 + 2x - 4y = 4$, $x^2 + y^2 - 6x + 2y = 6$

18. $x^2 + y^2 - 4x + 8y = -11$, $x^2 + y^2 + 6x - 16y = 48$

19. $x^2 + y^2 - 8x + 4y = 5$, $x^2 + y^2 + 16x - 6y = 8$

20. $x^2 + y^2 - 10x + 8y = 8$, $x^2 + y^2 + 14x - 4y = -4$

Select the members of the family in Problem 17 that satisfy the conditions given in Problems 21 to 28 by determining the appropriate values of k.

21. Radius equal to 2.5 **22.** Radius equal to 3

23. Center on $x - 2y = 0$ **24.** Center on $2x + 4y - 3 = 0$

25. Through $(2, 2)$ **26.** Through $(-1, 1)$

27. Through $(9, -1)$ **28.** Through $(10, 4)$

29. Prove that the radical axis of two non-concentric circles of equal radius is the perpendicular bisector of the line of centers.

30. Prove that the radical axes of three circles taken in pairs meet in a point provided the centers are not colinear. This point is called the *radical center*.

31. Prove that if $P_1(x_1, y_1)$ is a point external to $(x - h)^2 + (y - k)^2 = r^2$ and if T is the point of tangency of a tangent from P_1 to the circle, then the length t of the tangent is given by

$$t^2 = (x_1 - h)^2 + (y_1 - k)^2 - r^2$$

32. Prove that if the length of tangents from $P_1(x_1, y_1)$ to two circles are equal, then P_1 is on their radical axis.

4 THE CONICS

4.1. INTRODUCTION

In this chapter we shall study the general second-degree equation in two variables. If the variables are x and y, the equation is

$$Ax^2 + Bxy + Cy^2 + Dx + Ey + F = 0$$

provided A, B, C, D, E and F are constants. The curve made up of the set of points whose coordinates satisfy such an equation is called a *conic section* or a *conic*. This name is used since the curve can be obtained as the intersection of a right circular cone* and a plane. If the plane does not pass through the vertex, then the conic is

(a) a *parabola* if the plane is parallel to an element of the cone as in Fig. 4.1a,

---

* In order to generate a *right circular cone*, choose a fixed point on a fixed line and rotate another line passing through the fixed point so that this line goes around the fixed line making a constant angle with it. The fixed point is the *vertex* of the cone, and any position of the rotating line is an *element* of the cone. The two parts of the cone above and below the vertex are called *nappes*. The line through the vertex that makes equal angles with all elements of the cone is called the *axis*.

(b) an *ellipse* if the plane cuts entirely across one nappe of the cone as in Fig. 4.1b, and

(c) a *hyperbola* if the plane cuts both nappes of the cone as in Fig. 4.1c.

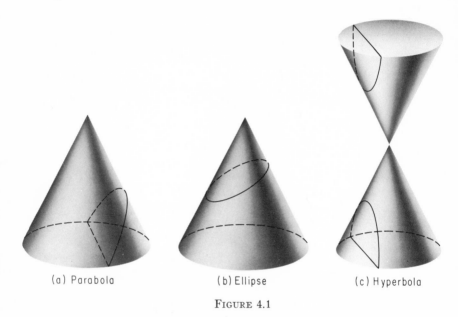

(a) Parabola   (b) Ellipse   (c) Hyperbola

FIGURE 4.1

The Greeks studied and named the three types of conics and discovered many of their properties. The properties discovered included the ones that we shall use as definitions in later articles of this chapter.

4.2. THE PARABOLA

After defining the parabola, we shall derive and discuss its equation.

DEFINITION. *The **parabola** is the set of points arranged in a plane so that for each point the undirected distances from a fixed point and from a fixed line are equal.*

The fixed point is called the *focus*, and the fixed line is called the *directrix*. The line through the focus and perpendicular to the directrix is called the *axis*. Finally, the line segment through the focus, perpendicular to the axis and intercepted by the parabola is called the *focal width* or *latus rectum*. These quantities are shown in Fig. 4.2.

In order that the final form of the equation shall be relatively simple, we shall use $x = h - a$ as the equation of directrix and the point $F(h+a, k)$ as the focus and, of course, $P(x, y)$ as any point

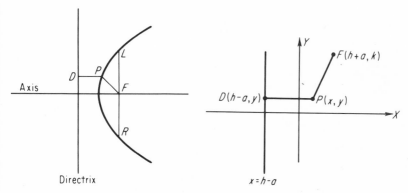

FIG. 4.2 The parabola. FIG. 4.3 Equation of a parabola.

of the set. Then, D has the coordinates $(h-a, y)$ since it is on the directrix and is the same distance as P from the X axis. Hence the definition

$$FP = DP,$$

by use of the distance formula, becomes

$$\sqrt{(x - h - a)^2 + (y - k)^2} = \sqrt{(x - h + a)^2 + (y - y)^2}.$$

Therefore, squaring each member gives

$$(x - h - a)^2 + (y - k)^2 = (x - h + a)^2.$$

Now, considering $x - h$ as a single quantity, we have

$$[(x - h) - a]^2 + (y - k)^2 = [(x - h) + a]^2.$$

Partially expanded this becomes

$$(x - h)^2 - 2a(x - h) + a^2 + (y - k)^2 = (x - h)^2 + 2a(x - h) + a^2.$$

Finally, collecting terms,

(1) $$(y - k)^2 = 4a(x - h).$$

This is the equation of the parabola with focus at $F(h + a, k)$ and $x = h - a$ as directrix.

If we now recall that the line through the focus and perpendicular to the directrix is called the axis, we see that the equation of the axis is

(2) $$y = k.$$

Furthermore, the intersection of the axis and the conic is the *vertex* of the conic. Hence, solving (1) and (2) simultaneously, we find that the vertex is at (h, k).

The following theorem may now be stated:

THEOREM 1. *The equation of the parabola with vertex at $(\boldsymbol{h}, \boldsymbol{k})$ and focus at $(\boldsymbol{h+a}, \boldsymbol{k})$ is*

(1) $$(y - k)^2 = 4a(x - h).$$

The following theorem can be demonstrated in a similar manner.

THEOREM 2. *The equation of the parabola with vertex at $(\boldsymbol{h}, \boldsymbol{k})$ and focus at $(\boldsymbol{h}, \boldsymbol{k+a})$ is*

(3) $$(x - h)^2 = 4a(y - k).$$

Equations (1) and (3) are called the *standard forms* of the equation of a parabola and reduce to

(1′) $$y^2 = 4ax \quad \text{and} \quad (3′) \quad x^2 = 4ay,$$

if the vertex (h, k) is at the origin.

The left member of (1) is positive or zero, since it is the square of a real quantity. Hence, the right member must be positive or zero. Consequently, a and $x - h$ must have the same sign or $x - h$ must be zero. Therefore, if $\boldsymbol{a > 0}$, *then* $\boldsymbol{x \geqq h}$, *and the curve is to the right of the vertex. If* $\boldsymbol{a < 0}$, *then* $\boldsymbol{x \leqq h}$ *and the curve is to the left of the vertex.* It can be shown in a similar manner that *the parabola (3) extends upward for* $\boldsymbol{a > 0}$ *and downward for* $\boldsymbol{a < 0}$.

The focal width is readily obtained by solving the equation of the line along which it lies simultaneously with that of the parabola and then using the distance formula to find the distance between the two points of intersection. If we use equation (1) for the parabola, then $x = h + a$ is the equation of the line along which the focal width lies and the points of intersection are $R(h+a, k+2a)$ and $L(h+a, k-2a)$ as shown in Fig. 4.4. The distance between them is

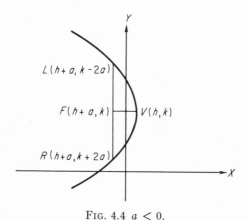

FIG. 4.4 $a < 0$.

$4|a|$. We can show similarly that the focal width of the parabola whose equation is the standard form (3) is also $4|a|$. Hence we have the theorem.

THEOREM 3. *The focal width of a parabola is* **$4|a|$**.

The reader should be able to visualize the sketch in Fig. 4.5 which shows relative positions of essential lines and points connected with a parabola. The length of the focal width LR is indicated and a parabola is sketched in.

EXAMPLE

What is the equation of the parabola with vertex at (2, 3) and focus at (4, 3)? Find the focal width and sketch the parabola.

Solution: The distance and direction from the vertex to the focus is always a, hence $a = 2$. Furthermore, the axis is parallel to the X axis, since the ordinates of the focus and vertex are equal; consequently, we must use standard form (1) for the equation.

Hence substituting $a = 2$, $h = 2$ and $k = 3$ in (1) we see that

$$(y - 3)^2 = 4(2)(x - 2)$$

is the equation of the desired parabola.

Since the focal width of any parabola is $4|a|$, we know, by inspection of the equation of the parabola under consideration, that its focal

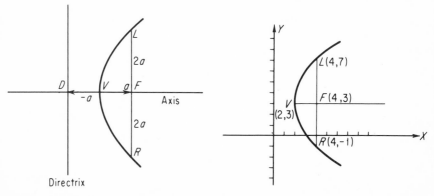

FIG. 4.5 Relative positions for parabolas.   FIG. 4.6 A parabola.

width is $4|2| = 8$. Furthermore, the graph does not extend to the left of the vertex, since $a > 0$. The facts disclosed in this discussion and the two points $(4, 7)$ and $(4, -1)$ determined by making use of the focal width were used in sketching Fig. 4.6.

EXERCISE 4.1

Find the equation of each parabola described in Problems 1 to 24. Sketch each parabola.

1. Vertex at $(3, 2)$, focus at $(4, 2)$

2. Vertex at $(1, -1)$, focus at $(-1, -1)$

3. Vertex at $(-3, 2)$, focus at $(-3, 5)$

4. Vertex at $(2, -3)$, focus $(2, -4)$

5. Vertex at $(-1, 1)$, $y = 3$ as directrix

6. Vertex at $(3, -2)$, $y = -5$ as directrix

7. Vertex at $(1, -2)$, $x = 4$ as directrix

8. Vertex at $(-2, -1)$, $x = -4$ as directrix

9. Focus at $(-5, 2)$, $x = -1$ as directrix

10. Focus at $(-3, 3)$, $x = -5$ as directrix

11. Focus at $(2, 3)$, $y = -1$ as directrix

12. Focus at $(-1, 0)$, $y = 4$ as directrix

13. Ends of focal width at $(-3, 0)$ and $(9, 0)$, vertex at $(3, -3)$

14. Ends of focal width at $(0, 0)$ and $(-4, 0)$, vertex at $(-2, 1)$

15. Ends of focal width at $(-5, 9)$ and $(-5, 1)$ vertex at $(-3, 5)$

16. Ends of focal width at $(-1, 5)$ and $(-1, -11)$ vertex at $(-5, -3)$

17. Vertex at $(-1, 2)$, axis parallel to the X axis, passing through $(-4, 8)$

18. Vertex at $(1, -3)$, axis parallel to the X axis, passing through $(3, 1)$

19. Vertex at $(4, -3)$, axis parallel to the Y axis, passing through $(0, -4)$

20. Vertex at $(3, 4)$, axis parallel to the Y axis, passing through $(-7, 9)$

21. Focal width 8, axis parallel to the Y axis, passing through $(5, 0)$ and $(9, -6)$

22. Focal width 4, axis parallel to the Y axis, passing through $(-2, -1)$ and $(2, 3)$

23. Focal width 12, axis parallel to the X axis, passing through $(-1, -3)$ and $(2, 3)$

24. Focal width 16, axis parallel to the X axis, passing through $(1, 3)$ and $(-2, -9)$

Find the equation that is satisfied by the coordinates of each point in the set that is equidistant from the given point and the given line in Problems 25 to 28.

25. $x = 1$, $(5, 3)$ **26.** $x = 4$, $(-4, 5)$

27. $y = -3$, $(6, 1)$ **28.** $y = 2$, $(3, -6)$

4.3. *THE ELLIPSE*

We shall now define and discuss another one of the conics.

DEFINITION. *An* **ellipse** *is the set of points located in a plane so that the sum of the distances of each from two fixed points is a constant.*

The fixed points are called the *foci* and the line through them is the *axis*. In order to obtain a general but relatively simple form for the equation of the ellipse, we shall choose the position of the coordinate axes so that the foci are at $F_1(h-c, k)$ and $F_2(h+c, k)$ as shown in Fig. 4.7. If $P(x, y)$ is any point on the ellipse and if $2a$ is the sum of its distances from the foci, then the definition of the ellipse becomes

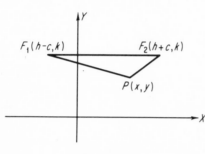

FIGURE 4.7

$$F_1P + F_2P = 2a.$$

We shall now translate this in terms of x, y, and appropriate constants. By use of the distance formula, we get

$$\sqrt{(x - h + c)^2 + (y - k)^2} + \sqrt{(x - h - c)^2 + (y - k)^2} = 2a.$$

If we think of $x - h$ as a single term and then transpose the second radical, square, and solve for the only remaining radical, we get

$$\sqrt{[(x - h) - c]^2 + (y - k)^2} = a - \frac{c}{a}(x - h).$$

Now squaring, collecting coefficients, and dividing by $a^2 - c^2$ gives

(1) $$\frac{(x - h)^2}{a^2} + \frac{(y - k)^2}{a^2 - c^2} = 1.$$

In the triangle PF_1F_2 the sum $2a$ of the sides PF_1 and PF_2 is greater than the side $F_1F_2 = 2c$; hence $a^2 - c^2$ is positive and we shall put

$$a^2 - c^2 = b^2$$

in equation (1) and have

(2)
$$\frac{(x - h)^2}{a^2} + \frac{(y - k)^2}{b^2} = 1$$

in which a is greater than b.

Equation (2) is the equation of the ellipse, since we can show that if $P(x, y)$ satisfies (2), then $F_1P + F_2P = 2a$ and we have shown that $P(x, y)$ satisfies (2) if $F_1P + F_2P = 2a$. The ratio c/a is called the *eccentricity*.

The point midway between the foci is called the *center* and is readily seen to be (h, k) since the foci are at $(h-c, k)$ and $(h+c, k)$. The intersections of the ellipse and its axis are called the *vertices* and are seen to be $(h-a, k)$ and $(h+a, k)$ by solving the ellipse (2) and its axis $y = k$ simultaneously. The quantities a and b are called the *semi-major* and *semi-minor axes*. Hence

(2)
$$\frac{(x - h)^2}{a^2} + \frac{(y - k)^2}{b^2} = 1$$

is the equation of the ellipse with center at $(\boldsymbol{h}, \boldsymbol{k})$, major axis parallel to the $\boldsymbol{X}$ axis and semi-axes $\boldsymbol{a}$ and $\boldsymbol{b}$.

The following theorem can be proved in a manner similar to that used in obtaining the one above.

The equation of the ellipse with center at $(\boldsymbol{h}, \boldsymbol{k})$, major axis parallel to the $\boldsymbol{Y}$ axis and semi-axes $\boldsymbol{a}$ and $\boldsymbol{b}$ is

(3)
$$\frac{(y - k)^2}{a^2} + \frac{(x - h)^2}{b^2} = 1.$$

Fig. 4.8 shows an ellipse and the pictorial values of a, b, and c. It also shows one of the latera recta (focal widths) and

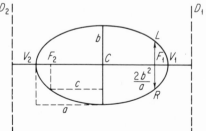

FIG. 4.8 The ellipse.

its length. The *latus rectum* is defined here, as in connection with the parabola, to be the segment of a line through the focus, perpendicular to the axis and intercepted by the conic. The reader should show that *the focal width or length of the latus rectum is* $\mathbf{2b^2/a}$.

EXAMPLE

Find the equation of the ellipse with center at $(2, 3)$, a focus at $(5, 3)$ and corresponding vertex at $(7, 3)$. Sketch the curve.

Solution: We shall first draw a sketch which shows the information given in this problem, then find the equation, and finally the ellipse. The distance from center to vertex is always a and is 5 in this problem; hence, $a = 5$; furthermore, $CF = c = 3$. Consequently, $b^2 = a^2 - c^2 = 5^2 - 3^2 = 4^2$. Finally we must use (2) since the major axis is parallel to the X axis; hence, the equation is

$$\frac{(x - 2)^2}{5^2} + \frac{(y - 3)^2}{4^2} = 1.$$

In sketching the curve, we shall make use of the given vertex, the other vertex and the ends of the latera recta. The given vertex and

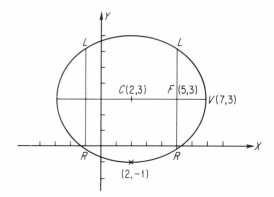

FIGURE 4.9

focus are $a = 5$ and $c = 3$ units to the right of the center; hence the other vertex and focus are 5 and 3 units to the left of the center as indicated in Fig. 4.9. The length of each latus rectum is

$$\frac{2b^2}{a} = \frac{2(4^2)}{5} = \frac{32}{5}.$$

Hence the points $\frac{16}{5}$ units above and below the foci are on the ellipse.

EXERCISE 4.2

Find the equation of each ellipse described in Problems 1 to 20. Sketch each one after finding the coordinates of the center, the vertices, the foci, and the ends of latera recta.

1. $a = 5, b = 3$, major axis parallel to the X axis, center at $(2, 1)$

2. $a = 13, b = 5$, major axis parallel to the X axis, center at $(-1, 2)$

3. $a = 5, b = 4$, major axis parallel to the Y axis, center at $(-2, -3)$

4. $a = 13, b = 12$, major axis parallel to the Y axis, center at $(-1, 3)$

5. $a = 25, c = 7$, major axis parallel to the Y axis, center at $(-3, -2)$

6. $a = 17, c = 8$, major axis parallel to the Y axis, center at $(-4, 3)$

7. $b = 7, c = 24$, major axis parallel to the X axis, center at $(3, -4)$

8. $b = 8, c = 15$, major axis parallel to the X axis, center at $(-5, 2)$

9. Center at $(-5, 1)$, a vertex at $(0, 1)$, a focus at $(-1, 1)$

10. Center at $(-3, 1)$, a vertex at $(14, 1)$, a focus at $(5, 1)$

11. Center at $(3, 2)$, a vertex at $(3, -3)$, a focus at $(3, -1)$

12. Center at $(2, 1)$, a vertex at $(2, -12)$, a focus at $(2, 6)$

13. Vertices at $(2, 8)$ and $(2, -2)$, a focus $(2, 3 + \sqrt{21})$

14. Vertices at $(-1, 2)$ and $(-1, -6)$, a focus at $(-1, -2 + \sqrt{7})$

15. Vertices at $(-4, -1)$ and $(2, -1)$, a focus at $(-1 + \sqrt{5}, -1)$

16. Vertices at $(8, 5)$ and $(-2, 5)$, a focus at $(-1, 5)$

17. Ends of the minor axis at $(-2, 2)$ and $(-2, 0)$, a vertex at $(1, 1)$

18. Ends of the minor axis at $(3, 5)$ and $(3, -3)$, a vertex at $(-2, 1)$

19. Ends of the minor axis at $(-1, 1)$ and $(-3, 1)$, a vertex at $(-2, 3)$

20. Ends of the minor axis at $(-3, -2)$ and $(1, -2)$, a vertex at $(-1, 1)$

Find the equation that is satisfied by the coordinates of the points in the set that is described in each of Problems 21 to 24.

21. The sum of the distances of each point from $(2, 3)$ and $(5, -1)$ is 7.

22. The sum of the distances of each point from $(4, -2)$ and $(5, 3)$ is 6.

23. The sum of the distances of each point from $(2, -1)$ and $(-3, 2)$ is 6.

24. The sum of the distances of each point from $(3, -4)$ and $(-2, -3)$ is 8.

4.4. THE HYPERBOLA

We shall now define and discuss the remaining conic.

DEFINITION. *A **hyperbola** is the set of points located in a plane so that the difference of the distances of each from two fixed points is a constant.*

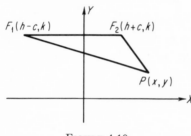

The fixed points are called the *foci* and the line through them is the *axis*. In order to obtain a general but relatively simple form for the equation of the hyperbola, we shall choose the position of the coordinate axes so that the foci are at $F_1(h-c, k)$ and $F_2(h+c, k)$ as shown in Fig. 4.10. If P (x, y) is any point on the hyperbola and if $2a$ is the difference of the distances from the foci, then the definition of the hyperbola becomes

FIGURE 4.10

$$F_1P - F_2P = 2a.$$

We shall now translate this in terms of x, y and appropriate constants. By use of the distance formula, we get

$$\sqrt{(x - h + c)^2 + (y - k)^2} - \sqrt{(x - h - c)^2 + (y - k)^2} = 2a.$$

If we think of $x - h$ as a single term and then transpose the second radical, square, and solve for the remaining radical, we get

$$\sqrt{[(x - h) - c]^2 + (y - k)^2} = \frac{c}{a}(x - h) - a.$$

Now, squaring, collecting coefficients, dividing by $a^2 - c^2$, and writing $-(c^2 - a^2)$ in place of $a^2 - c^2$ gives

(1)
$$\frac{(x - h)^2}{a^2} - \frac{(y - k)^2}{c^2 - a^2} = 1.$$

The inequality $a < c$ holds, since the difference between two sides of a triangle is less than the third side. Hence, $c^2 - a^2$ is positive, and we shall replace it by b^2 and have

(2)
$$\frac{(x - h)^2}{a^2} - \frac{(y - k)^2}{b^2} = 1.$$

Equation (2) is the equation of the hyperbola, since we can show that if $P(x, y)$ satisfies (2), then $F_1P - F_2P = 2a$ and we have shown that $P(x, y)$ satisfies (2) if $F_1P - F_2P = 2a$. The ratio c/a is called the *eccentricity*.

The point midway between the foci is called the *center* and is readily seen to be (h, k), since the foci are at $(h-c, k)$ and $(h+c, k)$. The intersections of the hyperbola and its axis are called the *vertices* and are seen to be $(h-a, k)$ and $(h+a, k)$ when the hyperbola (2) and its axis $y = k$ are solved simultaneously. The quantities a and b are called the *semi-transverse* and *semi-conjugate axes*. Hence

THEOREM.

(2)
$$\frac{(x - h)^2}{a^2} - \frac{(y - k)^2}{b^2} = 1$$

is the equation of the hyperbola with center at (h, k), axis parallel to the X axis and semi-axes a and b.

The following theorem can be proved in a manner similar to that used in obtaining the one above.

THEOREM. *The equation of the hyperbola with center at (h, k), axis parallel to the Y axis and semi-axes a and b is*

(3)
$$\frac{(y - k)^2}{a^2} - \frac{(x - h)^2}{b^2} = 1.$$

Fig. 4.11 shows a hyperbola and the pictorial values of a and c. It also shows a latus rectum and its length. The *latus rectum* is defined here, as in connection with the other conics, to be the segment of a line through the focus, perpendicular to the axis, and

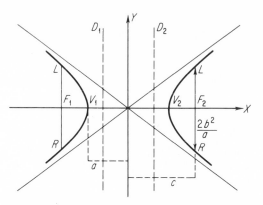

FIG. 4.11 The hyperbola.

intercepted by the conic. The reader should show that the *focal width or length of the latus rectum is* $\mathbf{2b^2/a.}$

EXAMPLE

Find the equation of the hyperbola with center at $(2, 3)$, a focus at $(7, 3)$, and corresponding vertex at $(5, 3)$.

Solution: The information given in this problem is shown in Fig. 4.12. The distance from center to vertex is always a and is 3 in this problem; hence $a = 3$; furthermore, $CF = c = 5$. Consequently,

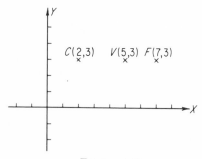

FIGURE 4.12

$$b^2 = c^2 - a^2 = 5^2 - 3^2 = 4^2.$$

Finally we must use (2) since the axis is parallel to the X axis; hence the equation is

$$\frac{(x-2)^2}{3^2} - \frac{(y-3)^2}{4^2} = 1.$$

4.5. *THE ASYMPTOTES*

To sketch the hyperbola it is desirable to make use of two lines called *asymptotes*, which are approached by the curve as x becomes larger and larger. If we solve (2) of Article 4.4 for $y - k$ we get

$$y - k = \pm \frac{b}{a} \sqrt{(x - h)^2 - a^2},$$

$$y - k = \pm \frac{b}{a} (x - h) \sqrt{1 - \frac{a^2}{(x - h)^2}}$$

by multiplying and dividing the right member by $x - h$. For h fixed, the value of $x - h$ becomes larger and larger as x does; hence it is clear that the expression $\sqrt{1 - \dfrac{a^2}{(x - h)^2}}$ approaches 1 as x gets larger and larger. Therefore, for large values of x, the hyperbola (2) of Art. 4.4 comes as close to coinciding with the lines

$$y - k = \pm \frac{b}{a} (x - h)$$

as one could wish. The reader should show that these asymptotes and those for the hyperbola whose equation is (3) of Article 4.4 can be obtained by replacing the 1 of standard form by zero and solving for $y - k$.

EXAMPLE

Sketch the graph of

$$\frac{(x - 2)^2}{3^2} - \frac{(y - 3)^2}{4^2} = 1.$$

Solution: This is the equation derived in the example of the previous article. Hence, as seen from the equation or the data which determined it, the axis is parallel to the X axis, the center is at $(2, 3)$, the vertices are $a = 3$ units to the right and left of the center, the foci are $c = \sqrt{3^2 + 4^2} = 5$ units to the right and left of the center, the ends of the latera recta are $b^2/a = \frac{16}{3}$ units above and below the foci, and the asymptotes are

$$y = 3 \pm \tfrac{4}{3}(x - 2)$$

as obtained from the equation of the hyperbola by replacing the 1 of standard form by zero and solving for y. The facts determined above were used in sketching the graph in Fig. 4.13.

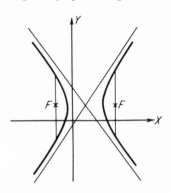

FIGURE 4.13

EXERCISE 4.3

Find the equation of each hyperbola described in Problems 1 to 20. Find the equations of the asymptotes and sketch them and the hyperbola after finding the coordinates of the center, vertices, foci, and ends of the latera recta.

1. $a = 4, b = 3$, transverse axis parallel to the X axis, center at $(2, 1)$

2. $a = 12, b = 5$, transverse axis parallel to the X axis, center at $(-1, 2)$

3. $a = 3, b = 4$, transverse axis parallel to the Y axis, center at $(-2, -3)$

4. $a = 5, b = 12$, transverse axis parallel to the Y axis, center at $(-1, 3)$

5. $a = 7, c = 25$, transverse axis parallel to the Y axis, center at $(-3, -2)$

6. $a = 8, c = 17$, transverse axis parallel to the Y axis, center at $(-4, 3)$

7. $b = 7, c = 25$, transverse axis parallel to the X axis, center at $(3, -4)$

8. $b = 8, c = 17$, transverse axis parallel to the X axis, center at $(-5, 2)$

9. Center at $(-5, 1)$, a vertex at $(-1, 1)$, a focus at $(0, 1)$
10. Center at $(-3, 1)$, a vertex at $(5, 1)$, a focus at $(14, 1)$
11. Center at $(3, 2)$, a vertex at $(3, 5)$, a focus at $(3, 7)$
12. Center at $(2, 1)$, a vertex at $(2, -4)$, a focus at $(2, 14)$
13. Vertices at $(2, 8)$ and $(2, -2)$, a focus at $(2, 3 + \sqrt{29})$
14. Vertices at $(-1, -6)$ and $(-1, 2)$, a focus at $(-1, 3)$
15. Vertices at $(-4, -1)$ and $(2, -1)$, a focus at $(-1 + \sqrt{13}, -1)$
16. Vertices at $(8, 5)$ and $(-2, 5)$, a focus at $(3 - \sqrt{34}, 5)$
17. Ends of the conjugate axis at $(-2, 2)$ and $(-2, 0)$, a vertex at $(1, 1)$
18. Ends of the conjugate axis at $(3, -3)$ and $(3, 5)$, a vertex at $(-2, 1)$
19. Ends of the conjugate axis at $(-3, 1)$ and $(-1, 1)$, a vertex at $(-2, -1)$
20. Ends of the conjugate axis at $(-3, -2)$ and $(1, -2)$, a vertex at $(-1, 1)$

Find the equation that is satisfied by the coordinates of each point in the set that is described in each of Problems 21 to 24.

21. The difference of the distances of each point from $(2, 3)$ and $(5, -1)$ is 3.
22. The difference of the distances of each point from $(4, -2)$ and $(5, 3)$ is 4.
23. The difference of the distances of each point from $(2, -1)$ and $(-3, 2)$ is 2.
24. The difference of the distances of each point from $(3, -4)$ and $(-2, -3)$ is 2.

4.6. REDUCTION TO STANDARD FORM

It is ordinarily a simple matter to determine pertinent facts concerning a conic if the equation is in standard form. Consequently it is desirable to be able to put the equation

$$Ax^2 + Cy^2 + Dx + Ey + F = 0$$

in standard form where A, C, D, E and F are constants and not both A and C are zero. In order to do this, we begin by completing the square of each quadratic in the equation. The next step depends on whether either A or C is zero. If one of them is zero, we have a parabola and must put the equation in the form

$$(y - k)^2 = 4a(x - h) \quad \text{or} \quad (x - h)^2 = 4a(y - k)$$

EXAMPLE 1

Put $y^2 - 12x - 4y - 56 = 0$ in standard form.

Solution: We complete the square of the quadratic in y by adding and subtracting 4. Thus we have $y^2 - 4y + 4 - 12x - 60 = (y - 2)^2 - 12x - 60 = 0$; hence $(y - 2)^2 = 12x + 60 = 4(3)(x + 5)$ is the standard form of the given equation.

If neither A nor C is zero, the equation represents an ellipse or a hyperbola and should be put in the form of equation (2) or (3) of Articles 4.3 or 4.4.

EXAMPLE 2

Put $9x^2 + 4y^2 - 18x + 16y - 11 = 0$ in standard form.

Solution: To complete the squares of the quadratics, we first factor the coefficient of x^2 out of the terms in x^2 and x and factor the coefficient of y^2 out of the terms in y^2 and y. Thus the equation becomes $9(x^2 - 2x) + 4(y^2 + 4y) - 11 = 0$. Now to complete the squares, we need only to add 1 in the first pair of parentheses and 4 in the second and to offset this by also adding $(9)(1)$ and $(4)(4)$ to the right member. If in addition to doing these things, we also add 11 to each member, we have

$$9(x^2 - 2x + 1) + 4(y^2 + 4y + 4) = 9 + 16 + 11$$
$$9(x - 1)^2 + 4(y + 2)^2 = 36$$

Finally, dividing each member by 36, putting 2^2 for 4 and 3^2 for 9, we see that

$$\frac{(x - 1)^2}{2^2} + \frac{(y + 2)^2}{3^2} = 1$$

is the standard form of the equation.

EXAMPLE 3

Put $9x^2 + 54x - 16y^2 + 64y - 127 = 0$ into standard form.

Solution: Factoring 9 from the first two terms and -16 from the next two, we have

$$9(x^2 + 6x) - 16(y^2 - 4y) - 127 = 0.$$

Now adding 127 to each member, completing the squares by adding 9 in the first pair of parentheses and 4 in the second, and offsetting these additions by adding $(9)(9)$ and subtracting $(16)(4)$ in the right member, we get

$$9(x^2 + 6x + 9) - 16(y^2 - 4y + 4) = 127 + 81 - 64$$
$$9(x + 3)^2 - 16(y - 2)^2 = 144$$

Finally, dividing through by 144 and writing 4^2 for 16 and 3^2 for 9, we see that

$$\frac{(x + 3)^2}{4^2} - \frac{(y - 2)^2}{3^2} = 1$$

is the standard form of the given equation.

4.7. THE RECTANGULAR HYPERBOLA

There is one special case of the hyperbola that deserves mention. It is the one in which the semi-axes are equal and is called a *rectangular hyperbola*. If $b = a$, the standard form of the hyperbola can be put in the form

$$(x - h)^2 - (y - k)^2 = a^2$$

if the axis is parallel to the X axis and

$$(y - k)^2 - (x - h)^2 = a^2$$

if the axis is parallel to the Y axis.

EXAMPLE

Find the equation of the equilateral hyperbola with center at $(2, -5)$ and a vertex at $(6, -5)$.

Solution: In this problem $a = 4$, since that is the distance between center and vertex; furthermore, the axis is parallel to the X axis.

Consequently, the equation is

$$(x - 2)^2 - (y + 5)^2 = 4^2$$

4.8. CONJUGATE HYPERBOLAS

If, in standard form, the left member of one hyperbola is the negative of the left member of another, the two are called *conjugate hyperbolas*. In keeping with this, $(x - 1)^2/3^2 - (y - 2)^2/5^2 = 1$ and $(y - 2)^2/5^2 - (x - 1)^2/3^2 = 1$ are conjugate hyperbolas.

4.9. ANOTHER DEFINITION OF THE CONICS

All three conics can be included in the following definition. The set of points so located in a plane that the undirected distance of each from a fixed point divided by its undirected distance from a fixed line is a constant e is called a *conic*. The fixed point is called the *focus*, the fixed line the *directrix*, and the constant e the *eccentricity*.

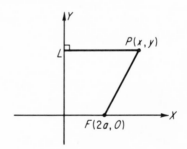

FIGURE 4.14

In order to derive the equation of the conic, we take the directrix along the Y axis, the focus at $F(2a, 0)$ and let $P(x, y)$ be any point of the set that forms the conic. Then, in symbolic form the definition becomes $FP = eDP$. Now if we use the distance formula and the coordinates of F and P, we have

$$\sqrt{(x - 2a)^2 + y^2} = ex$$

Finally, squaring and collecting coefficients of like terms, we find that

(1) $$(1 - e^2)x^2 + y^2 - 4ax + 4a^2 = 0$$

is the equation of the conic with eccentricity **e**, *a focus at* (**2a**, **0**), *and directrix along the* **Y** *axis.*

It can be shown in a similar manner that

(2) $$(1 - e^2)y^2 + x^2 - 4ay + 4a^2 = 0$$

is the equation of the conic with eccentricity **e**, *a focus at* (**0**, **2a**), *and directrix along the* **X** *axis.*

The type of conic is determined by the value of e as given in the following statement: The conic is an *ellipse*, a *parabola*, or a *hyperbola* according as e is less then, equal to, or greater than 1.

EXAMPLE

Determine the type of conic represented by

$$7x^2 + 16y^2 - 128x + 16 = 0$$

by evaluating e. Locate a focus.

Solution: Since this equation contains x, it must be compared to (1); hence the coefficient of y^2 must be 1. Therefore, we divide through by 16 and have

$$\tfrac{7}{16}x^2 + y^2 - 8x + 1 = 0$$

Consequently, $1 - e^2 = \tfrac{7}{16}$, $e^2 = \tfrac{9}{16}$ and $e = \tfrac{3}{4}$. Therefore, the conic is an ellipse. Since $-4a = -8$, we have $a = 2$ and a focus is at $(4, 0)$.

EXERCISE 4.4

Change the equation in each of Problems 1 to 12 to standard form.

1. $y^2 - 2y - 8x - 7 = 0$ 2. $y^2 + 6y + 4x + 1 = 0$

3. $x^2 + 4x + 12y - 8 = 0$ 4. $x^2 - 2x + 8y + 41 = 0$

5. $9x^2 + 16y^2 - 32y = 128$

6. $25x^2 + 144y^2 + 100x - 288y = 3456$

7. $9y^2 + 16x^2 - 54y - 32x = 47$

8. $64y^2 + 225x^2 + 128y - 900x = 13436$

9. $4x^2 - 9y^2 - 16x + 18y = 29$

10. $25x^2 - 16y^2 + 50x + 32y = 391$

11. $y^2 - 9x^2 + 4y - 18x = 14$

12. $25y^2 - 4x^2 - 100y - 24x = 36$

Determine the equation of each equilateral hyperbola described in Problems 13 to 16.

13. $a = 2$, center at $(2, -1)$, axis parallel to the X axis

14. A vertex at $(5, 2)$, center at $(1, 2)$

15. Vertices at $(3, -2)$ and $(3, 6)$

16. Vertices at $(-1, 4)$ and $(5, 4)$

Find the conjugate of the hyperbola given in each of Problems 17 to 20. Sketch each hyperbola and its conjugate.

17. $\dfrac{(x+3)^2}{3^2} - \dfrac{(y-1)^2}{4^2} = 1$ 18. $\dfrac{(x+1)^2}{5^2} - \dfrac{(y-2)^2}{2^2} = 1$

19. $\dfrac{(y+2)^2}{5^2} - \dfrac{(x-2)^2}{3^2} = 1$ 20. $\dfrac{(y-3)^2}{3^2} - \dfrac{(x+2)^2}{2^2} = 1$

21. Show that a rectangular hyperbola and its conjugate have the same eccentricity.

22. Show that conjugate hyperbolas have the same asymptotes.

23. Show that the asymptotes of a rectangular hyperbola are perpendicular.

24. What is the relation between the eccentricity of a hyperbola and its conjugate?

Determine the value of e and the type of conic represented by each of the following equations. Sketch each curve.

25. $3x^2 + 4y^2 - 16x + 16 = 0$

26. $y^2 - 12x + 36 = 0$

27. $-2x^2 + y^2 + 4x + 4 = 0$

28. $-3x^2 + y^2 + 12x + 36 = 0$

29. $-y^2 + x^2 - 4y + 4 = 0$

30. $x^2 - 8y + 16 = 0$

31. $8y^2 + 9x^2 + 72y + 144 = 0$

32. $y^2 + 2x^2 + 8y + 8 = 0$

5 *THE GENERAL SECOND DEGREE EQUATION*

5.1. *INTRODUCTION*

In this chapter, we shall investigate the effect on an equation of two different types of change in the position of the coordinate axes. One of these consists of changing the position of the origin while leaving the axes parallel to and oriented as the original axes. The other change is brought about by keeping the origin fixed and turning the axes. We shall show that each type of change can be used to simplify an equation.

5.2. *TRANSLATION*

We shall now discuss the first type of change in position of axes. It is characterized below.

DEFINITION. *The coordinate axes are said to be* **translated** *if the new axes are parallel to and oriented as the original ones.*

We shall now prove a theorem that gives the relation between the coordinates of a point referred to the two sets of axes.

THEOREM. *If the origin is translated to* (h, k) *and if* (x, y) *and* (x', y') *are the coordinates of a point* P *when referred to the original and new axes, respectively, then*

$$x = x' + h$$

and

$$y = y' + k.$$

Proof. The segment MP in Fig. 5.1 is perpendicular to OX and to $O'X'$, and NP is perpendicular to OY and $O'Y'$. Hence

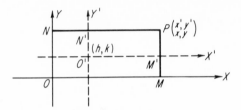

FIG. 5.1 Translation.

$MP = y$, $M'P = y'$, $NP = x$, and $N'P = x'$. Furthermore, $MM' = k$ and $NN' = h$. If we notice that $MP = M'P + MM'$ and $NP = N'P + NN'$ and substitute the values of these segments as given above, it follows that

$$y = y' + k \quad \text{and} \quad x = x' + h.$$

EXAMPLE

Determine the equation of the curve represented by

$$x^2 - 2x + y^2 + 6y - 15 = 0$$

if the origin is translated to $(1, -3)$.

Solution: Since the new origin is at $(1, -3)$ the equation referred to the new axes is obtained by replacing x by $x' + 1$ and y by $y' + (-3) = y' - 3$. Thus the given equation becomes

$$(x' + 1)^2 - 2(x' + 1) + (y' - 3)^2 + 6(y' - 3) - 15 = 0,$$
$$x'^2 + 2x' + 1 - 2x' - 2 + y'^2 - 6y' + 9 + 6y' - 18 - 15 = 0.$$

After collecting terms this reduces to the desired equation

$$x'^2 + y'^2 - 25 = 0.$$

5.3. SIMPLIFICATION OF AN EQUATION BY TRANSLATION

It is often possible to simplify an equation by translation, but it is sometimes difficult to choose the most desirable point for the new origin unless the problem is attacked systematically. Such an attack can be made by putting $x = x' + h$ and $y = y' + k$ in the given equation and then determining h and k in such a way as to make the equation reduce to a desirable form in the new coordinates. Generally, it is possible to make any two of the following vanish: (a) the coefficient of x, (b) the coefficient of y, (c) the constant term. It is often desirable to determine h and k so that the first degree terms vanish. This is not possible, however, unless h or k or both enter into the coefficients of x' and y' and then only if the resulting equations in h and k represent intersecting lines. The method of procedure may be clarified by considering a special case.

EXAMPLE

What point should be selected as the new origin in order to transform the equation $x^2 - 2x + y^2 + 6y - 15 = 0$ into a new equation without linear terms? Find the transformed equation.

Solution: In order to determine the desired point, we shall put

$$x = x' + h \quad \text{and} \quad y = y' + k$$

in the given equation. Thus we get

$$(x' + h)^2 - 2(x' + h) + (y' + k)^2 + 6(y' + k) - 15 = 0,$$

(1) $\quad x'^2 + 2hx' + h^2 - 2x' - 2h + y'^2 + 2ky' + k^2 + 6y'$
$$+ 6k - 15 = 0.$$

Collecting coefficients,

$$x'^2 + x'(2h - 2) + y'^2 + y'(2k + 6) + h^2 - 2h + k^2 + 6k$$
$$- 15 = 0.$$

The coefficients of x' and y' are obviously zero if

$$2h - 2 = 0 \quad \text{and} \quad 2k + 6 = 0.$$

Therefore, $\qquad\qquad h = 1 \quad \text{and} \quad k = -3.$

Consequently, the origin should be translated to $(1, -3)$. If this is done, the given equation becomes

$$x'^2 + y'^2 - 25 = 0$$

EXERCISE 5.1

Find the equation into which each equation in Problems 1 to 4 is transformed if the origin is translated to the given point.

1. $x^2 + y^2 - 4x - 2y + 2 = 0$, $(2, 1)$

2. $2x^2 - y^2 - 12x - 4y + 12 = 0$, $(3, -2)$

3. $4x^2 + 8x + 9y^2 + 54y + 49 = 0$, $(-1, -3)$

4. $y^2 - 8x - 2y - 31 = 0$, $(-4, 1)$

To what point must the origin be translated in order to eliminate the linear terms or a linear term and the constant from each of the following equations? What is each transformed equation?

5. $x^2 + y^2 - 2x - 4y + 1 = 0$

6. $x^2 + y^2 + 2x - 6y + 1 = 0$

7. $4x^2 + 9y^2 + 16x - 36y + 16 = 0$

8. $4x^2 + 25y^2 + 24x + 250y + 561 = 0$

9. $x^2 - 4y^2 - 10x - 8y + 17 = 0$

10. $9x^2 - 25y^2 - 72x + 50y - 106 = 0$

11. $y^2 - 4x - 2y - 19 = 0$

12. $x^2 + 4x + 8y - 20 = 0$

13. Remove the linear terms from $(y - 1)^2 = 4(x - 3)$ by a translation, or tell why it cannot be done.

14. Remove the linear terms from $(x + 2)^2 = 8(y - 1)$ by a translation, or tell why it cannot be done.

15. To what point must the origin be translated to remove the constant term and the linear term in x from $x^2 + 4x - 4y + 12 = 0$ by a translation?

16. To what point must the origin be translated to remove the constant term and the linear term in y from $y^2 + 2y + 4x - 11 = 0$ by a translation?

17. Find the equation into which $ax + ay + c = 0$ is transformed if the origin is translated to $(h, -h)$.

18. Find the equation into which $ax + by + c = 0$ is transformed if the origin is translated to $(bh, -ah - c/b)$.

19. Find the equation into which $y = mx + b$ is transformed if the origin is translated to $(-b/m, 0)$.

20. Show that the distance between two points is not altered by a translation of axes.

5.4. ROTATION

We shall now discuss the second type of change in position of axes. It is characterized in the definition given below.

DEFINITION. *The coordinate axes are said to be* **rotated** *if the origin remains fixed and both axes are turned through the same angle about the origin.*

The relation between the coordinates of a point referred to the original and new axes is given in the following theorem.

THEOREM. *If* (x, y) *are the coordinates of a point before the axes are rotated through an angle* θ *and if* (x', y') *are the coordinates after the rotation, then*

$$x = x' \cos \theta - y' \sin \theta,$$
$$y = x' \sin \theta + y' \cos \theta.$$

Proof. We shall use Fig. 5.2 in the proof. It is constructed by drawing two pairs of coordinate axes with the same origin and

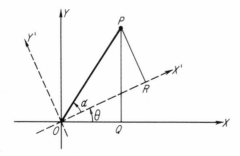

FIG. 5.2 Rotation.

making an angle θ less than $90°$ with one another; selecting any point P with coordinates (x, y) and (x', y') relative to the original and new axes, dropping perpendiculars PQ and PR to the X and X' axes and finally, connecting O and P. If α is the name of angle ROP then, using the definitions of the sine and cosine of a positive acute angle,

$$\cos (\alpha + \theta) = \cos \alpha \cos \theta - \sin \alpha \sin \theta$$

becomes

$$\frac{OQ}{OP} = \frac{OR}{OP} \cos \theta - \frac{RP}{OP} \sin \theta$$

$$OQ = OR \cos \theta - RP \sin \theta, \quad \text{multiplying by } OP,$$

$$x = x' \cos \theta - y' \sin \theta$$

since $OQ = x, OR = x'$ and $RP = y'$.

Furthermore,

$$\sin (\alpha + \theta) = \sin \alpha \cos \theta + \cos \alpha \sin \theta$$

becomes

$$\frac{QP}{OP} = \frac{RP}{OP} \cos \theta + \frac{OR}{OP} \sin \theta$$

$$QP = RP \cos \theta + OR \sin \theta, \quad \text{multiplying by } OP,$$

$$y = y' \cos \theta + x' \sin \theta$$

since $QP = y, RP = y'$ and $OR = x'$.

EXAMPLE

What does the equation $x^2 - y^2 - 4 = 0$ become when referred to a pair of axes which make an angle of $45°$ with the original pair?

Solution: The angle θ through which the axes are rotated is $45°$. Hence the new equation is obtained by putting

$$x = x' \cos 45° - y' \sin 45° = \frac{x' - y'}{\sqrt{2}},$$

and

$$y = x' \sin 45° + y' \cos 45° = \frac{x' + y'}{\sqrt{2}},$$

in the original equation since $\sin 45° = \cos 45° = 1/\sqrt{2}$. Thus, we get

$$\left(\frac{x' - y'}{\sqrt{2}}\right)^2 - \left(\frac{x' + y'}{\sqrt{2}}\right)^2 - 4 = 0.$$

Therefore, expanding and collecting like terms, we have

$$x'y' + 2 = 0$$

for the desired equation.

5.5. SIMPLIFICATION OF AN EQUATION BY ROTATION

We shall now develop a formula for the determination of the angle θ through which the axes must be rotated in order to eliminate the product term from the general equation of the second degree

$$Ax^2 + Bxy + Cy^2 + Dx + Ey + F = 0. \quad (B \neq 0)$$

To do this, we shall put $x = x' \cos \theta - y' \sin \theta$ and $y = x' \sin \theta + y' \cos \theta$ in the given equation and set the coefficient of $x'y'$ equal to zero. Thus we get $A(x' \cos \theta - y' \sin \theta)^2 + B(x' \cos \theta - y' \sin \theta)(x' \sin \theta + y' \cos \theta) + C(x' \sin \theta + y' \cos \theta)^2 + D(x' \cos \theta - y' \sin \theta) + E(x' \sin \theta + y' \cos \theta) + F = 0$. Expanding and collecting coefficients of like terms, we get

(1) $x'^{\,2}(A \cos^2 \theta + B \sin \theta \cos \theta + C \sin^2 \theta)$
$+ x'y'(-2A \sin \theta \cos \theta + B \cos^2 \theta$
$- B \sin^2 \theta + 2C \sin \theta \cos \theta) +$
$y'^{\,2}(A \sin^2 \theta - B \sin \theta \cos \theta + C \cos^2 \theta)$
$+ x'(D \cos \theta + E \sin \theta) + y'(-D \sin \theta$
$+ E \cos \theta) + F = 0.$

Hence in order to eliminate the product term, we must have

$$B(\cos^2 \theta - \sin^2 \theta) + (C - A)\, 2 \sin \theta \cos \theta = 0.$$

Using the formulas for the sine and cosine of twice an angle, this becomes

(2) $B \cos 2\theta + (C - A) \sin 2\theta = 0.$

Finally, adding $(A - C) \sin 2\theta$ to each member of (2) and dividing each member of the resulting equation by $B \sin 2\theta$, we have

$$\cot 2\theta = \frac{A - C}{B}, \quad B \neq 0.$$

Consequently, we can now state the theorem given below.

THEOREM. *In order to eliminate the product term from*

$$Ax^2 + Bxy + Cy^2 + Dx + Ey + F = 0, \quad B \neq 0,$$

the axes must be rotated through an angle θ determined by the equation $\cot 2\theta = \dfrac{A - C}{B}$.

The phrase *an* angle θ is used instead of *the* angle θ, since there are infinitely many angles which satisfy the trigonometric equation. It is customary in rotation of axes to choose the smallest positive angle that satisfies the equation. Since there is always an angle 2θ between $0°$ and $180°$ that satisfies the equation of the theorem, *an equation without product term can always be obtained by rotating through an acute angle.*

The theorem gives the value of $\cot 2\theta$ but we must use the value, exact value, of $\sin \theta$ and of $\cos \theta$ in the rotation formulas. Therefore, we must be able to find them. We can find $\tan \theta$ by making use of the identity

$$(1) \qquad\qquad \cot 2\theta = \frac{1 - \tan^2 \theta}{2 \tan \theta}.$$

We then can find $\sin \theta$ and $\cos \theta$ by making use of the identity

$$(2) \qquad\qquad \tan \theta = \frac{\sin \theta}{\cos \theta}.$$

If $\tan \theta = a/b$, it does not follow that $\sin \theta = a$ and $\cos \theta = b$ but rather that $\sin \theta = ka$ and $\cos \theta = kb$; hence squaring each member of these two equations and adding corresponding members, we have $1 = k^2(a^2 + b^2)$ since $\sin^2 \theta + \cos^2 \theta = 1$. Therefore, it follows that $k = 1/\sqrt{a^2 + b^2}$ and

$$(3) \qquad \sin \theta = \frac{a}{\sqrt{a^2 + b^2}} \quad \text{and} \quad \cos \theta = \frac{b}{\sqrt{a^2 + b^2}}$$

EXAMPLE

Rotate the axes so as to eliminate the product term from

$$2x^2 + 24xy - 5y^2 - 9 = 0$$

Solution: In keeping with the theorem, we must rotate through an angle θ determined by the equation

$$\cot 2\theta = \frac{A - C}{B} = \frac{2 - (-5)}{24} = \frac{7}{24}$$

Consequently, by use of (1), we have

$$\frac{1 - \tan^2 \theta}{2 \tan \theta} = \frac{7}{24}$$

$24 - 24 \tan^2 \theta = 14 \tan \theta,$ clearing of fractions,

$24 \tan^2 \theta + 14 \tan \theta - 24 = 0$

$2(4 \tan \theta - 3)(3 \tan \theta + 4) = 0,$ factoring,

$\tan \theta = \frac{3}{4}, -\frac{4}{3}$

We shall use $\frac{3}{4}$ since we want to rotate through an acute angle. Now, by use of (3), we see that $\sin \theta = \frac{3}{5}$ and $\cos \theta = \frac{4}{5}$, since $\sqrt{3^2 + 4^2} = 5$. Therefore, the rotation formulas become

$$x = \frac{4x' - 3y'}{5} \text{ and } y = \frac{3x' + 4y'}{5}.$$

Now, putting these values in the given equation, we have

$$2x^2 + 24xy - 5y^2 - 9$$

$$= 2\left(\frac{4x' - 3y'}{5}\right)^2 + 24\frac{4x' - 3y'}{5}\frac{3x' + 4y'}{5} - 5\left(\frac{3x' + 4y'}{5}\right)^2 - 9$$

$$= \frac{1}{25}[2(16x'^2 - 24x'y' + 9y'^2) + 24(12x'^2 + 7x'y' - 12y'^2)$$

$$- 5(9x'^2 + 24x'y' + 16y'^2) - 225]$$

$$= \frac{1}{25}[x'^2(32 + 288 - 45) + x'y'(-48 + 168 - 120)$$

$$+ y'^2(18 - 288 - 80) - 225]$$

$$= \frac{1}{25}(275x'^2 - 350y'^2 - 225)$$

$$= 11x'^2 - 14y'^2 - 9 = 0.$$

EXERCISE 5.2

Find the new equation if the axes are rotated through the indicated angle in Problems 1 to 8.

1. $x^2 + 3xy + y^2 = 2$, $45°$ $5x'^2 - y'^2 = 4$

2. $2x^2 - xy + 2y^2 = 9$, $135°$

3. $x^2 - \sqrt{3}\,xy + 2y^2 = 3$, $30°$

4. $x^2 - 2\sqrt{3}\,xy - y^2 = 2$, $60°$

5. $13x^2 + 24xy + 6y^2 = 6$, $\theta = \arccos\left(\frac{4}{5}\right)$, θ acute

6. $9x^2 - 24xy + 2y^2 = 7$, $\theta = \arcsin\left(\frac{3}{5}\right)$, θ obtuse $18x'^2 - 7y'^2 = 7$

7. $5x^2 + 4xy + 2y^2 = 6$, $\theta = \arcsin(1/\sqrt{5})$, θ acute

8. $7x^2 + 3xy + 3y^2 = 5$, $\theta = \arccos(-1/\sqrt{10})$, θ obtuse

Find the sine and cosine of the smallest positive angle through which the axes can be rotated so as to eliminate the product term in each of equations 9 to 16.

9. $7x^2 + \sqrt{3}\,xy + 6y^2 = 2$ $\sin\theta = \tfrac{1}{2}$ $\cos\theta = \dfrac{\sqrt{3}}{2}$

10. $7x^2 - \sqrt{3}\,xy + 6y^2 = 2$

11. $7x^2 + \sqrt{3}\,xy + 7y^2 = 2$

12. $x^2 - 9xy + y^2 = 5$

13. $2x^2 + 24xy - 5y^2 = 6$

14. $13x^2 + 7xy - 11y^2 = 19$ $\sin\theta = .1\sqrt{2}$ $\cos\theta .7\sqrt{2}$

15. $2x^2 + 4xy - y^2 = 11$

16. $9x^2 - 3xy + 5y^2 = 8$

17. Prove that $x^2 + y^2 = r^2$ is unaltered by a rotation.

18. Find the equation into which $x^2 - y^2 = 2a^2$ is transformed if the axes are rotated through $45°$.

19. Show that both linear terms cannot be removed by a rotation.

20. Show that the distance between two points is not altered by a rotation.

5.6. TYPES OF CONICS AND THE GENERAL QUADRATIC EQUATION

The equation

$$A'x^2 + C'y^2 + D'x + E'y + F' = 0.$$

represents

(a) an ellipse if $-A'C' < 0$, since A' and C' are of the same sign for an ellipse;

(b) a parabola if $-A'C' = 0$, since A' or C' is zero for a parabola; or

(c) a hyperbola if $-A'C' > 0$, since A' and C' are of opposite signs for a hyperbola.

Hence if we combine these three statements, we have the following theorem.

THEOREM 1. *The equation*

$$A'x^2 + C'y^2 + D'x + E'y + F' = 0$$

(with A and C not both zero)

represents an ellipse, a parabola, or a hyperbola when $-A'C'$ *is respectively negative, zero, or positive.*

We shall now consider the general quadratic

(1) $$Ax^2 + Bxy + Cy^2 + Dx + Ey + F = 0$$

in two variables and show that

$$B^2 - 4AC = B'^{\,2} - 4A'C'$$

where

(2) $$A'x'^{\,2} + B'x'y' + C'y'^{\,2} + D'x' + E'y' + F' = 0$$

is the equation into which (1) is transformed by rotating the axes through an angle θ.

If we examine (1) of Art. 5.5, we see that

$$A' = A \cos^2 \theta + C \sin^2 \theta + B \sin \theta \cos \theta,$$
$$C' = A \sin^2 \theta + C \cos^2 \theta - B \sin \theta \cos \theta,$$

and

$$B' = 2(C - A) \sin \theta \cos \theta + B(\cos^2 \theta - \sin^2 \theta).$$

Therefore,

$$A' = \tfrac{1}{2}A(1 + \cos 2\theta) + \tfrac{1}{2}C(1 - \cos 2\theta) + \tfrac{1}{2}B \sin 2\theta$$

and

$$C' = \tfrac{1}{2}A(1 - \cos 2\theta) + \tfrac{1}{2}C(1 + \cos 2\theta) - \tfrac{1}{2}B \sin 2\theta$$

since $\quad \sin^2 \theta = \tfrac{1}{2}(1 - \cos 2\theta), \cos^2 \theta = \tfrac{1}{2}(1 + \cos 2\theta)$

and $\quad\quad\quad\quad\quad\quad \sin \theta \cos \theta = \tfrac{1}{2} \sin 2\theta.$

Hence

$$2A' = A + A \cos 2\theta + C - C \cos 2\theta + B \sin 2\theta$$
$$= [A + C] + [(A - C) \cos 2\theta + B \sin 2\theta]$$

and

$$2C' = A - A \cos 2\theta + C + C \cos 2\theta - B \sin 2\theta$$
$$= [A + C] - [(A - C) \cos 2\theta + B \sin 2\theta].$$

Since $4A'C'$ is the product of the sum and the difference of two quantities, we have

$$4A'C' = (A + C)^2 - [(A - C) \cos 2\theta + B \sin 2\theta]^2$$
$$= (A + C)^2 - [(A - C)^2 \cos^2 2\theta$$
$$+ 2B(A - C) \sin 2\theta \cos 2\theta + B^2 \sin^2 2\theta].$$

Furthermore, since

$$B' = -2(A - C) \sin \theta \cos \theta + B(\cos^2 \theta - \sin^2 \theta)$$
$$= -(A - C) \sin 2\theta + B \cos 2\theta,$$

it then follows that

$$B'^2 = (A - C)^2 \sin^2 2\theta - 2B(A - C) \sin 2\theta \cos 2\theta + B^2 \cos^2 2\theta.$$

Consequently,

$$B'^2 - 4A'C' = (A - C)^2 \sin^2 2\theta - 2B(A - C) \sin 2\theta \cos 2\theta$$
$$+ B^2 \cos^2 2\theta - (A + C)^2 + (A - C)^2 \cos^2 2\theta$$
$$+ 2B(A - C) \sin 2\theta \cos 2\theta + B^2 \sin^2 2\theta = (A - C)^2$$
$$- (A + C)^2 + B^2 = B^2 - 4AC,$$

since $\sin^2 2\theta + \cos^2 2\theta = 1$.

We have shown therefore that $\quad B'^2 - 4A'C' = B^2 - 4AC$

regardless of the angle θ through which the axes are rotated. If θ is determined by $\cot 2\theta = (A - C)/B$, then $B' = 0$ and we have

$$B'^2 - 4A'C' = -4A'C' = B^2 - 4AC.$$

Therefore, we have the following theorem.

THEOREM 2. *The equation*

$$Ax^2 + Bxy + Cy^2 + Dx + Ey + F = 0$$

represents an ellipse, a parabola, or a hyperbola when $B^2 - 4AC$ is respectively negative, zero, or positive.

EXAMPLE 1

Determine the type of conic represented by each of the following equations:

(a) $\qquad 8x^2 + 8xy - 2y^2 + x - 3y + 8 = 0$

(b) $\qquad 8x^2 + 2xy + 8y^2 + x - 3y + 8 = 0$

(c) $\qquad 8x^2 + 8xy + 2y^2 + x - 3y + 8 = 0.$

Solution: We shall use Theorem 2 to identify each conic.

(a) The conic is a hyperbola, since

$$B^2 - 4AC = 8^2 - 4(8)(-2) = 128 > 0.$$

(b) The conic is an ellipse, since

$$B^2 - 4AC = 2^2 - 4(8)(8) = -252 < 0.$$

(c) The conic is a parabola, since

$$B^2 - 4AC = 8^2 - 4(8)(2) = 0.$$

EXAMPLE 2

Identify the conic represented by

$$7x^2 - 6\sqrt{3}\,xy + 13y^2 - 4\sqrt{3}\,x - 4y - 12 = 0,$$

remove the product term by rotation, sketch the curve referred to the new axes, and draw the original axes with the same origin as the new ones.

Solution: The conic is an ellipse since $B^2 - 4AC = (-6\sqrt{3})^2 - 4(7)13 = -256 < 0$. In order to remove the product term, we must rotate the coordinate axes through the angle θ determined by cot $2\theta =$ $(A - C)/B$. Hence

$$\cot 2\theta = \frac{7 - 13}{-6\sqrt{3}} = \frac{1}{\sqrt{3}}$$

and $2\theta = 60°$. Therefore, $\theta = 30°$ and the formulas for rotation become

$$x = x' \cos \theta - y' \sin \theta$$

$$= x' \frac{\sqrt{3}}{2} - y' \frac{1}{2}$$

and

$$y = x' \sin \theta + y' \cos \theta$$

$$= x' \frac{1}{2} + y' \frac{\sqrt{3}}{2}$$

since $\sin 30° = \frac{1}{2}$ and $\cos 30° = \sqrt{3}/2$.

Therefore, putting in these values for x and y, the given equation becomes

$$7\left(\frac{\sqrt{3}\,x'}{2} - \frac{y'}{2}\right)^2 - 6\sqrt{3}\left(\frac{\sqrt{3}\,x'}{2} - \frac{y'}{2}\right)\left(\frac{x'}{2} + \frac{\sqrt{3}\,y'}{2}\right)$$

$$+ 13\left(\frac{x'}{2} + \frac{\sqrt{3}\,y'}{2}\right)^2 - 4\sqrt{3}\left(\frac{\sqrt{3}\,x'}{2} - \frac{y'}{2}\right)$$

$$- 4\left(\frac{x'}{2} + \frac{\sqrt{3}\,y'}{2}\right) - 12 = 0.$$

Now collecting coefficients and dividing by 4, this equation becomes

$$x'^2 + 4y'^2 - 2x' - 3 = 0;$$

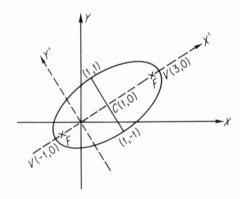

FIGURE 5.3

and we shall put it into standard form to sketch the curve more readily. The standard form is $(x' - 1)^2/2^2 + y'^2/1^2 = 1$. The center is at $(1, 0)$, the semi-axes are $a = 2$ and $b = 1$, and the major axis is parallel to the X' axis. The graph is shown in Fig. 5.3, and the original axes are indicated by the solid lines.

EXERCISE 5.3

Identify the conic represented by the equation in each of Problems 1 to 12.

1. $x^2 + 2xy + y^2 + 2x - 5y + 8 = 0$
2. $9x^2 + 6xy + y^2 + 4x + 3y + 7 = 0$ *Parabola*
3. $4x^2 - 4xy + y^2 + 5x - 2y + 3 = 0$
4. $2x^2 - 8xy + 8y^2 - 3x + 9y - 11 = 0$
5. $x^2 + 2xy + 3y^2 + 2x - 5y + 8 = 0$
6. $9x^2 + 6xy + 2y^2 + 4x + 3y + 7 = 0$
7. $4x^2 - 4xy + 2y^2 + 5x - 2y + 3 = 0$
8. $2x^2 - 8xy + 9y^2 - 3x + 9y - 11 = 0$
9. $x^2 + 2xy - y^2 + 2x - 5y + 8 = 0$
10. $8x^2 + 6xy + y^2 + 4x + 3y + 7 = 0$
11. $3x^2 - 4xy + y^2 + 5x - 2y + 3 = 0$
12. $x^2 - 8xy + 8y^2 - 3x + 9y - 11 = 0$

Remove the product and linear terms or the product term, a linear term, and the constant from the equation in Problems 13 to 20. Sketch each graph relative to the final position of the axes.

13. $x^2 - 2\sqrt{3}\,xy + 3y^2 + (4 - 16\sqrt{3})x - (4\sqrt{3} + 16)y + 4 = 0$ $(y'-1)^2 = 8x'$ $y''^2 = 8x''$
14. $x^2 + 2xy + y^2 - 8\sqrt{2}\,x + 8 = 0$
15. $5x^2 + 6xy + 5y^2 - 4\sqrt{2}\,x - 12\sqrt{2}\,y + 8 = 0$
16. $26x^2 + 6y^2 - 20\sqrt{3}\,xy + (12 + 36\sqrt{3})x + (12\sqrt{3} - 36)y - 36 = 0$
17. $5x^2 - 4xy + 8y^2 + 10\sqrt{5}\,x - 4\sqrt{5}\,y - 11 = 0$
18. $11x^2 + 24xy + 4y^2 + 26x + 32y - 5 = 0$
19. $9x^2 - 24xy + 16y^2 + 220x + 40y + 300 = 0$
20. $9x^2 + 24xy + 16y^2 - 20x - 110y + 50 = 0$ *Take home quiz*

5.7. *INVARIANTS*

We noticed in Art. 5.6 that the value of $B^2 - 4AC$ is unaltered regardless of the angle through which the axes are rotated. This is an example of the following definition.

DEFINITION. *A function of the coefficients of a general equation that is unaltered by a transformation of the coordinate axes is called an* **invariant** *of the equation relative to that change in axes.*

EXAMPLE

In the second degree equation in two unknowns, $I \equiv A + C$ involves only the coefficients of second degree terms. Since these coefficients are not altered by a translation, it follows that I is an invariant of a conic relative to translation.

EXERCISE 5.4

1. Prove that $D^2 + E^2 - 4F$ is an invariant of $x^2 + y^2 + Dx + Ey + F = 0$ relative to translation and rotation.

2. Prove that $A + C + F \equiv L$ is an invariant of $Ax^2 + Bxy + Cy^2 + Dx + Ey + F = 0$ relative to rotation. *Suggestion.* See (1) of Art. 5.5.

3. Prove that $4(AC + CF + FA) - B^2 - D^2 - E^2 \equiv J$ is an invariant of $Ax^2 + Bxy + Cy^2 + Dx + Ey + F = 0$ relative to rotation.

4. Prove that $4ACF + BDE - (AE)^2 - (CD)^2 - (FB)^2 = \theta$ is an invariant of $Ax^2 + Bxy + Cy^2 + Dx + Ey + F = 0$ relative to translation.

5. Prove that $4ACF + BDE - (AE)^2 - (CD)^2 - (FB)^2 = \theta$ is an invariant of $Ax^2 + Bxy + Cy^2 + Dx + Ey + F = 0$ relative to rotation.

6 ALGEBRAIC CURVES

6.1. INTRODUCTORY CONCEPTS AND DEFINITIONS

We studied equations of the form $Ax + By + C = 0$ in Chapter 2 and the general second degree equation $Ax^2 + Bxy + Cy^2 + Dx + Ey + F = 0$ in Chapter 4 and found their graphs to be straight lines and conics, respectively. They are special cases of the more general class of curves called algebraic curves. A plane curve is called an *algebraic curve* if it is the set of points which satisfy an equation $f(x, y) = 0$ when $f(x, y)$ is a polynomial in x and y, that is, when each term is of the form $Kx^m y^n$ where K is a constant and m and n are nonnegative integers. Thus the graph of the polynomial equation $f(x, y) = x^3 y - 2xy^2 - x + 1 = 0$ is an algebraic curve. The polynomial is of degree four since that is the largest sum obtained by adding the exponents of x and y in any term of the polynomial.

The abscissas and the ordinates of points of intersection of the graph of $f(x, y) = 0$ and the coordinate axes are obtained by solving $f(x, 0) = 0$ for x and solving $f(0, y) = 0$ for y. The ordinate of each intersection of the curve and the Y axis is called a *y-intercept;* furthermore, the abscissa of each intersection of the curve and the X axis is called an *x-intercept.* Thus the y-intercept of $f(x, y) = x^2 - 5y - 9$ $= 0$ is $-\frac{9}{5}$, since that is the solution of $f(0, y) = -5y - 9 = 0$. The solutions of $f(x, 0) = x^2 - 9 = 0$ are $x = \pm 3$; hence the x-intercepts are ± 3.

6.2. POLYNOMIALS IN X

An expression in the form

$$a_0 x^n + a_1 x^{n-1} + \cdots + a_{n-1}x + a_n$$

when each coefficient is a constant and n is a positive integer is called a *polynomial in x.* It is of degree n if $a_0 \neq 0$. In keeping with this definition, $3ix^2 - 1$, $(x^3 - 1)^3$, and $3x^8 - \sqrt{7}\,x^2 - 4$ are polynomials of degree 2, 9, and 8, respectively. The expressions

$$\sqrt[3]{x}, \; x^2 + 2\sqrt{x} + 1, \quad \text{and} \quad \frac{x+3}{x^2-1}$$

are not polynomials.

If a polynomial in x is given in factored form or is readily factorable, then it is a simple matter to obtain the graph of y equal to the polynomial. We can find the x-intercepts by putting the factors separately equal to zero and can determine as many other points on the graph as desired by assigning values to x and computing each corresponding value of y.

EXAMPLE 1

Sketch the graph of

$$y = (x + 2)(x - 1)(x - 3)$$

Solution: If we set each factor of the right-hand member equal to zero and solve, we find that $x = -2, 1, 3$ are the x-intercepts. We shall assign to x a value less than the smallest zero, a value between each consecutive pair of zeros and a value larger than the largest zero and find each corresponding value of y. The resulting number pairs are shown in the following table. In locating the pairs, remember that one space represents one unit on the x axis and six on the y axis as indicated in Fig. 6.1.

x	-3	0	2	4	large pos.	Num. large neg.
y	-24	6	-4	18	large pos.	Num. large neg.

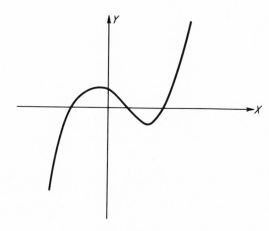

FIGURE 6.1

EXAMPLE 2

Sketch the graph of

$$y = (x - 1)(x - 3)^2(x - 4)$$

Solution: If we set each factor of the right-hand member equal to zero and solve, we find that the x-intercepts are $x = 1, 3, 3, 4$. Furthermore, if we assign the values to x as shown in the table below, we obtain the values shown for y. For example, if $x = 5$, the value of y is $(5 - 1)(5 - 3)^2(5 - 4) = (4)(2)^2(1) = 16$. This and other pairs of values are given in the table.

x	0	$.5$	1.5	2	3.5	5
y	36	10.9375	-2.8125	-2	$-.3125$	16

We can see readily that the graph shown in Fig. 6.2 is reasonable since

if $x < 1$, then each factor is positive and $y > 0$;

if $1 < x < 3$, then the factor $x - 4 < 0$, all others are positive, and $y < 0$;

if $3 < x < 4$, then the factor $x - 4 < 0$ all others are positive, and $y < 0$;

if $x > 4$, then all factors are positive and $y > 0$

The reader should notice that each interval between two consecutive zeros, as well as the values of x less than the smallest zero and greater than the largest, has been considered. In sketching the curve one space represents one unit on the x axis and two units on the y axis as seen in Fig. 6.2.

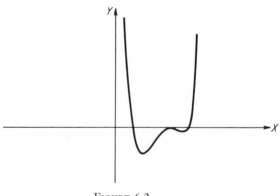

FIGURE 6.2

EXAMPLE 3

Sketch the graph of

$$y = (x^2 + x + 3)(x - 3)$$

Solution: If we set the second factor equal to zero and solve, we find that $x = 3$ is an intercept; furthermore, we see that x is imaginary if we set the first factor equal to zero and solve. Consequently, no intercept corresponds to that factor. We shall assign several values to x and find each corresponding value of y. These number pairs are listed in the table.

x	numerically large, neg.	-1	0	1	2	4	large pos.
y	numerically large, neg.	-12	-9	-10	-9	23	large pos.

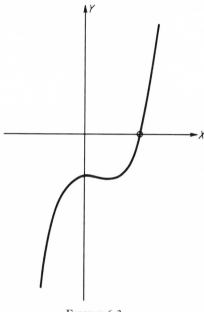

FIGURE 6.3

In sketching the graph one space represents 5 units on the x axis and 4 units on the y axis as seen in Fig. 6.3.

EXERCISE 6.1

Find the x-intercepts and sketch the graph of each of the following equations.

1. $y = x + 3$

2. $y = -x + 2$

3. $y = 2x - 5$

4. $y = -3x - 4$

5. $y = 2x^2 - 3x - 5$

6. $y = -2x^2 + 5x - 2$

7. $y = -x^2 + 2x + 3$

8. $y = 3x^2 - x - 2$

9. $y = (x + 2)(x)(x - 1)$

10. $y = (x + 1)(x - 1)(x - 3)$

11. $y = (-x - 3)(x + 1)(x - 2)$

12. $y = (x + 4)(-x + 1)(x - 2)$

13. $y = (x + 1)^2(x - 1)$

14. $y = (x - 2)^2(x - 3)$

15. $y = (x + 2)^2(x - 3)$

16. $y = (x + 3)^2(x - 1)$

17. $y = (x^2 + 3x + 1)(x - 1)$

18. $y = (x^2 - 2x - 2)(x - 2)$

19. $y = (x^2 + 2x + 3)(x + 1)$

20. $y = (x^2 - x + 1)(x - 1)$

21. $y = (x + 2)(x)(x - 1)(x - 3)$

22. $y = (x + 3)(x + 1)(x - 1)(x - 2)$

23. $y = (-x + 3)(x - 1)(x + 1)(x + 2)$

24. $y = (x + 2)(x)(x - 1)(-x + 3)$

25. $y = (x - 2)^2(x + 1)(x + 3)$

26. $y = (x + 1)^2(x + 3)(x - 1)$

27. $y = (x - 1)^2(-x + 2)(x + 3)$

28. $y = (x + 2)^2(x + 3)(-x + 1)$

29. $y = (x^2 + 3x + 1)(x - 2)(x + 1)$

30. $y = (x^2 + x + 2)(x + 2)(x - 3)$

31. $y = (x^2 + 2x + 3)(x + 1)^2$

32. $y = (x^2 + 4x + 2)(x - 2)^2$

6.3. SYMMETRY

This article and the two that follow are necessary here because an understanding of the concepts involved in them simplifies the discussion of curves.

DEFINITION. *Two points P_1 and P_2 are said to be* **located symmetrically with respect to a third point P** *if P is the midpoint of the line segment that joins them.*

The points P_1 and P_2 in Fig. 6.4 are situated symmetrically with respect to P, since it is the midpoint of the segment that connects them.

DEFINITION. *Two points P_1 and P_2 are said to be* **located symmetrically with respect to a line** *if the line is the perpendicular bisector of the segment that joins them.*

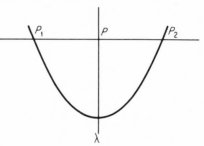

FIG. 6.4 Symmetry.

The points P_1 and P_2 in Fig. 6.4 are symmetrically located with respect to the line λ, since it is the perpendicular bisector of the segment P_1P_2.

DEFINITION. *A curve is* **symmetrical with respect to a point P** *if for each point P_1 on the curve there is a point P_2 on it such that P_1 and P_2 are symmetrically located with respect to the point P.*

Thus, a circle is symmetrical with respect to its center.

DEFINITION. *A curve is* **symmetrical with respect to a line** *if for each point P_1 on the curve, there is a point P_2 on it such that P_1 and P_2 are symmetrically located with respect to the line. The line is called an* **axis of symmetry.**

The curve in Fig. 6.4 is symmetrical with respect to the line λ, since corresponding to each point on the curve there is a second point placed so that the two points are symmetrically located with respect to λ. Furthermore, a square is symmetrical with respect to a diagonal.

We shall be primarily interested in determining whether a curve whose equation is given is symmetrical with respect to the origin, the X axis and the Y axis, and shall prove three theorems that furnish appropriate tests.

THEOREM 1. *A curve is symmetrical with respect to the origin if and only if its equation is unchanged or multiplied by* -1 *when* x *is replaced by* $-x$ *and* y *by* $-y$ *simultaneously, that is, if and only if* $f(-x, -y) = \pm f(x, y)$, *where the equation of the curve is* $f(x, y) = 0$.

Proof. The points (x, y) and $(-x, -y)$ are symmetrically located with respect to the origin since the origin is the midpoint of the segment that joins them. This symmetry and the fact that the graphs of $f(x, y) = 0$ and $kf(x, y) = 0$ are identical are used in the proof. Hence, if the equation of the curve is unaltered or multiplied by -1 when x and y are replaced by $-x$ and $-y$, respectively, then corresponding to each point $P_1(x, y)$ on the curve the symmetrically located point $P_2(-x, -y)$ is also on the curve, since its coordinates satisfy the equation of the curve. The constant -1 is specifically named since no other constant can be introduced by replacing x and y by $-x$ and $-y$, respectively. Consequently, the curve is symmetrical with respect to the origin.

If $f(-x, -y) \neq \pm f(x, y)$, then $(-x, -y)$ does not satisfy the equation and, consequently, is not on the locus. Since $(-x, -y)$ and (x, y) are symmetrically located with respect to the origin and the first is not on the locus, whereas the second is, the curve is not symmetrical with respect to the origin.

THEOREM 2. *A curve is symmetrical with respect to the* X *axis if and only if its equation is unchanged or multiplied by* -1 *when* y *is replaced by* $-y$, *that is, if and only if* $f(x, -y) = \pm f(x, y)$ *where the equation of the curve is* $f(x, y) = 0$.

Proof. The points $P_1(x, y)$ and $P_2(x, -y)$ are symmetrically located with respect to the X axis since the axis is the perpendicular bisector of the segment between P_1 and P_2. Hence if the equation of a curve is unaltered or multiplied by -1 when y and $-y$ are replaced, then corresponding to each point $P_1(x, y)$ on the curve the symmetrically located point $P_2(x, -y)$ is also on it. Consequently, by definition, the curve is symmetrical with respect to the X axis.

If $f(x, -y) \neq \pm f(x, y)$, then $(x, -y)$ does not satisfy the equation and, consequently, is not on the locus. Since $(x, -y)$ and (x, y) are symmetrically located with respect to the X axis and since the first point is not on the locus and the second is, the curve is not symmetrical with respect to the X axis. ·

THEOREM 3. *A curve is symmetrical with respect to the* **Y** *axis if and only if its equation is unchanged or multiplied by* -1 *when* **x** *is replaced by* $-x$, *that is, if and only if* $f(-x, y) = \pm f(x, y)$ *where the equation of the curve is* $f(x, y) = 0$.

Proof. The proof of this theorem is almost identical with that of Theorem 2 and can be obtained from it by replacing $(x, -y)$ by $(-x, y)$ and X by Y.

EXAMPLE

Test

$$f(x, y) = x^2 - 3x^2y + y^3 - 2 = 0$$

for symmetry with respect to the origin and each coordinate axis.

Solution: Since $f(-x, -y)$ is obtained from $f(x, y)$ by replacing x by $-x$ and y by $-y$, we have

$$
\begin{aligned}
f(-x, -y) &= (-x)^2 - 3(-x)^2(-y) + (-y)^3 - 2 \\
&= x^2 + 3x^2y - y^3 - 2 \\
&\neq \pm f(x, y)
\end{aligned}
$$

and the curve is not symmetrical with respect to the origin.
Furthermore,

$$
\begin{aligned}
f(x, -y) &= x^2 - 3x^2(-y) + (-y)^3 - 2 \\
&= x^2 + 3x^2y - y^3 - 2 \\
&\neq \pm f(x, y)
\end{aligned}
$$

and the curve is not symmetrical with respect to the X axis.
Finally,

$$
\begin{aligned}
f(-x, y) &= (-x)^2 - 3(-x)^2y + y^3 - 2 \\
&= x^2 - 3x^2y + y^3 - 2 \\
&= f(x, y)
\end{aligned}
$$

and the curve is symmetrical with respect to the Y axis.

6.4. ASYMPTOTES

The concept given in the following definition makes the drawing of certain curves simpler than would otherwise be the case.

DEFINITION. *If the distance between a variable point on a curve and a fixed line becomes and remains less than any preassigned, arbitrarily small, positive number as the point recedes infinitely far out on the curve, the line is said to be an* **asymptote** *of the curve.*

The asymptotes of a hyperbola were discussed and their equations derived in Article 4.5. We shall restrict our further study of asymptotes to those parallel to one of the coordinate axes and shall present two methods for determining them. If an equation in x and y is solved for y in terms of x, it may happen that a value of x, say a, makes the denominator of the right member zero without making the numerator zero. If there is such a value of x, it cannot be used, because no value of y corresponds to it inasmuch as division by zero is not a permissible operation. If, however, x is sufficiently near to a, y is numerically larger than any preassigned number. We shall now show that the distance from the line $x - a = 0$ to any point $P_1(x_1, y_1)$ on a curve, and infinitely far from the origin, is as small as we please under the conditions stated above. The equation of the line, $x - a = 0$, is already in normal form if $a > 0$; therefore, we substitute the coordinates of P_1 in it in order to obtain the distance d and direction from the line to P_1. Thus, we have $d = x_1 - a$; $x_1 - a$, however, is as small as we please for x_1 is sufficiently near a. The proof is similar if a is negative.

It can be shown in a similar manner that $y = b$ is an asymptote of a curve if x becomes and remains larger than any preassigned number when y is sufficiently near b. Hence we have the following theorem.

THEOREM. *The line* $x - a = 0$ *is an asymptote of a curve if* $x - a$ *is a factor of the denominator after the equation has been* *solved for **y** in terms of **x** and all common factors have been removed from the denominator and numerator. The line **y** − **b** = **0** is an asymptote of a curve if **y** − **b** is a factor of the denominator after the equation has been solved for **x** in terms of **y**, and all common factors removed from the denominator and numerator.*

The following method for finding horizontal and vertical asymptotes is often easier to use than the preceding one and will be stated without proof and then illustrated.

*In order to find the horizontal asymptotes of a curve, set the coefficient of the highest power of **x** equal to zero and solve for **y**. In order to find the vertical asymptotes of a curve, set the coefficient of the highest power of **y** equal to zero and solve for **x**.*

EXAMPLE 1

Discuss the graph of

$$F(x, y) = xy - 2x + y - 3 = 0$$

by finding the intercepts and asymptotes and testing for symmetry. Sketch the curve.

Solution: Replacing y by zero, we have

$$F(x, 0) = x \cdot 0 - 2x + 0 - 3$$
$$= -2x - 3$$
$$= 0 \text{ for } x = -\tfrac{3}{2}.$$

Hence *the x-intercept is* $-\dfrac{3}{2}.$ Similarly,

$$F(0, y) = 0 \cdot y - 2 \cdot 0 + y - 3$$
$$= y - 3$$
$$= 0 \text{ for } y = 3.$$

Therefore, *the y-intercept is 3.*

We can find the asymptotes by means of the theorem since we can solve the equation for x and y but shall find them by means of the statement following the theorem. The highest power of x is x itself and its coefficient is $y - 2$; *hence* $y - 2 = 0$ *is an asymptote.* Similarly, $x + 1 = 0$ *is an asymptote* since $x + 1$ is the coefficient of the highest power of y.

In order to test for symmetry, we notice that

$$F(x, -y) = x(-y) - 2x - y - 3$$
$$= -xy - 2x - y - 3$$
$$\neq \pm F(x, y),$$
$$F(-x, y) = -xy + 2x + y - 3$$
$$\neq \pm F(x, y),$$

and

$$F(-x, -y) = xy + 2x - y - 3$$
$$\neq \pm F(x, y).$$

Consequently, the curve is not symmetrical with respect to either axis or the origin. The facts above and the table below were used in sketching the curve shown in Fig. 6.5.

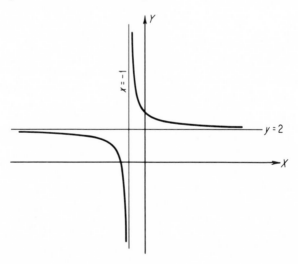

FIGURE 6.5

x	Numerically large, neg.	-5	-3	-2	0	2	3	5	Large, positive
y	Near but less than 2	$\frac{7}{4}$	$\frac{3}{2}$	1	3	$\frac{7}{3}$	$\frac{9}{4}$	$\frac{13}{6}$	Near but greater than 2

6.5. *TANGENTS AT THE ORIGIN*

If a curve passes through the origin, its behavior at and near the origin should be determined as a part of the preliminary discussion before sketching. This can be done by considering only those terms of lowest degree in x and y since others are negligible for small values of x and y. Specifically, *in order to find the tangent or tangents at the origin, equate to zero the terms of the equation for which the sum of the exponents of* x *and* y *is smallest.*

EXAMPLE

Discuss the graph of $f(x, y) = xy - 4x - y = 0$ by finding the intercepts, symmetry, asymptotes and tangents at the origin and then sketch the graph.

Solution: Intercepts. $f(x, 0) = 4x = 0$; hence $x = 0$ an intercept. Similarly, $f(0, y) = -y = 0$ and $y = 0$ is an intercept.
Symmetry.

$$f(x, -y) = -xy - 4x + y \neq \pm f(x, y)$$
$$f(-x, y) = -xy + 4x - y \neq \pm f(x, y)$$
$$f(-x, -y) = xy + 4x + y \neq \pm f(x, y)$$

Consequently, the graph is not symmetrical with respect to either coordinate axis or to the origin.

Asymptotes. The highest power of y is y itself and its coefficient is $x - 1$; hence $x - 1 = 0$ is an asymptote. The coefficient of the highest power of x is $y - 4$; consequently, $y - 4 = 0$ is an asymptote.

Tangents at the origin. This curve passes through the origin since the constant term is zero. The equation of the tangent at the origin is $-4x - y = 0$, since these are the terms of lowest degree in x and y set equal to zero. This tangent, the asymptotes, and the graphs are shown in Fig. 6.6.

This interesting and sometimes useful theorem will be stated without proof; *an asymptote to a curve of degree* n *may intersect the curve in at most* $(n - 2)$ *points.*

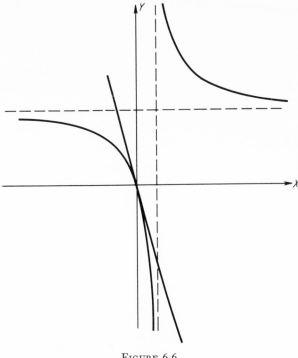

FIGURE 6.6

6.6. RATIONAL FUNCTIONS

The example of the last article if solved for y becomes

$$y = \frac{4x}{x - 1}$$

and is a special case of a rational function. Any function expressible in the form

$$y = \frac{N(x)}{D(x)}$$

when $N(x)$ and $D(x)$ are polynomials is called a *rational function*. Quite often, without resorting to any appreciable amount of plotting of points, a reasonably accurate sketch of the graph can be constructed by making use of the intercepts, symmetry, asymptotes, and tangents at the origin.

EXAMPLE 1

Sketch the graph of

$$y = \frac{x - 1}{(x + 1)(x - 2)}$$

by making use of the intercepts, symmetry, asymptotes, and tangents, if any, at the origin.

Solution: Intercepts. If we replace x by zero, we see that $y = \frac{1}{2}$ is an intercept; furthermore, $x = 1$ is an intercept, since that is the value of x that corresponds to $y = 0$.

Symmetry. The given equation is equivalent to

$$f(x, y) = y - \frac{x - 1}{(x + 1)(x - 2)} = 0$$

Therefore,

$$f(x, -y) = -y - \frac{x - 1}{(x + 1)(x - 2)} \neq \pm f(x, y)$$

and the curve is not symmetrical with respect to the X axis. Furthermore, $f(-x, y) \neq \pm f(x, y)$ and $f(-x, -y) \neq \pm f(x, y)$; hence the curve is not symmetrical with respect to the Y axis or the origin.

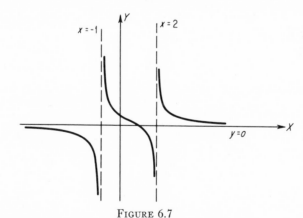

FIGURE 6.7

Asymptotes. With the equation in the given form, it is clear that $x = -1$ and $x = 2$ are asymptotes since $x + 1$ and $x - 2$ are factors of the denominator after the equation is solved for y and all common factors are removed from the numerator and denominator. In order to determine whether there are horizontal asymptotes, we shall clear the given equation of fractions and transpose all terms to one member. Thus we have

$$(x + 1)(x - 2)y - x + 1 = x^2y - xy - 2y - x + 1 = 0.$$

Now we see that $y = 0$ is an asymptote, since y is the coefficient of the highest power of x.

Tangents at the origin. There are no tangents at the origin, since equation of the curve is not satisfied by $(0, 0)$.

In order to determine what use to make of the asymptotes, we notice that $y > 0$ if $x > 2$, $y < 0$ if $1 < x < 2$, $y > 0$ if $-1 < x < 1$, and $y < 0$ if $x < -1$.

The graph, the intercepts, and the asymptotes are shown in Fig. 6.7.

EXAMPLE 2

Sketch the graph of

$$f(x, y) = y - \frac{x^3}{(x + 2)(x - 3)} = 0$$

by making use of the intercepts, symmetry, asymptotes, and tangents, if any, at the origin.

Solution: Intercepts. Since $f(x, 0) = x^3/(x + 2)(x - 3) = 0$ for $x = 0$, we see that zero is the x-intercept; furthermore, $f(0, y) = y = 0$ for $y = 0$ and zero is the y-intercept.

Symmetry. In order to test for symmetry, we find that

$$f(x, -y) = -y - \frac{x^3}{(x + 2)(x - 3)} \neq \pm f(x, y)$$

$$f(-x, y) = y + \frac{x^3}{(-x + 2)(-x - 3)} \neq \pm f(x, y)$$

$$f(-x, -y) = -y + \frac{x^3}{(-x + 2)(-x - 3)} \neq \pm f(x, y).$$

Asymptotes. The vertical asymptotes are $x = -2$ and $x = 3$ since $x + 2$ and $x - 3$ are factors of the denominator when the equation is solved for y and all common factors are removed from numerator and denominator. Furthermore, if $f(x, y) = 0$ is taken out of fractional form by multiplying by $(x + 2)(x - 3)$, we have $(x + 2)(x - 3)y - x^3 = 0$. Now, since the coefficient of the highest power of x is a constant, it is clear that there are no horizontal asymptotes.

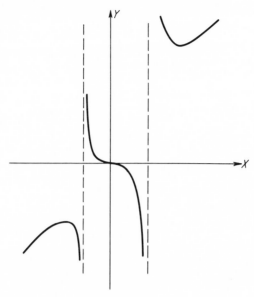

FIGURE 6.8

Tangents at the origin. The term of lowest degree in $(x + 2)(x - 3)y - x^3 = 0$ is $-6y$; hence, $y = 0$ is a tangent at the origin.

EXERCISE 6.2

Sketch the graph of each of the following equations by making use of the intercepts, symmetry, asymptotes, tangents at the origin, and as many points as needed.

1. $y = \dfrac{3}{x - 2}$

2. $y = \dfrac{5}{x + 3}$

3. $y = \dfrac{2}{(x + 1)(x - 2)}$

4. $y = \dfrac{6}{(x + 2)(2x - 1)}$

5. $y = \dfrac{x}{x + 3}$

6. $y = \dfrac{x + 2}{x + 1}$

7. $y = \dfrac{2x - 5}{x + 2}$

8. $y = \dfrac{x - 3}{3x + 1}$

9. $y = \dfrac{x + 2}{(x + 3)(x - 1)}$

10. $y = \dfrac{x}{(x + 1)(x - 2)}$

11. $y = \dfrac{2x - 3}{(x + 2)(2x - 1)}$ **12.** $y = \dfrac{3x - 2}{(x + 3)(2x - 3)}$

13. $y = \dfrac{x - 3}{x^2 + x + 1}$ **14.** $y = \dfrac{x + 2}{x^2 - x + 2}$

15. $y = \dfrac{2x}{2x^2 - x + 1}$ **16.** $y = \dfrac{3x - 4}{x^2 + 2x + 2}$

17. $y = \dfrac{x(x - 2)}{x^2 - 2x + 2}$ **18.** $y = \dfrac{(x - 1)(2x + 3)}{2x^2 + x + 2}$

19. $y = \dfrac{(2x + 3)x}{x^2 + 2}$ **20.** $y = \dfrac{(3x - 2)(x - 3)}{x^2 + 1}$

21. $y = \dfrac{(2x - 1)(x - 2)}{(3x - 2)(x + 3)}$ **22.** $y = \dfrac{(x + 1)(x - 3)}{(x + 2)(x - 2)}$

23. $y = \dfrac{(3x + 4)(x - 1)}{(2x - 3)(x + 2)}$ **24.** $y = \dfrac{(2x + 5)(x - 3)}{(x + 1)(2x - 5)}$

25. $y = \dfrac{(x + 1)(x)(x - 1)}{(x + 2)(x - 2)}$ **26.** $y = \dfrac{(x + 2)(x)(x - 1)}{(x + 3)(x - 2)}$

27. $y = \dfrac{(x + 3)(x + 1)}{(x + 2)(x - 1)(x - 3)}$ **28.** $y = \dfrac{(x + 2)(x - 1)}{(x + 3)(x + 1)(x - 2)}$

29. $y(x - 3)x = x^2 - 3x + 2$

30. $x^2 y + a^2 y = a^3$, witch of Agnesi

31. $x^2 y + a^2 y = b^2 x$, serpentine

32. $a^2 y = x^3$, cubical parabola

6.7. FUNCTIONS OF THE FORM y^2 EQUAL TO A RATIONAL FUNCTION

In the last two articles we have studied y equal to a rational function and found one value of y for each usable value of x. In the chapter on conics we studied y^2 equal to a linear function of x and equal to a quadratic function of x and found two values of y for each usable value of x, that is two values of y for each value of x in the domain of definition. We shall continue our study of double valued relations in this article. The procedure will be very much the same as that used in the last two articles. The graph of $y^2 = f(x)$ is symmetrical with respect to the X axis.

Values of x for which y^2 is negative must be ruled out, since for each of them y is imaginary and only pairs of real numbers are used in location points.

EXAMPLE 1

Sketch the graph of

$$y^2 = (x + 3)(x - 1)(x - 2)$$

by making use of the intercepts, symmetry, asymptotes, and excluded values.

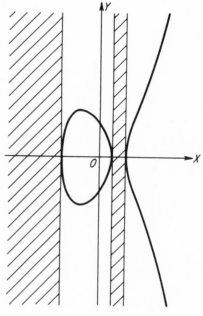

FIGURE 6.9

Solution: Intercepts. The x-intercepts are $x = -3, 1, 2$, since those are the values of x if $y = 0$; furthermore, if $x = 0$, then $y^2 = 6$. Consequently, the y-intercepts are $y = \pm \sqrt{6}$.

Symmetry. The graph is symmetrical with respect to the X axis, since $(-y)^2 = y^2$. It is not symmetrical with respect to the Y axis, since replacing x by $-x$ changes the equation. It is not symmetrical with respect to the origin, since changing x to $-x$ and y to $-y$ alters the equation.

Asymptotes. There are no horizontal or vertical asymptotes since the coefficients of the highest power of x and of y are constants.

Excluded values. Since $y^2 = (x + 3)(x - 1)(x - 2)$, it changes sign only as x passes through -3, 1, and 2. If $x < -3$, then $y^2 < 0$, since each factor is negative. If $-3 < x < 1$, then $x - 2 < 0$, $x - 1 < 0$ and $x + 3 > 0$; hence $y^2 > 0$. If $1 < x < 2$, then $x - 2 < 0$, $x - 1 > 0$ and $x + 3 > 0$; hence, $y^2 < 0$. If $x > 0$, each factor is positive and $y^2 > 0$. Consequently, the excluded regions are $x < -3$ and $1 < x < 2$. These regions are shaded in Fig. 6.9. The table given below is a further aid in sketching the curve.

x	-3	-2	-1	0	1	2	3	3.5	large
y^2	0	12	12	6	0	0	12	97.5/4	large
y	0	± 3.46	± 3.46	± 2.45	0	0	± 3.46	± 4.86	

EXAMPLE 2

Sketch the graph of

$$y^2 = \frac{x-1}{x^2-4} = \frac{N(x)}{D(x)}$$

by making use of the intercepts, symmetry, asymptotes, and excluded values, and of a table of values.

Solution: Intercepts. If $x = 0$, then $y^2 = \frac{1}{4}$; hence $y = \pm\frac{1}{2}$ are intercepts. Furthermore, $x = 1$ is an intercept, since that is the value of x for $y = 0$.

Symmetry. The given equation is not changed if y is replaced by $-y$; hence, the curve is symmetrical with respect to the X axis. By applying the usual tests, we see that the curve is not symmetrical with respect to the Y axis or the origin.

Asymptotes. The lines $x = \pm 2$ are asymptotes since these are the values of x for which the denominator is zero. The highest power of x is x^2, and after clearing of fractions, its coefficient is y^2; hence $y = 0$ is an asymptote.

Excluded values. We cannot use values of x for which the numerator $x - 1$ and the denominator $x^2 - 4$ are of opposite signs, since then y^2 would be negative and y imaginary. It is clear that $N = x - 1 \gtrless 0$ when $x \gtrless 1$, and $D = x^2 - 4 > 0$ when $x > 2$ and when $x < -2$, and $D = x^2 - 4 < 0$ when $-2 < x < 2$ as indicated in Fig. 6.10.

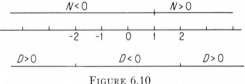

FIGURE 6.10

A study of the figure shows that y^2 is negative when $x < -2$ and when $1 < x < 2$ and zero or positive for all other values of x. Consequently, $x < -2$ and $1 < x < 2$ must be excluded. The facts devel-

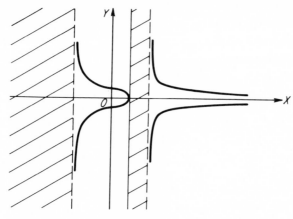

FIGURE 6.11

oped above and the table of values given below are used in sketching
the graph shown in Fig. 6.11.

x	-1.5	-1	$-.5$	0	$.5$	1	2.5	3	4
y^2	$\frac{10}{7}$	$\frac{2}{3}$	$\frac{2}{5}$	$\frac{1}{4}$	$\frac{2}{15}$	0	$\frac{2}{3}$	$\frac{2}{5}$	$\frac{1}{4}$
y	± 1.2	$\pm.8$	$\pm.6$	$\pm.5$	$\pm.4$	0	$\pm.8$	$\pm.6$	$\pm.5$

EXERCISE 6.3

Make use of the intercepts, symmetry, asymptotes, and a set of
pairs of values to sketch the graphs of the following equations.

1. $y^2 = (x + 2)(x - 1)$

2. $y^2 = (x + 1)(x - 3)$

3. $y^2 = x(x - 2)$

4. $y^2 = (x + 2)(x + 1)$

5. $y^2 = (x + 2)(x - 1)(x - 3)$

6. $y^2 = (x + 3)x(x - 2)$

7. $y^2 = (x + 4)(x + 2)(x + 1)$

8. $y^2 = (x - 1)(x - 2)(x - 3)$

9. $y^2 = x^2(x - 1)$

10. $y^2 = (x + 2)^2(x - 2)$

11. $y^2 = x^3$

12. $y^2 = (x - 1)^3$

13. $y^2 = (x + 2)(x + 1)(x)(x - 3)$

14. $y^2 = (x + 1)(x)(x - 1)(x - 2)$

15. $y^2 = (x + 1)^2(x - 1)(x - 4)$

16. $y^2 = (x + 2)(x - 1)^2(x - 3)$

17. $y^2 = (x - 1)/(x + 1)$

18. $y^2 = (x + 2)/(x - 3)$

19. $y^2 = (x + 1)/x(x - 1)$

20. $y^2 = (x - 4)/(x - 3)(x + 1)$

21. $y^2 = x(x - 1)/(x + 2)$

22. $y^2 = (x + 3)(x - 2)/(x - 3)$

23. $y^2 = (x + 2)(x + 1)/(x - 1)(x - 3)$

24. $y^2 = (x + 3)(x - 1)/(x - 2)(x + 1)$

25. $y^2 = x^2/(x + 4)(x - 1)$

26. $y^2 = (x - 2)^2/x(x + 1)$

27. $y^2 = (x + 1)(x - 1)/x^3$

28. $y^2 = (x + 2)(x + 1)/(x - 1)^3$

29. $x^3 + xy^2 + ax^2 = ay^2$, strophoid

30. $x^3 + xy^2 + ay^2 = 3ax^2$, trisectrix

31. $x^3 + xy^2 = 2ay^2$, cissoid

32. $x^3 + 3xy^2 = a(x^2 - y^2)$, folium

33. $ay^2 = x^3$, semi-cubical parabola

34. $(a^2 - x^2)y^2 = a^2x^2$, $a \neq 0$, arc light

35. $x^4 - 2ax^3 + a^2y^2 = 0$, top

36. $x^2y^2 = x^2 + y^2$

6.8. THE GRAPH BY FACTORING

If the left member of $f(x, y) = 0$ can be factored into $f_1(x, y)$ and $f_2(x, y)$, where $f_1(x, y)$ and $f_2(x, y)$ are real non-constant polynomials, then the graph of $f(x, y)$ is made up of the graphs of $f_1(x, y) = 0$ and $f_2(x, y) = 0$. This statement is easily proved, since $f(x, y) = f_1(x, y)f_2(x, y) = 0$ if and only if $f_1(x, y) = 0$ or $f_2(x, y) = 0$.

EXAMPLE

Sketch the graph of

$$f(x, y) = x^3 - 2x^2y + xy^2 - 4x + 8y - 2y^3 = 0.$$

Solution: The factors of $f(x, y)$ are $f_1(x, y) = x^2 + y^2 - 4$ and $f_2(x, y) = x - 2y$. Hence the graph of the given equation is made up

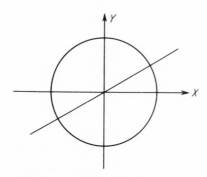

FIGURE 6.12

of the graphs of $f_1 = 0$ and $f_2 = 0$. The former is a circle of radius 2 with center at the origin, and the latter is a line through the origin with slope $\frac{1}{2}$. The combined graph is shown in Fig. 6.12.

6.9. INTERSECTIONS OF CURVE

The points of intersections of two curves are those points that are on both curves; hence they are the points whose rectangular coordinates satisfy the equations of both curves. Therefore the coordinates of the intersections are obtained by solving the equations simultaneously. In solving them, we may obtain imaginary values of x or y or both. If either or both are imaginary, the corresponding pair of values of x and y satisfy the equations but are not the coordinates of a point of intersection because only pairs of real numbers are used as coordinates of a point.

Approximations to the points of intersection can be obtained by sketching the curves about the same axes and then estimating the coordinates of each intersection.

EXAMPLE 1

Find the coordinates of the points of intersection of

(1) $x - y + 2 = 0$

and

(2) $(x + 1)^2 + (y - 5)^2 = 16.$

Solution: We shall solve this pair of equations by substitution. To do this, we first solve (1) for y and get $y = x + 2$. We now substitute this for y in (2) and have

$$(x + 1)^2 + (x + 2 - 5)^2 = 16$$
$$x^2 + 2x + 1 + x^2 - 6x + 9 = 16$$
$$2x^2 - 4x + 10 = 16$$
$$x^2 - 2x + 5 = 8$$
$$x^2 - 2x - 3 = 0$$
$$x = 3, -1$$

We now obtain each corresponding value of y by substituting the values of x in $y = x + 2$. Thus we find that $y = 3 + 2 = 5$ for $x = 3$ and $y = -1 + 2 = 1$ for $x = -1$. Consequently, the intersection of the graphs are at $(3, 5)$ and $(-1, 1)$.

EXAMPLE 2

Find the coordinates of the intersections of

(1) $x^2 + 2y^2 = 17$

and

(2) $xy - y^2 = 2.$

Solution. We shall solve this system by substitution. Solving (2) for x gives $x = (2 + y^2)/y$. Substituting this for x in (1) leads to

$$\left(\frac{2 + y^2}{y}\right)^2 + 2y^2 = 17$$
$$4 + 4y^2 + y^4 + 2y^4 = 17y^2, \quad \text{expanding and multiplying by } y^2,$$
$$3y^4 - 13y^2 + 4 = 0, \quad \text{collecting,}$$
$$y^2 = 4, \tfrac{1}{3}$$
$$y = \pm 2, \pm \sqrt{3}/3.$$

The corresponding values of x are ± 3, $\pm 7\sqrt{3}/3$; hence the intersections are $(3, 2)$, $(-3, -2)$, $(7\sqrt{3}/3, \sqrt{3}/3)$, and $(-7\sqrt{3}/3, -\sqrt{3}/3)$.

EXERCISE 6.4

Sketch the graph of each equation in Problems 1 to 16 after factoring.

1. $x^2 - 4y^2 = 0$

2. $9x^2 - y^2 = 0$

3. $4x^2 - 9y^2 = 0$

4. $25x^2 - 36y^2 = 0$

5. $y^3 - xy^2 + 4xy - 4x^2 = 0$

6. $x^3 + x^2y - 6xy - 6y^2 = 0$

7. $3x^3 - 12x^2 - 2x^2y + 11xy - 2y^2 = 0$

8. $3y^3 + 6y^2 + 2xy^2 - 3y + 8xy + 2x - 8x^2 = 0$

9. $x^3 - 2x^2 - x^2y - 3x + 2xy + xy^2 + 3y - y^3 = 0$

10. $x^3 - 4x^2 + x^2y - 4xy + xy^2 + y^3 = 0$

11. $2x^3 - x^2y - 16x - 4xy + 2xy^2 + 8y + 2y^2 - y^3 = 0$

12. $x^3 + x^2y - 3x + 2xy + xy^2 - 6y + 4y^2 + 2y^3 = 0$

13. $x^3 - x^2y - x^2 - xy^2 + y^3 + y^2 - x + y + 1 = 0$

14. $4x^3 + 4x^2y - xy^2 - y^3 - 4x - 4y = 0$

15. $8x^3 - 4x^2y - 16x^2 + 8xy + 2xy^2 - y^3 = 0$

16. $3x^3 - 2x^2y - 12x^2 + 8xy + 3xy^2 - 2y^3 = 0$

Find the coordinates of each point of intersection of the following pairs of curves.

17. $y = x - 1$
    $y^2 = 3x - 5$

18. $y = 2x + 1$
    $y^2 = 5x + 4$

19. $y = 2x - 5$
    $(y - 1)^2 = 2x$

20. $y = x + 4$
    $(y - 2)^2 = 3x + 4$

21. $y = 2x - 2$
    $4(x - 1)^2 - (y - 2)^2 = 4$

22. $y = x - 5$
    $(x - 1)^2 - 4(y + 2)^2 = 4$

23. $y = 2x - 1$
    $4(x - 2)^2 + (y - 5)^2 = 4$

24. $y = x - 3$
    $(x - 2)^2 + 4(y - 1)^2 = 4$

25. $x^2 + y^2 = 13$
    $2x^2 - y^2 = -1$

26. $x^2 + y^2 = 5$
    $x^2 - 3y^2 = 1$

27. $x^2 - y^2 = 5$
$2x^2 - 3y^2 = 6$

28. $x^2 - y^2 = 7$
$3x^2 - 4y^2 = 12$

29. $x^2 + y^2 = 8$
$x^2 - xy = 8$

30. $x^2 - y^2 = 24$
$y^2 + xy = -4$

31. $x^2 - y^2 = 12$
$x^2 + 3xy = -8$

32. $x^2 - 2y^2 = -7$
$x^2 - xy = 5$

By making use of the fact that the roots of a quadratic are equal if and only if the discriminant is zero, determine b so that the line is tangent to the curve in each of the following problems.

33. $y = x - b$
$x^2 + xy = -8$

34. $y = x + b$
$xy - 2x^2 = 2$

35. $y = 2x - b$
$2xy - 5x^2 = 1$

36. $y = 3x + b$
$10x^2 - y^2 = -10$

6.10. COMPOSITION OF ORDINATES

If the equation of a curve is given or can be placed in the form $y = f(x) + g(x)$, it is often a simple matter to obtain the desired graph by sketching the graphs of $y_1 = f(x)$ and $y_2 = g(x)$ as a preliminary step. We then make use of the fact that $y = y_1 + y_2$ for any value of x for which both y_1 and y_2 are defined.

EXAMPLE

Sketch the graph of

$$y = 2x + \sqrt{4 - x^2}$$

by addition of ordinates.

Solution: The graph of $y_1 = 2x$ is a straight line that has slope 2 and passes through the origin. The graph of $y_2 = \sqrt{4 - x^2}$ is defined for all real x numerically less than or equal to 2, whereas the graph of $y_1 = 2x$ is defined for all real x. Hence the graph of the given function is defined only for x between -2 and 2. The value of y_1 is negative, zero, or positive when x is respectively negative, zero or positive; but y_2 is never negative, since it is equal to the square root of a nonnegative number. The component graphs are shown as dotted curves in Figure 6.13 and the combined graph is shown as a solid curve.

If $y = f(x) - g(x)$, $y = f(x) \cdot g(x)$, or $y = f(x)/g(x)$, $g(x) \neq 0$, the graph can be obtained in a manner similar to that above. Thus if $y = f(x) \cdot g(x)$, the graph can be obtained from those of $y_1 = f(x)$ and $y_2 = g(x)$ by multiplying y_1 by y_2 for each x that is used.

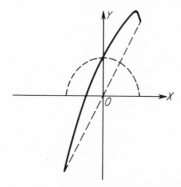

FIGURE 6.13

EXERCISE 6.5

Sketch the graphs of the following functions by use of composition of ordinates.

1. $y = x + \sqrt{x + 2}$ 2. $y = 2x + \sqrt{x^2 + x}$

3. $y = x + \sqrt{2x - 1}$ 4. $y = 3x + \sqrt{x^3 - x}$

5. $y = 2x - \sqrt{3x + 1}$ 6. $y = -x + \sqrt{x^2 - x}$

7. $y = 3x - \sqrt{-x + 3}$ 8. $y = x - \sqrt{x^3 - 4x}$

9. $y = x\sqrt{x - 1}$ 10. $y = 2x\sqrt{x^2 - 2x}$

11. $y = x\sqrt{2 - x}$ 12. $y = 3x\sqrt{x^3 - x}$

13. $y = 2x/\sqrt{x - 1}$ 14. $y = x/\sqrt{x^2 + x}$

15. $y = \sqrt{x^2 - 4}/x$ 16. $y = \sqrt{x + 1}/(x - 1)$

7 *TRANSCENDENTAL CURVES*

7.1. *INTRODUCTION*

In Chapter 6 we studied algebraic curves. In this chapter, we shall study transcendental curves. These are the graphs of the transcendental functions, including the logarithm, the exponential, the trigonometric functions, and combinations of them.

7.2. *THE LOGARITHMIC CURVE*

The reader who has had work in computation with logarithms may be familiar with the following definition and graph, However, a review of them is desirable at this point.

DEFINITION. *The **logarithm** of a positive number to a base is the exponent of the power to which the base must be raised in order to produce the number.*

We write $\log_b x = y$ and read "the logarithm of x to the base b is y."

An alternate symbolic form of the definition is

$$\log_b x = y \quad \textit{if and only if} \quad b^y = x.$$

Thus, $\log_4 64 = 3$ since $4^3 = 64$ and $\log_8 64 = 2$ since $8^2 = 64$.

Figure 7.1 shows a part of the graph of $y = \log_{10} x$. The curve passes through $(1, 0)$, since $\log 1 = 0$ regardless of the base. Furthermore, $x = 0$ is an asymptote, since as x gets nearer and nearer

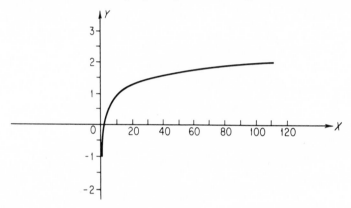

FIG. 7.1 Graph of $y = \log_{10} x$.

to zero, y becomes numerically larger and larger. The table given below, constructed by assigning values to x and computing each corresponding value of $y = \log_{10} x$, was used in sketching the curve.

x	negative	very small		.01	.1	1	10	100	large
y	not real	negative but numerically large		-2	-1	0	1	2	large

Any positive number other than 1 can be used as a base. Why can we not use 1, zero, or a negative number as a base?

7.3. THE EXPONENTIAL CURVE

Another curve, closely associated with the logarithmic curve, is described in the following definition.

DEFINITION. *An equation of the form* $y = a^x$ $(a > 0, \neq 1)$ *is called an* **exponential equation** *and the corresponding curve is known as an* **exponential curve.**

We shall now sketch the graphs of $y = 10^x$ and $y = e^x$ ($e = 2.718$ . . .) by making use of the intercepts, symmetry, excluded values, asymptotes, and several points that are determined by assigning values to x and computing each corresponding value of y.

x	-2	-1	0	1	1.5	2	large, pos.	numerically large, neg.
$y = 10^x$	.01	.1	1	10	31.6	100	large, pos.	small, pos.
$y = e^x$	.14	.37	1	2.72	4.48	7.39	large, pos.	small, pos.

The last two columns are used in order to call attention to the behavior of the curve for values of x that are not included in the table.

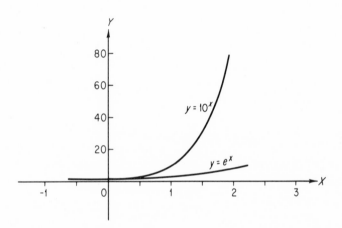

Fig. 7.2 Exponential curves.

We can quickly see that $y = 1$ is an intercept of each curve; furthermore, $y = 0$ is an asymptote, there is no symmetry, and negative values of y are excluded as seen from Fig. 7.2.

7.4. THE CATENARY

The graph of the quation

(1) $$y = \frac{a}{2}\left(e^{x/a} + e^{-x/a}\right)$$

is called a *catenary*. It has the same shape as a uniform slack flexible string that is suspended by fastening two points. The sketch given in Fig. 7.3 is for the catenary with $a = 1$ and is called the hyperbolic cosine of x. The table was constructed by assigning values to x and computing each corresponding value of y. It does not include

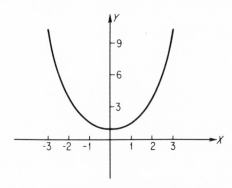

FIG. 7.3 The catenary.

negative values of x, since the curve is symmetrical with respect to the Y *axis*.

x	0	1	2	3
e^x	1	2.72	7.39	20.09
e^{-x}	1	.37	.14	.05
$y = \frac{1}{2}(e^x + e^{-x})$	1	1.54	3.76	10.07

EXERCISE 7.1

Sketch the graph of each of the following curves:

1. $y = 2^x$ **2.** $y = 5^x$

3. $y = 3^{x+1}$ **4.** $y = 7^{x-2}$

5. $y = 5^{-x}$ **6.** $y = 3^{-x+1}$

7. $y = (\frac{1}{4})^{x+2}$ **8.** $y = (\frac{1}{3})^{2x-3}$

9. $y = 2^{x^2-x}$ **10.** $y = 5^{x^2+x-1}$

11. $y = 3^{2x^2-3x+1}$ **12.** $y = 7^{2-x-x^2}$

13. $y = \log_2 x$ **14.** $y = \log_3 x$

15. $y = \log_{10} 5x = \log_{10} 5 + \log_{10} x$

16. $y = \log_{10} 3x$

17. $y = \log x - 2$

18. $y = \log 2x - 1$

19. $y = \log (x - 2)$

20. $y = \log 2(x - 1)$

21. $y = \log_{10} (x^2 + 3)$

22. $y = \log_{10} (x^2 + x - 1)$

23. $y = \log_e (x^2 + x + 3)$

24. $y = \log_e (x^2 - 2x + 2)$

25. $y = \log_e (x + 1)(x - 2)$

26. $y = \log_e (x - 3)(x - 1)$

27. $y = \log_{10} (x^2 - 2x)$

28. $y = \log_{10} (x^2 - 9)$

29. $y = (e^x - e^{-x})/2$. This curve is called the *hyperbolic sine* of x and is abbreviated as sinh x.

30. $y = (e^x - e^{-x})/(e^x + e^{-x})$. This curve is called the *hyperbolic tangent* of x and is abbreviated as tanh x.

31. What change takes place in the graph of $y = b^x$ as b decreases toward 1? As b increases beyond bound?

32. What change takes place in the graph of $y = \log_b x$ as b decreases toward 1? As b decreases from 1 toward zero?

7.5. PERIODIC FUNCTIONS

It should not be surprising to us that we study functions of the type described below, since we know that the seasons and tides and other phenomena occur and re-occur at regular intervals.

DEFINITION. *If $f(x + p) = f(x)$ for all x in the domain of definition, then $f(x)$ is said to be periodic. If p is the smallest positive number for which this is true, then $f(x)$ is of periodic p. If a periodic function has a range of $2A$ in its values, then A is said to be the* **amplitude** *of the function.*

ILLUSTRATIVE EXAMPLE 1

Since sin $(x + 2\pi) = $ sin x for all x for which sin x is defined, it follows that sin x is periodic and has 2π as a period. The largest value of sin x is 1, and the smallest value is -1; hence the range is $1 - (-1) = 2$, and the amplitude is $\frac{1}{2}(2) = 1$.

ILLUSTRATIVE EXAMPLE 2

The period of $y = 13 + 3 \cos x$ is 2π, since $13 + 3 \cos (x + 2\pi)$ $= 13 + 3 \cos x$ for all x in the domain of definition of $\cos x$. The largest and smallest values of $13 + 3 \cos x$ occur for $x = 0$ and $x = \pi$ and are 16 and 10; hence the range is $16 - 10 = 6$, and the amplitude is $\frac{1}{2}(6) = 3$.

7.6. THE SINE CURVE

The periodicity, symmetry with respect to the origin, and amplitude of sin x will be used in order to sketch the graph of $y = \sin x$. The periodicity and amplitude are given at the end of Article 7.5. We see that sin x is symmetrical with respect to the origin, since $\sin (-x) = - \sin x$.

Since sin x is of period 2π, we can obtain as much of the graph of $y = \sin x$ as we please by using a strip of horizontal length 2π as a pattern. Furthermore, because of the symmetry with respect to the origin, it is possible to obtain the part of the graph from $x = 0$

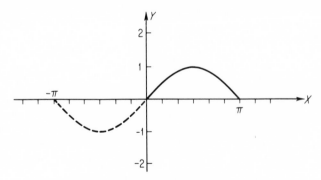

FIG. 7.4 $y = \sin x$.

to $x = -a$ by using that from $x = 0$ to $x = a$ as a pattern. In particular, if we sketch the part of the graph from $x = 0$ to $x = \pi$, it can be used as a pattern to obtain the part from $x = 0$ to $x = -\pi$. (*See* Fig. 7.4.) We then have a strip of horizontal length 2π and can use it as a pattern for obtaining as much of the graph as is desired.

The table shows corresponding values of x and $y = \sin x$ for several values of x from 0 to $\pi = 180°$.

x	0	$\pi/6$	$\pi/4$	$\pi/3$	$\pi/2$	$2\pi/3$	$3\pi/4$	$5\pi/6$	
$y = \sin x$	0	.50	.71	.87	1.00	.87	.71	.50	0

The corresponding values of x and y are used as the coordinates of a point, several such points are located, and a smooth curve is drawn through them. The solid part of the curve in Fig. 7.4 was obtained from the entries in the table and the other part secured by means of the property $\sin(-x) = -\sin x$. We now have a strip of the curve of horizontal length 2π and can obtain as much of the graph as we wish by using this as a pattern.

7.7. THE COSINE CURVE

The graph of $y = \cos x$ is obtained in a manner similar to that used in sketching the graph of $y = \sin x$. The graph is symmetrical with respect to the Y axis, since $\cos(-x) = \cos x$; furthermore,

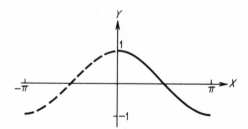

Fig. 7.5 $y = \cos x$.

$\cos x$ is of period 2π. These two facts and the accompanying table are used in sketching the part of the curve shown in Fig. 7.5.

x	0	$\pi/6$	$\pi/4$	$\pi/3$	$\pi/2$	$2\pi/3$	$3\pi/4$	$5\pi/6$	π
$y = \cos x$	1	.87	.71	.50	0	$-.50$	$-.71$	$-.87$	-1

The solid part was obtained from the entries in the table and the remainder drawn by means of the property $\cos(-x) = \cos x$. We now have a strip of horizontal length 2π and can use it as a pattern for securing as much of the graph as we wish.

7.8. *THE TANGENT CURVE*

In order to sketch the graph of $y = \tan x$, we make use of the fact that $\tan x$ is periodic with period π and that $\tan(-x) = -\tan x$, showing it to be symmetrical with respect to the origin.

x	0	$\pi/6$	$\pi/4$	$\pi/3$	$\pi/2$
$y = \tan x$	0	$\sqrt{3}/3$	1	$\sqrt{3}$	∞

The part from $-\pi/2$ to 0 can be obtained from the portion from $\pi/2$ to 0 by use of the relation $\tan(-x) = -\tan x$. Then, we have a strip of horizontal length π and can get any desired amount of the curve by using the section from $-\pi/2$ to $\pi/2$ as a pattern.

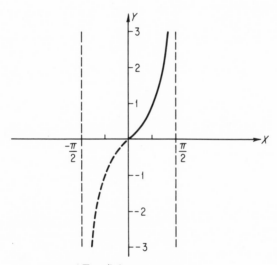

FIG. 7.6 $y = \tan x$.

The reader should notice that the ordinates of the curve increase as x increases from $-\pi/2$ to $\pi/2$. The asymptotes are

$$x = \pm \frac{\pi}{2}, \pm 3\frac{\pi}{2}, \pm 5\frac{\pi}{2}, \cdots \pm \frac{(2n+1)\pi}{2}, \cdots,$$

since $y = \tan x$ approaches infinity as x approaches any one of these values.

7.9. *THE GRAPH OF TRIGONOMETRIC FUNCTIONS OF* $bx + c$

To sketch the graph of a trigonometric function of $bx + c$, we use three trigonometric facts along with the ability to draw the graph of each function of x. These facts are:

(1) *Multiplying an angle by a constant divides the period of the function by that constant.*

(2) *Adding* c *to the angle* bx *moves the graph* c/b *units to the left without otherwise changing it.*

(3) *Multiplying a periodic function of an angle by a constant multiplies the amplitude by that constant.*

EXAMPLES

(1) The period of $y = \sin 4x$ is $2\pi/4 = \pi/2$, since that of $y = \sin x$ is 2π.

(2) The graph of $y = \sin (4x + 3)$ is $\frac{3}{4}$ of a unit to the left of the graph of $y = \sin 4x$.

(3) The amplitude of $y = 5 \sin x$ is 5, since that of $y = \sin x$ is one.

(4) The graph of $y = 3 \cos (\frac{1}{2}x + 5)$ has a period of $2\pi \div \frac{1}{2} = 4\pi$, the graph is $5 \div \frac{1}{2} = 10$ units to the left of that of $y = 3 \cos \frac{1}{2}x$, and the amplitude is 3.

7.10. *THE INVERSE TRIGONOMETRIC FUNCTIONS*

The equation $x = \sin y$ tells us that y is an angle whose sine is x. This can be and often is abbreviated for a suitably restricted y by writing $y = \arcsin x$ or $y = \sin^{-1} x$, but each abbreviation must be thought of as meaning that y is the unique angle in the restricted domain whose sine is x. We thus see that $x = \sin y$ and $y = \arcsin x$ are two ways of giving the same relation between x and the suitably restricted y. The equations $x = \sin y$ and $y = \arc \sin x$ are equivalent. Therefore, as can be verified by location of several points, the graph of $x = \sin y$ is as shown in Fig. 7.7. Consequently, part of that figure is also the graph of $y = \arcsin x$. It is clear that in the figure for $x = \sin y$ there are three values of y for each value of x, except 1 and −1, in the range of the function. Now, since the figure can be extended indefinitely in each direction, there are an unlimited number of values of y satisfying $x = \sin y$ for any given usable value of x.

In order to have a single valued relation, we limit the range of y. It could be limited in a variety of ways, but we shall limit it by restricting y to the interval from $-\pi/2$ to $\pi/2$, inclusive, as indicated by the solid part of the curve. Some writers use $y = \arcsin x$ to indicate that the range has been restricted and refer to the graph

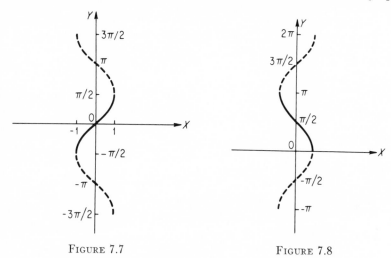

FIGURE 7.7   FIGURE 7.8

with restricted range as the *principal branch* of the graph and to each value of y on the principal branch as a principal value.

A similar discussion can be given for $y = \arccos x = \cos^{-1} x$ and $y = \arctan x = \tan^{-1} x$ as obtained by solving $x = \cos y$ and $x = \tan y$, respectively. Instead of doing so, we shall merely recall from trigonometry that the range of $y = \arccos x$ and $y = \arctan x$ are restricted as indicated in the table below so as to have single valued relations.

Function	Domain	Range
$y = \arcsin u$	$-1 \leq u \leq 1$	$-\pi/2 \leq \arcsin u \leq \pi/2$
$y = \arccos u$	$-1 \leq u \leq 1$	$0 \leq \arccos u \leq \pi$
$y = \arctan u$	$-\infty < u < \infty$	$-\pi/2 < \arctan u < \pi/2$

The graph of $y = \arccos x$ is shown as the solid part of Fig. 7.8 and that of $y = \arctan x$ as the solid part of Fig. 7.9. There are two branches other than the principal branch given in each figure.

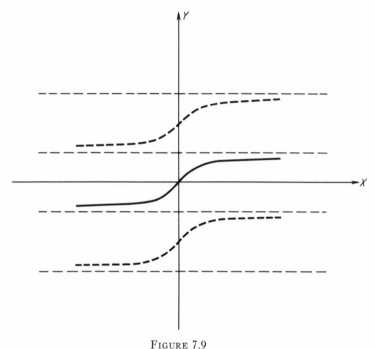

FIGURE 7.9

EXERCISE 7.2

Find the period and amplitude of the function in each of Problems 1 to 12.

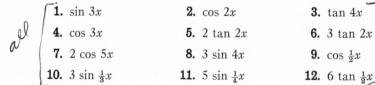

1. $\sin 3x$	**2.** $\cos 2x$	**3.** $\tan 4x$
4. $\cos 3x$	**5.** $2 \tan 2x$	**6.** $3 \tan 2x$
7. $2 \cos 5x$	**8.** $3 \sin 4x$	**9.** $\cos \frac{1}{2}x$
10. $3 \sin \frac{1}{3}x$	**11.** $5 \sin \frac{1}{4}x$	**12.** $6 \tan \frac{1}{2}x$

Find the period and amplitude of the first function in each of Problems 13 to 24, and find the position of its graph relative to the graph of the second function.

13. $y = 2 \cos (3x + \pi)$, $y = 2 \cos 3x$

14. $y = 3 \tan (2x + \pi/2)$, $y = 3 \tan 2x$

15. $y = 2 \sin (4x + \pi)$, $y = 2 \sin 4x$

16. $y = 4 \sin (2x + 2\pi)$, $y = 4 \sin 2x$

17. $y = 5 \tan (\frac{1}{2}x + \pi)$, $y = 5 \tan \frac{1}{2}x$

18. $y = 2 \cos (x/3 + 2\pi)$, $y = 2 \cos x/3$

19. $y = 3 \tan (\frac{1}{4}x + \pi)$, $y = 3 \tan \frac{1}{4}x$

20. $y = 4 \cos (\frac{1}{2}x + \pi/2)$, $y = 4 \cos \frac{1}{2}x$

21. $y = 6 \sin (3x - \pi)$, $y = 6 \sin 3x$

22. $y = 3 \sin (6x - 2\pi)$, $y = 3 \sin 6x$

23. $y = 2 \cos (4x - 3\pi)$, $y = 2 \cos 4x$

24. $y = 5 \tan (5x - 5\pi)$, $y = 5 \tan 5x$

In each of Problems 25 to 28, sketch the graphs of the four functions about the same axes.

25. $y = \cos x$, $y = \cos 2x$, $y = \cos (2x + \pi)$, $y = 2 \cos (2x + \pi)$

26. $y = \sin x$, $y = \sin 3x$, $y = \sin (3x - \pi)$, $y = 2 \sin (3x - \pi)$

27. $y = \tan x$, $y = \tan 2x$, $y = \tan (2x + \pi/2)$, $y = 3 \tan (2x + \pi/2)$

28. $y = \sin x$, $y = \sin \frac{1}{2}x$, $y = \sin (\frac{1}{2}x - \pi/3)$, $y = 4 \sin (\frac{1}{2}x - \pi/3)$

Sketch the graphs of the following pairs of functions about the same axes.

29. $y = \arcsin x$, $y = \sin x$

30. $y = \arccos x$, $y = \cos x$

31. $y = \arctan x$, $y = \tan x$

32. $y = \arcsin x$, $y = \sin x$ for $-\pi/2 \le x \le \pi/2$

Sketch the graphs of the following functions.

33. $y = x + \sin x$	**34.** $y = x - \cos x$
35. $y = 2x - \tan x$	**36.** $y = \sin x + \cos x$
37. $y = x \sin x$	**38.** $y = x \cos x$
39. $y = x \tan x$	**40.** $y = x/\cos x$
41. $y = 2x + e^x$	**42.** $y = x + \log x$
43. $y = e^x + \sin x$	**44.** $y = \cos x - \cosh x$
45. $y = x + \sin (\pi/2)x$	**46.** $y = \cos x - 2 \sin x$
47. $y = \sin x + \sin 2x$	**48.** $y = \cos x + 2 \cos 3x$

8 *POLAR COORDINATES*

8.1. *INTRODUCTION*

We are accustomed to locating points by means of a rectangular coordinate system. There are, however, other methods that are more practicable in some situations. One such method is known as a *polar coordinate system*. Using this system, we locate a point by

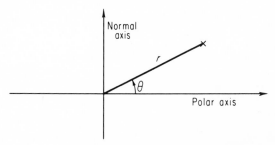

Fig. 8.1 Locating a point.

giving its *distance and direction from a given point on a given line.* The given point is called the *pole*, and the given line is known as the *polar axis*. The distance r from the pole to the point is called the *radius vector*, and the angle θ from the polar axis to the radius

146

vector is called the *amplitude* or *vectorial angle*. The *polar coordinates* of a point are written in the form (r, θ) as shown in Fig. 8.1. As in trigonometry, the radius vector may be rotated through any counterclockwise or clockwise angle; hence θ may take on any positive or negative value. Distances measured along the radius vector from the pole are defined to be positive and those measured in the opposite direction, that is, along the radius vector produced through the pole, are negative by definition. The line through the pole and perpendicular to the polar axis is known as the *normal axis*.

8.2. PAIRS OF COORDINATES FOR A POINT

Since many pairs of polar coordinates can be used to represent the same point, polar representation is not unique. The point (r, θ) can be given the coordinates $(r, \theta + k360°)$, where k is any integer,

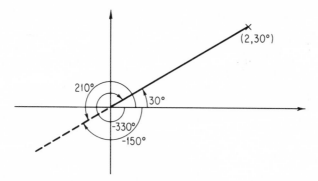

Fig. 8.2 Multiple names.

since each of these angles determines the same direction as θ and r is the distance from the pole in each case. If r is preceded by a negative sign, it is understood that the distance must be measured in a negative direction, that is, along the extension through the pole of the terminal side of the vectorial angle. If this custom is observed, $(-r, 180° + \theta)$ represents the same point as (r, θ).

EXAMPLE

Locate the point $(2, 30°)$ and give three other pairs of coordinates for it.

Solution: The point is shown in Fig. 8.2. The point also has the coordinates $(-2, 210°)$, since $210°$ is $180°$ more than $30°$ and the radius vector is minus that used in the original pair of coordinates. Furthermore $(2, -330°)$ and $(-2, -150°)$ are two more pairs of coordinates for the point, since $-330°$ has the same terminal side as $30°$ and $-150°$ has the same terminal side as $210°$.

8.3. TESTS FOR SYMMETRY AND INTERCEPTS

The amount of labor required for sketching a curve whose equation is given in terms of polar coordinates is often reduced if we make use of the symmetry and intercepts of the curve. We shall give tests for symmetry with respect to the polar axis, the pole, and the normal axis.

If a polar equation $f(r, \theta) = 0$ is unchanged

(a) *when θ is replaced by $-\theta$, the curve is symmetrical with respect to the polar axis;*

(b) *when θ is replaced by $180° + \theta$, the curve is symmetrical with respect to the pole;*

(c) *when θ is replaced by $180° - \theta$, the curve is symmetrical with respect to the normal axis.*

If we look at Fig. 8.3, we see from congruent triangles that the polar axis is the perpendicular bisector of PP_1; hence statement (a).

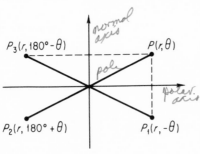

FIG. 8.3 Symmetry.

Furthermore, the pole is the midpoint of PP_2 thus proving statement (b). Finally, since the normal axis is the perpendicular bisector of PP_3 (c) is also true.

There are also other tests for symmetry. For example, a curve is symmetrical with respect to the polar axis if its polar equation is unchanged when θ is replaced by $180° - \theta$ and r is simultaneously replaced by $-r$, even though any symmetry with respect to the polar axis may fail to show up when the test given by (a) is used. The curious and capable student can devise other tests for symmetry if he makes use of the fact that replacing θ by $-\theta$ is equivalent to a reflection in the polar axis, substituting $-r$ for r is a reflection in the pole, and replacing θ by $180° - \theta$ is a reflection in the normal axis.

EXAMPLE 1

Test $f(r, \theta) = r - 4 \cos 2\theta = 0$ for symmetry.

Solution: Since

$$f(r, -\theta) = r - 4 \cos 2(-\theta)$$
$$= r - 4 \cos 2\theta$$
$$= f(r, \theta)$$

the curve is symmetrical with respect to the polar axis
    Now

$$f(-r, \theta) = -r - 4 \cos 2\theta$$
$$\neq \pm f(r, \theta).$$

Consequently, this test does not show any symmetry which may exist with respect to the pole. However,

$$f(r, 180° + \theta) = r - 4 \cos 2(180° + \theta)$$
$$= r - 4 \cos (360° + 2\theta)$$
$$= r - 4 \cos 2\theta$$
$$= f(r, \theta),$$

and the curve is symmetrical with respect to the pole in spite of the fact that the first test used did not show that symmetry.
    Finally,

$$f(r, 180° - \theta) = r - 4 \cos 2(180° - \theta)$$
$$= r - 4 \cos (360° - 2\theta)$$
$$= r - 4 \cos (-2\theta)$$
$$= r - 4 \cos 2\theta$$
$$= f(r, \theta)$$

and the curve is symmetrical with respect to the normal axis.

The *intercepts* are the values of r for which θ is an integral multiple of 90°. We therefore get the intercepts by solving the equations in r that are obtained by putting $\theta = 0°, 90°, 180°, 270°, \ldots$ in $f(r, \theta) = 0$.

EXAMPLE 2

What are the intercepts of $f(r, \theta) = r - 4 \cos 2\theta = 0$?

Solution: $f(r, 0°) = r - 4 \cos 0° = r - 4 = 0$ for $r = 4$ and $(4, 0°)$ is an intercept.

$f(r, 90°) = r - 4 \cos 180° = r + 4 = 0$ for $r = -4$ and $(-4, 90°)$ is an intercept.

$f(r, 180°) = r - 4 \cos 360° = r - 4 = 0$ for $r = 4$ and $(4, 180°)$ is an intercept.

$f(r, 270°) = r - 4 \cos 540° = r + 4 = 0$ for $r = -4$ and $(-4, 270°)$ is an intercept.

Only trigonometric functions of θ enter into $f(r, \theta)$; hence there is no reason for testing further for intercepts since all six basic trigonometric functions have 360° as a period.

8.4. CONSTRUCTION OF THE GRAPH

The graph of $f(r, \theta) = 0$ consists of those and only those points (r, θ) whose coordinates satisfy the equation $f(r, \theta) = 0$. The graph can be sketched by assigning values to θ, computing each corresponding value of r, locating the points thus determined, and drawing a smooth curve through them. The amount of labor is ordinarily reduced if we make use of the symmetry and intercepts of the curve.

It is often a troublesome task to determine a suitable range of values to be assigned to θ. It is usually desirable to start with $\theta = 0°$ and assign values at small intervals until we have obtained a sufficient number of points to be able to sketch the desired part of the curve or until we begin to retrace a portion of the curve already obtained.

EXAMPLE 1

Sketch the graph of $f(r, \theta) = r - 4 \cos 2\theta = 0$.

Solution: We saw in Examples 1 and 2 of Article 8.3 that the curve is symmetrical with respect to the axes and the pole and that its intercepts are $(4, 0°)$, $(-4, 90°)$, $(4, 180°)$, and $(-4, 270°)$.

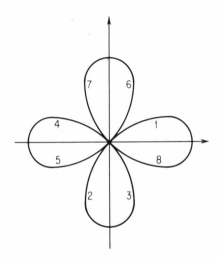

FIG. 8.4 A rose.

We shall now construct a table which shows corresponding values of θ, 2θ, $\cos 2\theta$, and r and shall locate the points (r, θ). The other entries in the table are included only as intermediate steps in determining r.

θ	0°	15°	$22\frac{1}{2}°$	30°	45°	60°	$67\frac{1}{2}°$	75°	90°
2θ	0°	30°	45°	60°	90°	120°	135°	150°	180°
$\cos 2\theta$	1	$\sqrt{3}/2$	$\sqrt{2}/2$	$\frac{1}{2}$	0	$-\frac{1}{2}$	$-\sqrt{2}/2$	$-\sqrt{3}/2$	-1
r	4	$2\sqrt{3}$	$2\sqrt{2}$	2	0	-2	$-2\sqrt{2}$	$-2\sqrt{3}$	-4

The half-loops numbered 1 and 2 in Fig. 8.4 are obtained by means of the points indicated in the table, those numbered 3 and 4 are the results of the symmetry with respect to the normal axis, and the others are a result of the symmetry with respect to the polar axis. We could have begun with 1 and 2, obtained 5 and 6 because of the symmetry with respect to the pole, and then obtained the remainder by symmetry with respect to the two axes. The numbers in the half-loops indicate the order in which they are obtained if the symmetry is not used, and increasing values of θ are assigned until we get the entire curve. The curve is called a four-leaf rose.

EXAMPLE 2

Test

$$r^2 = a^2 \sin \theta, \qquad a = 2$$

for symmetry and intercepts and sketch its graph.

Solution: The curve is symmetrical with respect to the pole, since

$$f(r, \theta) = r^2 - a^2 \sin \theta$$

and

$$\begin{aligned} f(-r, \theta) &= (-r)^2 - a^2 \sin \theta \\ &= r^2 - a^2 \sin \theta \\ &= f(r, \theta) \end{aligned}$$

and with respect to the normal axis, since

$$\begin{aligned} f(r, 180° - \theta) &= r^2 - a^2 \sin (180° - \theta) \\ &= r^2 - a^2 \sin \theta \\ &= f(r, \theta) \end{aligned}$$

The test given in Art. 8.3 does not enable us to make a statement concerning symmetry with respect to the polar axis.

The intercepts are readily seen to be $(0, 0°)$, $(\pm 2, 90°)$ and $(0, 180°)$, since $\sin 0° = \sin 180° = 0$ and $\sin 90° = 1$. Since $\sin 270° = -1$, there is no intercept corresponding to $\theta = 270°$.

The part of the curve in Fig. 8.5 in the first and third quadrants is obtained from the points located in the table, and then the parts in the second and fourth are obtained by means of the symmetry with respect to the normal axis.

θ	0°	30°	45°	60°	90°
$\sin \theta$	0	$\frac{1}{2}$	$\sqrt{2}/2$	$\sqrt{3}/2$	1
r^2	0	2.00	$2\sqrt{2}$	$2\sqrt{3}$	4
r	0	± 1.41	± 1.68	± 1.86	± 2

We should notice that the values of θ that make $\sin \theta$ negative must be excluded, since we are interested only in real values of r. Hence $180° < \theta < 360°$ is excluded. It is interesting to note that there are points on the curve in the third and fourth quadrants, even though angles in these quadrants must be excluded. Such points are accounted for by the negative values of r that correspond to angles in the first and second quadrants.

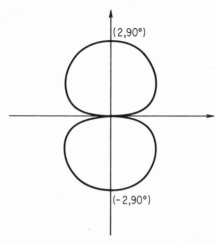

FIGURE 8.5

EXERCISE 8.1

Locate all points whose coordinates are given in Problems 1 to 4 and give three other pairs of coordinates for each.

1. $(2, 45°)$, $(3, 120°)$, $(5, -120°)$, $(3, 270°)$, $(-2, 30°)$, $(-4, -75°)$

2. $(1, 165°)$, $(3, 30°)$, $(-2, 120°)$, $(0, 17°)$, $(3, -135°)$, $(-5, -60°)$

3. $(5, 60°)$, $(6, 300°)$, $(0, 209°)$, $(-2, 135°)$, $(4, -60°)$, $(-3, -120°)$

4. $(4, 315°)$, $(5, 135°)$, $(3, -45°)$, $(0, 111°)$, $(-7, 90°)$, $(-8, -150°)$

After testing for symmetry, intercepts, and excluded values of θ, sketch the graph of each curve whose equation is given below.

5. $\theta = 45°$ **6.** $\theta = -210°$

7. $\theta = -135°$ **8.** $\theta = 330°$

9. $r = 2$ **10.** $r = -3$

11. $r = -5$ **12.** $r = 6$

13. $r = 4 \sin \theta$ **14.** $r = 8 \cos \theta$

15. $r = 5 \cos \theta$ **16.** $r = 7 \sin \theta$

17. $r = \sin 2\theta$ **18.** $r = 3 \cos 2\theta$

19. $r = \cos 4\theta$ **20.** $r = 2 \sin 4\theta$

21. $r = 2 \cos 3\theta$ **22.** $r = 3 \sin 5\theta$

23. $r = 4 \cos 5\theta$ **24.** $r = \sin 3\theta$

25. $r = 2(\sin \theta + 1)$ **26.** $r = 3(\cos \theta + 1)$

27. $r = 4(\cos \theta - 1)$ **28.** $r = 2(\sin \theta - 1)$

29. $r = 2 \sin \theta + 3$ **30.** $r = 3 \sin \theta + 2$

31. $r = 3 \cos \theta - 2$ **32.** $r = 2 \cos \theta - 4$

33. $r = \csc \theta$ **34.** $r = \sec \theta$ *In notebook*

35. $r = \cot \theta$ **36.** $r = \tan \theta$

37. $r = 2 \sin \dfrac{\theta}{3}$ **38.** $r = \cos^3 \dfrac{\theta}{2}$

39. $r = 4 \cos \dfrac{2\theta}{3}$ **40.** $r = \sin^2 \dfrac{\theta}{4}$

41. $r = \dfrac{2}{1 - \sin \theta}$ **42.** $r = \dfrac{3}{1 - \cos \theta}$

43. $r = \dfrac{6}{1 + \cos \theta}$ *In notebook*   **44.** $r = \dfrac{5}{1 + \sin \theta}$

45. $r = \dfrac{3}{2 + \sin \theta}$ **46.** $r = \dfrac{4}{3 + \cos \theta}$

47. $r = \dfrac{2}{2 - \cos \theta}$ **48.** $r = \dfrac{5}{4 - \sin \theta}$

49. $r = \dfrac{3}{1 + 2 \cos \theta}$ **50.** $r = \dfrac{2}{1 - 3 \cos \theta}$

51. $r = \dfrac{4}{1 - 3 \sin \theta}$ **52.** $r = \dfrac{3}{1 + 2 \sin \theta}$

53. $r = \sin^2 \theta$ **54.** $r = \cos^2 \theta$

55. $r = \cos^2 2\theta$ **56.** $r = \sin^2 2\theta$

57. $r^2 = \cos \theta$ **58.** $r^2 = \sin \theta$

59. $r^2 = 4 \sin \theta$ **60.** $r^2 = 9 \cos \theta$

61. The roses $r = \cos (2n + 1)\theta$, n a positive integer

62. The roses $r = \sin (2n + 1)\theta$, n a positive integer

63. The roses $r = \sin 2n\theta$, n a positive integer

64. The roses $r = \cos 2n\theta$, n a positive integer

65. The cardiod $r = 2a(\cos \theta + 1)$

66. The cardioid $r = 2a(\sin \theta + 1)$

67. The limaçon $r = 2a \sin \theta + b$

68. The limaçon $r = 2a \cos \theta + b$

69. The cissoid $r = a \tan \theta \sin \theta$

70. The spiral of Archimedes $r = a\theta$, θ in radians

71. The lemniscate $r^2 = a^2 \sin 2\theta$

72. The lituus $r^2\theta = \pi$, θ in radians

8.5. RELATIONS BETWEEN RECTANGULAR AND POLAR COORDINATES

We shall now use Fig. 8.6 and derive several equations that can be used for converting an equation that is given in terms of rectangular or polar coordinates into one using the other type of coordinate

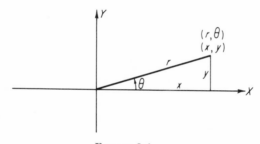

FIGURE 8.6

system. If we use the definitions of the sine and cosine of an angle, we have $\sin \theta = y/r$ and $\cos \theta = x/r$. Solving for x and y, we get

$$(1) \qquad x = r \cos \theta \quad \text{and} \quad y = r \sin \theta.$$

Equations (1) can be used to change an equation into polar coordinates if it is given in rectangular coordinates.

If we use the Pythagorean theorem and the definition of the tangent of an angle, we obtain

$$r^2 = x^2 + y^2 \quad \text{and} \quad \tan \theta = \frac{y}{x}.$$

Solving for r and θ, we see that

(2) $$r = \sqrt{x^2 + y^2} \quad \text{and} \quad \theta = \text{arc tan} \frac{y}{x} + k\pi$$

can be used to put an equation in terms of rectangular coordinates if it is given in polar form. It is often desirable to use a combination of Eqs. (1) and (2).

EXAMPLES

Write

$$(a) \quad x^2 + 2x + y^2 = 0$$

and $$(b) \quad r = 2a \cos \theta$$

in another type of coordinate system.

Solution of (a): To express the given equation in terms of polar coordinates, we shall use

$$x = r \cos \theta \quad \text{and} \quad y = r \sin \theta.$$

Thus, we have

$$\begin{aligned}
x^2 + 2x + y^2 &= (r \cos \theta)^2 + 2r \cos \theta + (r \sin \theta)^2 \\
&= r^2 \cos^2 \theta + 2r \cos \theta + r^2 \sin^2 \theta \\
&= r^2 + 2r \cos \theta
\end{aligned}$$

since $$\sin^2 \theta + \cos^2 \theta = 1.$$

Hence $$r + 2 \cos \theta = 0$$

is the desired equation. No part of the curve was lost in omitting the pole $r = 0$, since $r + 2 \cos \theta = 0$ passes through the pole.

Solution of (b): If we use the first of Eqs. (2) and the first of Eqs. (1), we have

$$r = \sqrt{x^2 + y^2}$$

and $$\cos \theta = \frac{x}{r} = \frac{x}{\sqrt{x^2 + y^2}}.$$

Substituting for $\cos \theta$ and r in the given equation, we see that

$$\sqrt{x^2 + y^2} = \frac{2ax}{\sqrt{x^2 + y^2}}$$

and, therefore, $\qquad x^2 + y^2 = 2ax$

is the desired equation as we see by multiplying by $\sqrt{x^2 + y^2}$.

EXERCISE 8.2

Express each equation in Problems 1 to 20 in terms of polar coordinates.

1. $x = 2$ 2. $y = 3$

3. $x + 2y = 1$ 4. $2x - 3y = 5$

5. $x^2 + y^2 = 9$ 6. $x^2 + y^2 = 4$

7. $y^2 = 4x$ 8. $x^2 = 9y$

9. $4x^2 + 9y^2 = 36x$ 10. $9x^2 - y^2 = 9y$

11. $y^2 = x^3$ 12. $(2a - x)y^2 = x(x - a)^2$

13. $(x - a)^2 + (y - b)^2 = a^2 + b^2$ 14. $(x^2 + y^2)x = y^2$

15. $y^2 = 16 - 8x$ 16. $4x^2 + 3y^2 + 6y = 9$

17. $(x^2 + y^2)^{\frac{3}{2}} = x^2 - y^2 - 2xy$ 18. $x(x^2 + y^2) = a(3x^2 - y^2)$

19. $x^4 - y^4 = 2xy$ 20. $(x^2 + y^2)^2 = 2a^2xy$

Express each equation in Problems 21 to 40 in terms of rectangular coordinates.

21. $r \cos \theta = 2$ 22. $r \sin \theta = 3$

23. $r = \dfrac{1}{\cos \theta + 2 \sin \theta}$ 24. $r = \dfrac{5}{2 \cos \theta - 3 \sin \theta}$

25. $r = 3$ 26. $r = 2$

27. $r = 4 \cot \theta \csc \theta$ 28. $r = 9 \tan \theta \sec \theta$

29. $4r + 5r \sin^2 \theta = 36 \cos \theta$ 30. $10r \cos^2 \theta - r = 9 \sin \theta$

31. $r = \sec \theta \tan^2 \theta$ 32. $2ar - r^2 \cos \theta = a^2 \cos \theta$

33. $r = 2a \cos \theta + 2b \sin \theta$ 34. $r = \tan \theta \sin \theta$

35. $r = \dfrac{4}{1 + \cos \theta}$ 36. $r = \dfrac{3}{2 + \sin \theta}$

37. $r = \cos 2\theta - \sin 2\theta$ 38. $r = a(4 \cos \theta - \sec \theta)$

39. $r^2 = \tan 2\theta$ 40. $r^2 = a^2 \sin 2\theta$

8.6. THE EQUATION OF A SET OF POINTS

The steps in determining the equation of a set of points in terms of polar coordinates are essentially the same as in rectangular coordinates. Take (r, θ) as the coordinates of the typically located point, and translate the symbolic geometric statement of the problem into an equation in r and θ. As in the case of rectangular coordinates, the frame of reference (position of axes) should be chosen to fit the conditions of the particular problem. For instance, if a fixed point is given, the pole may be chosen at this point. If there is a line of symmetry, the polar axis or the normal axis may well be chosen along this line.

EXAMPLE

Find the equation of a curve if the radius vector of each point on it is equal to a constant times the cosine of the vectorial angle.

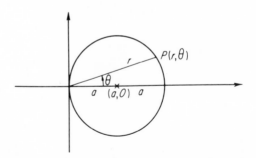

FIG. 8.7 A polar locus.

Solution: We shall use $2a$ for the constant and represent a typical member of the set by $P(r, \theta)$; then the symbolic geometric statement of the problem becomes

$$OP = 2a \cos \theta.$$

Since $OP = r$,   the desired equation is

$$r = 2a \cos \theta.$$

The graph is symmetrical with respect to the polar axis and can be obtained by assigning values to θ, calculating each corresponding value of r, and drawing a smooth curve through the points (r, θ) thus determined. The curve is the circle shown in Fig. 8.7.

8.7. POLAR EQUATION OF A STRAIGHT LINE

To derive the polar equation of a line, we shall draw any line L; let the distance OA (considered positive as in the normal form of the equation of a line) from the origin to the line be p; let ω be the angle from the X axis to the normal; and finally, let $P(r, \theta)$ be any point on the given line. Now angle AOP is $\theta - \omega$, and from the right triangle we have

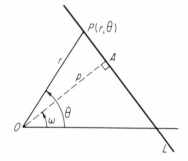

$$\cos (\theta - \omega) = \frac{p}{r}; \text{ hence}$$

$$(1) \qquad r \cos (\theta - \omega) = p$$

is the polar form of the equation of L, since it is a relation between r and θ

Fig. 8.8 A line.

that is true for points on L and not true for other points. There are four special cases of (1) that are worth remembering. They are as follows:

If $\omega = 0°$ or $180°$, the line is parallel to the normal axis and its equation is

$$r \cos \theta = p \quad \text{or} \quad r \cos \theta = -p.$$

If $\omega = 90°$ or $270°$, the line is parallel to the polar axis and its equation is

$$r \sin \theta = p \quad \text{or} \quad r \sin \theta = -p.$$

If (1) is expanded by use of the identity for the cosine of the difference of two angles, it takes the form

$$(2) \qquad r \cos \theta \cos \omega + r \sin \theta \sin \omega = p$$

If we now make use of the relations $x = r \cos \theta$ and $y = r \sin \theta$, (2) can be written as

$$x \cos \omega + y \sin \omega = p.$$

The reader should recognize this as the normal form of equation of a line as given in Article 2.9. That this is the normal form should not be surprising since both (1) and the normal form give the equation of a line in terms of the same two quantities. These are the angle the normal to the line makes with the X axis and the length of this normal.

8.8. POLAR EQUATION OF A CIRCLE

We shall now derive the polar form of the equation of a circle of radius a and center at $C(r_1, \theta_1)$. We shall represent any point on the circle by $P(r, \theta)$ as in Fig. 8.9, then we shall use the law of cosines and see that

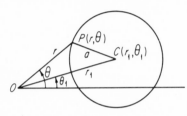

FIG. 8.9 A circle.

$$a^2 = r^2 + r_1^2 - 2rr_1 \cos (\theta - \theta_1)$$

is the polar form of the equation of the circle with center at (r_1, θ_1) and radius equal to a. Several special cases of this equation are simple and useful.

If the center is at the origin, the equation of the circle becomes

$$r = \pm a$$

since then $r_1 = 0$.

If the center is at $(a, 0°)$, the equation of the circle is

$$r = 2a \cos \theta$$

since substituting a for r_1 and $0°$ for θ_1 in the general equation it becomes

$$a^2 = r^2 + a^2 - 2ar \cos \theta.$$

Now collecting like terms and solving for r, we have $r = 2a \cos \theta$ as given above.

If the center is at $(a, 180°)$, the equation of the circle reduces to

$$r = -2a \cos \theta$$

since on substituting a for r_1 and $180°$ for θ_1 in the general equation, we have

$$a^2 = r^2 + a^2 - 2ar \cos (\theta - 180°)$$
$$-r^2 = +2ar \cos \theta, \cos (\theta - 180°) = -\cos \theta,$$
$$r = -2a \cos \theta, \quad \text{dividing by } -r.$$

Similarly, if the center is at $(a, 90°)$ or $(a, 270°)$, the equation of the circle becomes

$$r = 2a \sin \theta \quad \text{or} \quad r = -2a \sin \theta.$$

8.9. POLAR EQUATION OF A CONIC

In order to derive the polar equation of a noncircular conic, we shall use the definition in terms of eccentricity as given in Article 4.9, choose the pole as focus and a line perpendicular to the polar axis and two a units to the left of the pole as directrix. These things are shown in Fig. 8.10. If we now apply the definition of a conic, we get

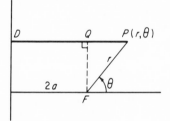

$$FP = eDP$$
$$r = e(DQ + QP)$$
$$= e(2a + r \cos \theta)$$

FIGURE 8.10

since $DQ = 2a$ and $\cos FPQ = \cos \theta = QP/r$. Now solving this equation for r, we see that

$$r = \frac{2ae}{1 - e \cos \theta}$$

is the standard polar form of the equation of the noncircular conic with eccentricity **e,** *a focus at the pole, and corresponding directrix perpendicular to the polar axis and* **2a** *units to the left of the pole.*

It can be shown in a similar manner that

$$r = \frac{2ae}{1 + e \cos \theta}$$

is the equation of the noncircular conic with eccentricity **e,** *focus at the pole, and corresponding directrix perpendicular to the polar axis and* **2a** *units to the right of the pole.*

Furthermore,

$$r = \frac{2ae}{1 - e \sin \theta} \quad \text{or} \quad r = \frac{2ae}{1 + e \sin \theta}$$

is the equation of the noncircular conic with eccentricity **e**, *focus at the pole, and corresponding directrix perpendicular to the normal axis and* **2a** *units below or above the pole.*

EXAMPLE

Identify and sketch the graph of

$$r = \frac{4}{3 - \cos \theta}.$$

Solution: The constant term in the denominator must be one for standard polar form; hence we divide numerator and denominator by 3 and get

$$r = \frac{\frac{4}{3}}{1 - \frac{1}{3} \cos \theta}.$$

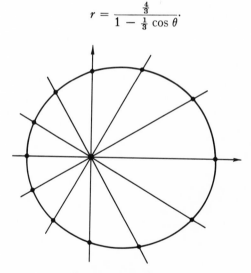

Fig. 8.11 An ellipse.

Therefore, $e = \frac{1}{3}$ and $a = 2$; hence the graph is an ellipse with a focus at the pole and corresponding directrix four units to the left of the pole. The facts above, symmetry with respect to the polar axis, and the table given below were used in sketching the graph in Fig. 8.11.

θ	0°	30°	60°	90°	120°	150°	180°
$\cos \theta$	1	.87	.5	0	$-.5$	$-.87$	-1
r	2	1.87	1.6	1.33	1.14	1.04	1

EXERCISE 8.3

Find the equation of each set of points described in problems 1 to 16. Check each line, circle, and conic equation by use of the appropriate general equation.

1. A line perpendicular to the polar axis and 3 units to the right of the normal axis; 3 units to the left of the normal axis

2. A line parallel to the polar axis and 5 units above; 5 units below it

3. A line whose normal from the pole is 4 units long and makes an angle of 60° with the polar axis　$r \cos(\theta - 60°) = 4$

4. A line whose normal from the pole is 2 units long and makes an angle of 150° with the polar axis

5. A circle with center at (6, 90°) and radius 6

6. A circle with center at (3, 45°) and radius 8

7. A circle with center at (2, 240°) and radius 7　$45 = r^2 - 4r \cos(\theta - 240°)$

8. A circle with center at (5, 180°) and radius 5

9. A parabola with focus at the pole and directrix perpendicular to the polar axis and 3 units to the right of the normal axis

10. A parabola with focus at the pole and directrix parallel to and 4 units below the polar axis

11. An ellipse with eccentricity $\frac{1}{2}$, a focus at the pole and corresponding directrix parallel to and 8 units above the polar axis

12. A conic with eccentricity 2, a focus at the pole and corresponding directrix parallel to and 6 units to the left of the normal axis

13. The curve with each point on it a distance from the pole that is equal to the tangent of the vectoral angle of the point

14. The curve such that the distance of each point on it from the pole is equal to three times the sine of twice the vectorial angle

15. The parabola with vertex at the pole and focus at $(a, 0)$. Check the equation by transforming $y^2 = 4ax$ to polar form

16. The midpoints of the segments of the tangents to $x^2 + y^2 = a^2$ that are intercepted by the coordinate axis

Identify and sketch the graph of each of the following curves.

17. $r \cos \theta = 2$
a line 2 units rt of normal axis

18. $r \sin \theta = 5$

19. $r \cos \theta = -3$

20. $r \sin \theta = -4$

21. $r \cos (\theta - 30°) = 6$

22. $r \cos (\theta - 120°) = 3$

23. $r^2 + 9 - 6r \cos (\theta - 45°) = 4$

24. $r^2 + 25 - 10r \cos (\theta - 210°) = 16$

25. $r = 5$

26. $r = 6 \cos \theta$

27. $r = -4 \sin \theta$

28. $r = 2 \sin \theta$

29. $r = \dfrac{4}{1 - \cos \theta}$

30. $r = \dfrac{6}{1 + \sin \theta}$

31. $r = \dfrac{2}{1 - \sin \theta}$

32. $r = \dfrac{4}{1 + \cos \theta}$

33. $r = \dfrac{8}{2 + \sin \theta}$

34. $r = \dfrac{6}{3 - \sin \theta}$

35. $r = \dfrac{4}{4 + \cos \theta}$

36. $r = \dfrac{10}{2 - \cos \theta}$

37. $r = \dfrac{6}{2 - 3 \sin \theta}$

38. $r = \dfrac{12}{3 + 4 \cos \theta}$

39. $r = \dfrac{10}{2 - 5 \cos \theta}$

40. $r = \dfrac{6}{3 + 6 \sin \theta}$

8.10. *PAIRS OF POLAR EQUATIONS*

In solving a pair of equations in rectangular coordinates, we find those points that have equal values of x and equal values of y. Because rectangular coordinates have exactly one pair of coordinates for each point and exactly one point for each pair of coordinates, we get all the points of intersection of two curves if we solve their equations simultaneously.

If we solve a pair of polar equations simultaneously, we obtain those points that have equal values of r and equal values of θ but do not necessarily get all points of intersection of the curves. This is true because a point of intersection of two curves may have one pair of coordinates so far as one of the curves is concerned and another pair relative to the other curve. There are ways of finding all points of intersection of two curves whose equations are in polar form, but we shall not present them here.

In order to solve two polar equations simultaneously and obtain the points that have the same values of r and same values of θ on both curves, we can begin by solving each equation for r, continue by solving the equation in θ obtained by equating the two expressions for r, and finally, substitute the values obtained for θ in either expression for r to obtain each corresponding value of r.

EXAMPLE 1

Solve

(1) $$r^2 = 4 \sin \theta$$

and

(2) $$r^2 = 4 \cos \theta$$

simultaneously and sketch their graphs on the same set of axes.

Solution: Dividing each member of (1) by the corresponding member of (2), we have

$$1 = \tan \theta$$

and $$\theta = 45°, 225°.$$

We shall obtain each corresponding value of r by means of (1). Thus

$$r^2 = 4 \sin 45° = 2\sqrt{2},$$
$$r = \pm 1.68 \quad \text{if} \quad \theta = 45°$$

and r is imaginary if $\theta = 225°$.

Therefore, the points on the two curves that have equal values of r and equal values of θ are $P_1(1.68, 45°)$ and $P_2(-1.68, 45°)$, and these are solutions of the pair of equations. There may, however, be other points at which the curves intersect.

We shall now sketch the two curves on the same set of axes. Eq. (1) was discussed in Example 2 of Article 8.4 and its graph given in Fig. 8.5. It is shown as the solid curve in Fig. 8.12. The graph of (2) is symmetrical with respect to the polar axis, since

$$f(r, -\theta) = r^2 - 4 \cos \theta$$
$$= f(r, \theta)$$

and is symmetrical with respect to the pole, since $f(-r, \theta) = f(r, \theta)$. Furthermore, values of θ from 90° to 270° must be excluded since the

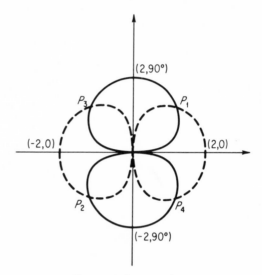

FIG. 8.12 Intersections.

corresponding values of r are imaginary. The table of values given below and the symmetry discovered earlier in this discussion are used in sketching the curve.

θ	0°	30°	45°	60°	90°
$\cos \theta$	1	$\sqrt{3}/2$	$\sqrt{2}/2$	$\frac{1}{2}$	0
r	±2	±1.86	±1.68	±1.41	0

The curves obviously cross one another at a point in each quadrant and at the origin in spite of the fact that we found only two solutions for the pair of equations. These extra crossings are not solutions of the pair of equations since no single one has the same coordinates from Eq. (1) as from Eq. (2). For example, the coordinates of the crossing in the second quadrant are (1.68, 135°) and (−1.68, 315°) from (1) and (2), respectively.

Finally, the curves intersect at the origin since $r^2 = 4 \sin \theta$ is zero if $\theta = 0°$ and $r^2 = 4 \cos \theta$ is zero if $\theta = 90°$.

EXERCISE 8.4

Solve the following pairs of equations simultaneously after sketching their graphs.

1. $r = 6 \sin \theta$
   $r = 3$

2. $r = 2 \cos \theta$
   $r = \sqrt{3}$

3. $r \sin \theta = 2$
   $r = 4$

4. $r \cos \theta = 1$
   $r = 2$

5. $r = 3$
   $r = 3 \sin^2 \theta$

6. $r = 1$
   $r = 4 \cos^2 \theta$

7. $r = 1$
   $r = 2 \sin 2\theta$

8. $r = \sqrt{2}$
   $r = 2 \cos 2\theta$

9. $r = a \cos \theta$
   $r \cos \theta = a$

10. $r = a \sin \theta$ $a, 90°$ $a, 270°$
    $r \sin \theta = a$

11. $r = 1 - \cos \theta$
    $r = 3 \cos \frac{1}{2}\theta$

12. $r = 1 + \cos \theta$
    $r = \cos \frac{1}{2}\theta$

13. $r = 3 \cos \theta$
    $r = 3 \sin \theta$

14. $r = 2 \sin 2\theta$
    $r = 2 \cos 2\theta$

15. $r = \sin \theta$
    $r = 1 + \cos \theta$

16. $r = \cos \theta$
    $r = 1 + 3 \sin \theta$

17. $r = 3 \cos \theta$
    $r = 1 + \cos \theta$

18. $r = 5 \sin \theta$
    $r = 2 + \sin \theta$

19. $r = a(1 + \cos \theta)$
    $r = a/(1 - \cos \theta)$

20. $r = 3 + \cos \theta$
    $r = 3 - \sin \theta$

21. $r = \sin \theta$
    $r^2 = \sin 2\theta$

22. $r = \cos \theta$
    $r^2 = \cos 2\theta$

23. $r = 2 \cos \theta$
    $r^2 = 4 \cos \theta$

24. $r = -3 \sin \theta$
    $r^2 = 9 \sin \theta$

9 *PARAMETRIC EQUATIONS*

9.1. PARAMETRIC REPRESENTATION

In the last chapter we found a method of representation of equations which sometimes makes them simpler to handle than they would be if we used retcangular coordinates. We shall now consider another method.

If, in an equation $f(x, y) = 0$, x and y are expressed in terms of a third variable in such a way that the given relation between x and y holds, the third variable is called a *parameter*. The equations between x and the third variable and y and the third variable are known as a *parametric representation of* $f(x, y) = 0$ or a part thereof.

ILLUSTRATIVE EXAMPLE 1

If the angle t is chosen as the parameter, we can use

$$x = 2 \sin t \quad \text{and} \quad y = 2 \cos t$$

as a parametric representation for the circle $x^2 + y^2 = 4$ because then

$$x^2 + y^2 = (2 \sin t)^2 + (2 \cos t)^2$$
$$= 4(\sin^2 t + \cos^2 t) = 4.$$

and every point of the graph is thus representable.

168

We can obtain a parametric representation for an equation in two variables in many cases by

(1) *setting one of the two variables equal to an arbitrary function of the parameter,*

(2) *substituting this in the given equation for the variable, and,*

(3) *solving for the second variable in terms of the parameter.*

We must realize, however, that it may be difficult or impossible to solve for the second variable. This procedure may lead to a complicated function of the parameter unless care and thought are given to choosing the arbitrary function of the parameter that is equated to the first variable. A desirable representation must be simple and must give the entire curve, unless otherwise noted.

ILLUSTRATIVE EXAMPLE 2

If we let $x = 2 \sec t$ in the equation $x^2 - y^2 = 4$, then

$$(2 \sec t)^2 - 4 = y^2,$$
$$4(\sec^2 t - 1) = y^2$$
$$4 \tan^2 t = y^2, \quad \text{since } 1 + \tan^2 t = \sec^2 t.$$

Therefore, $y = \pm 2 \tan t.$

Hence $x = 2 \sec t$, $y = 2 \tan t$ and $x = 2 \sec t$, $y = -2 \tan t$ are two parametric representations for the equation of the given equilateral hyperbola.

9.2. THE CONICS

We shall now give a desirable parametric representation for the equation of each type of conic. The curious and capable student can determine other forms which may be used.

The hyperbola. The standard form of the equation of the hyperbola is

(1)
$$\frac{(x - h)^2}{a^2} - \frac{(y - k)^2}{b^2} = 1$$

or

(2)
$$\frac{(y - k)^2}{a^2} - \frac{(x - h)^2}{b^2} = 1$$

when the transverse axis is parallel to the X or the Y axis, respectively.

To express either in parametric form, we should find and use some simple identity which gives the difference of the squares of two quantities equal to unity. The trigonometric identity $\sec^2 t - \tan^2 t = 1$ meets this requirement. Therefore, in order to express (1) in parametric form, we put

$$\frac{x - h}{a} = \sec t \quad \text{and} \quad \frac{y - k}{b} = \tan t.$$

Then, solving for x and y, we have the following theorem.

THEOREM.

$$x = h + a \sec t \quad \text{and} \quad y = k + b \tan t$$

are parametric equations of the hyperbola with semi-axes a and b, center at (h, k), and transverse axis parallel to the X axis.

These equations are materially simpler if the center is at the origin, since we then have $(h, k) = (0, 0)$. The equations are further simplified if we have an equilateral hyperbola as in the second illustrative example of Article 9.1.

The reader should show that $y = k + a \sec t$, $x = h + b \tan t$ is a parametric representation of (2).

The ellipse and circle. The standard form of the equation of the ellipse is

(3)
$$\frac{(x - h)^2}{a^2} + \frac{(y - k)^2}{b^2} = 1$$

or

(4)
$$\frac{(y - k)^2}{a^2} + \frac{(x - h)^2}{b^2} = 1$$

according as the major axis is parallel to the X or the Y axis.

We shall obtain a parametric representation of (3) and leave it as a problem for the reader to express (4) in a similar form. Equation (3) states that the sum of the squares of two quantities is unity. This should remind us of the trigonometric identity $\sin^2 t + \cos^2 t$

$= 1$. Hence, if we put $(x - h)/a = \sin t$ and $(y - k)/b = \cos t$ and solve for x and y, we have the following theorem.

THEOREM.

$$x = h + a \sin t \quad and \quad y = k + b \cos t$$

are parametric equations for the ellipse with center at (h, k), semi-axes a and b, and major axis parallel to the X axis.

If we recognize the fact that the equation of a circle can be obtained from that of an ellipse by putting $b = a$ and if we make the corresponding changes in the theorem stated for the ellipse, we see that

$$x = h + a \sin t \quad and \quad y = k + a \cos t$$

is a parametric form of the equation of the circle with radius a and center at (h, k).

The first illustrative example in Article 9.1 gives a particular case of this theorem in which $h = k = 0$ and $a = 2$.

The parabola. The standard form of the equation of the parabola is

(5) $\qquad (y - k)^2 = 4a(x - h)$ or (6) $\qquad (x - h)^2 = 4a(y - k)$

when the axis is parallel to the X or the Y axis, respectively.

In order to express either of these equations in parametric form, we should represent x by some function of the parameter t so that y is comparatively simple, Since, in (5), $x - h$ and a are of the same sign, we shall let $x - h = at^2$; then $(y - k)^2 = 4a^2t^2$ and $y - k = 2at$. Consequently, we have the following theorem.

THEOREM. *The equations*

$$x = h + at^2 \quad and \quad y = k + 2at$$

are parametric equations for the parabola with vertex at (h, k), axis parallel to the X axis, and distance and direction from the vertex to the focus equal to a.

The reader should find a similar representation for the parabola with (6) as its equation and for the ones with vertices at the origin.

EXERCISE 9.1

1. Express the circle $x^2 + y^2 = 9$ in parametric form with (a) $x = 3 \cos \theta$, (b) $y = 3 - t$.

2. Express the ellipse $4x^2 + y^2 = 4$ in parametric form with (a) $y = 2 \sin t$, (b) $x = \sqrt{1 - t^2}$.

3. Express the hyperbola $y^2 - 4x^2 = 4$ in parametric form with (a) $x = \sqrt{t^2 - 1}$, (b) $y = 2 \sec t$.

4. Express the parabola $x^2 = y$ in parametric form with (a) $x = t$, (b) $x = \sqrt{2} \sin t$.

5. Find a parametric representation for $xy = a^2$.

6. Express $y = mx + b$ in a parametric form.

7. Express $ax + by + c = 0$ in parametric form.

8. Find a parametric representation for $x^2 - xy + 1 = 0$ with $x = \tan t$.

9. Show that if we let $x = 3t$ in $x^2 + y^2 = 9$, then $y = 3 \sqrt{1 - t^2}$. By considering the restrictions on y, determine the part of the circle that is not obtained from the parametric form.

10. Show that if we let $x = a \sin t$ in $xy = a^2$, then $y = a \csc t$. By considering the restrictions on x and y, determine the part of the hyperbola that is not obtained by use of the parametric form.

11. Show that if we put $y = 4 \sin \frac{1}{2} t$ in $y^2 = 8x$, then $x = 1 - \cos t$; furthermore, show that only a part of the parabola is obtained by considering the restrictions imposed on x and y. What part is obtained?

12. Show that only a part of the line $x + y = 1$ is obtained from the parametric form $x = - \tan^2 t$, $y = \sec^2 t$, and determine that part.

9.3. ELIMINATION OF THE PARAMETER

No one method of eliminating a parameter may be applied equally well to all cases. Any method which was used in algebra or trigonometry for eliminating a variable may prove desirable at times. We shall now give two examples.

EXAMPLE 1

Eliminate the parameter from

$$x = \frac{t^2}{4} \quad \text{and} \quad y = t + 1$$

and identify the curve.

Solution: If we solve the second equation for t, we obtain $t = y - 1$. Putting this expression for t in the first equation, we get

$$x = \frac{(y - 1)^2}{4}.$$

Therefore, the desired equation is

$$(y - 1)^2 = 4x.$$

It represents a parabola with vertex at $(0, 1)$, axis parallel to the X axis, and focus at $(1, 1)$.

EXAMPLE 2

Eliminate the parameter from

$$x = \sin t \quad \text{and} \quad y = 2 \cos t.$$

Solution: If we multiply each member of the first equation by 2, square each new member, and add to the squares of the corresponding members of the second equation, we obtain

$$\begin{aligned}
(2x)^2 + y^2 &= (2 \sin t)^2 + (2 \cos t)^2 \\
&= 4 \sin^2 t + 4 \cos^2 t \\
&= 4, \text{ since } \sin^2 t + \cos^2 t = 1.
\end{aligned}$$

Therefore, $4x^2 + y^2 = 4$

is the equation obtained by eliminating the parameter from the given equations. The reader should recognize it as an ellipse with center at the origin, major axis along the Y axis and of length 4, and minor axis equal to 2.

9.4. THE CURVE FROM PARAMETRIC EQUATIONS

To obtain the graph from a parametric form of the equation, we assign a set of values to the parameter, compute each corresponding value of x and y, locate the points (x, y), and draw a smooth curve through them.

This, however, may give only a part of the graph of the rectangular coordinate equation obtained by eliminating the parameter. This fact is illustrated in Example 2.

EXAMPLE 1

Sketch the graph of

$$x = 2 \sin \theta \quad \text{and} \quad y = 2 \cos \theta$$

by assigning values to θ, computing the rectangular coordinates of the corresponding points, and drawing a smooth curve through the points thus determined.

Solution:

θ	0°	30°	60°	90°	120°	150°	180°	210°	240°	270°	300°	330°
x	0	1	$\sqrt{3}$	2	$\sqrt{3}$	1	0	-1	$-\sqrt{3}$	-2	$-\sqrt{3}$	-1
y	2	$\sqrt{3}$	1	0	-1	$-\sqrt{3}$	-2	$-\sqrt{3}$	-1	0	1	$\sqrt{3}$

The accompanying table was constructed by assigning values to θ and computing the corresponding values of x and y. It was not continued further, since any trigonometric function of θ is equal to that same function of $360° + \theta$. The points (x, y) determined by the table were located and used in sketching the graph shown in Fig. 9.1.

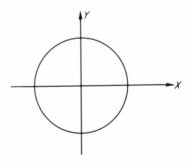

FIGURE 9.1

EXAMPLE 2

Sketch the graph of

$$x = \sec^2 \theta \quad \text{and} \quad y = -\tan^2 \theta.$$

Eliminate the parameter between the two equations and compare the graph of the resulting rectangular coordinate equation with that of the parametric form.

Solution: Since $x = \sec^2 \theta$ is always greater than or equal to 1 and $y = -\tan^2 \theta$ is always negative or zero for real angles, it follows that the graph obtained from the parametric form of the equation lies entirely in the fourth quadrant to the right of $x = 1$ and at the point $(1, 0)$ on the X axis.

θ	0°	30°	60°	90°
$x = \sec^2 \theta$	1	$\frac{4}{3}$	4	∞
$y = -\tan^2 \theta$	0	$-\frac{1}{3}$	-3	$-\infty$

The table is not continued further because assigning additional values of θ will merely give points (x, y), which have already been determined. The part of the graph that is obtained from the given parametric form is shown as a solid line in Fig. 9.2.

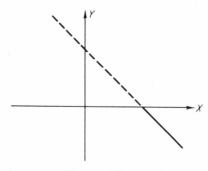

FIGURE 9.2

If we eliminate the parameter by adding x and y we get $x + y = 1$, since $\sec^2 \theta - \tan^2 \theta = 1$. Hence the graph of the equation obtained by eliminating the parameter is the entire line shown in Fig. 9.2.

This example illustrates the necessity of being careful not to impose unintended restrictions on the range of x and y in choosing a parametric form of the equation.

We can use $x = \sin^2 \theta$, $y = \cos^2 \theta$ as another parametric form of the equation, since then $x + y = 1$. If we use this form, we get only that portion of the line intercepted between the axes.

EXERCISE 9.2

Sketch the graph of each pair of parametric equations given below. Eliminate the parameter from each pair. Determine whether the entire curve or only a part of it is obtained from the parametric form of the equation.

1. $x = 3 + t$, $y = 2 - t$ **2.** $x = 1 + 2t$, $y = 3 + 2t$

3. $x = 2 - 3t$, $y = t + 1$ **4.** $x = 3 + t$, $y = 2t - 1$

5. $x = t + 2$, $y = t^2$ **6.** $x = 1 - t$, $y = 2 + t^2$

7. $x = t + t^2$, $y = t + 1$ **8.** $x = t^2 - 2t$, $y = t - 1$

9. $x = (t - 1)/(t + 2)$, $y = (t + 2)/(t - 1)$

10. $x = 2(t^2 - 1)/(2t - 1)$, $y = (2t - 1)/(t^2 - 1)$

11. $x = t - 1$, $y = t/(t - 1)$

12. $x = t - 2$, $y = t^2 - 4$

13. $x = 2/(1 + t^2)$, $y = 2t/(1 + t^2)$

14. $x = 3t/(1 + t^3)$, $y = 3t^2/(1 + t^3)$

15. $x = t(t^2 - 8)$, $y = t^2 - 8$

16. $x = t - 1$, $y = (t - 1)/t$

17. $x = 2^t$, $y = 2^{-t}$

18. $x = \sin t$, $y = \csc t$

19. $x = \sec t - \tan t$, $y = \sec t + \tan t$

20. $x = \sin t + \cos t$, $y = \sin t - \cos t$

21. $x = \cos t - 1$, $y = 2 \sin t - 1$

22. $x = a \cos^3 t$, $y = a \sin^3 t$

23. $x = \tan t - \cot t$, $y = \tan t + \cot t$

24. $x = a \sin t$, $y = b \cos t$

25. $x = \cos 2\theta$, $y = 2 \cos^2 \theta$

26. $x = \cos^2 \theta - 1$, $y = \cos \theta + 1$

27. $x = 2 - \sin t$, $y = \sqrt{\sin^2 t - 4 \sin t}$

28. $x = \cos^2 t$, $y = \cos^3 t$

9.5. *THE PATH OF A PROJECTILE*

We shall assume that a projectile is fired with an initial velocity of V_0, that it makes an angle θ with the horizontal, and that its motion is caused entirely by its initial velocity and direction and the acceleration g of gravity, thus ignoring air resistance. Under these conditions it is readily seen that the horizontal component of the initial velocity is $V_0 \cos \theta$ and the vertical component is $V_0 \sin \theta$. Hence the horizontal distance traveled in t seconds is $V_0 t \cos \theta$ and the vertical is $V_0 t \sin \theta - \frac{1}{2}gt^2$, since the distance traversed in t seconds because of the action of gravity alone is $\frac{1}{2}gt^2$. Consequently, if $P(x, y)$ is any point on the path of the projectile, its coordinates after t seconds are

$$x = V_0 t \cos \theta$$

and

$$y = V_0 t \sin \theta - \frac{1}{2} gt^2.$$

These are parametric equations of the path. If we eliminate the parameter t from them, we see that

$$y = x \tan \theta - \frac{gx^2}{2V_0{}^2} \sec^2 \theta$$

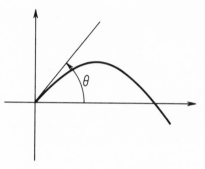

FIG. 9.3 Path of a projectile.

is the rectangular equation. Hence, under the conditions given in the problem, the path of a projectile is a parabola.

9.6. *THE CYCLOID*

We shall now derive the equations of a curve that is often used in bridge arches.

DEFINITION. *The curve traced by a given point on the circumference of a circle as the circle rolls without slipping along a straight line is called a* **cycloid.**

We shall use the X axis as the given straight line, a circle of radius a as the rolling circle, and shall choose the position of the Y axis in such a way that the given point P on the rolling circle passes through the origin. Hence $OD =$ arc PD. In the figure,

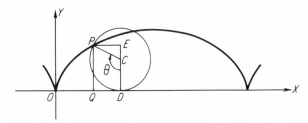

FIG. 9.4 A cycloid.

PQ and CD are perpendicular to the X axis and PE is perpendicular to CD. Therefore, the coordinates of P are

$$x = OQ = OD - PE \quad \text{and}$$
$$y = QP = DC + CE.$$

If we let the angle θ (in radians) between DC and CP be the parameter, we have $OD =$ arc $PD = a\theta$, $PE = a \sin \theta$, $DC = a$, and $CE = a \cos ECP = -a \cos \theta$. Consequently,

$$x = a(\theta - \sin \theta) \quad \text{and}$$
$$y = a(1 - \cos \theta)$$

are a pair of parametric equations for a cycloid provided the given point passes through the origin, the X axis is the given line, and the circle is of radius a.

9.7. THE TROCHOIDS

We shall now consider the equations of a generalization of the cycloid.

DEFINITION. *Given a circle of radius a and a point b units from the center on a radius or a radius extended, then the path traced by the point, as the circle rolls along a line, is called a **trochoid.***

A trochoid is known as a **prolate cycloid** *or a* **curtate cycloid** *according as b > a or b < a.*

The parametric form of the equation of a trochoid is obtained in the same manner as that of a cycloid and is

$$x = a\theta - b \sin \theta \quad and$$
$$y = a - b \cos \theta.$$

9.8. THE EPICYCLOID AND HYPOCYCLOID

DEFINITION. *The path traced by a given point on the circumference of a moving circle as it rolls without slipping along the circumference of a fixed circle is called an* **epicycloid** *or an* **hypocycloid** *when the moving circle is respectively outside or inside the fixed circle. A point common to such a curve and the fixed circle is a* **crest** *of the curve.*

We shall let a represent the radius of the rolling circle, b the radius of the fixed circle, θ the angle from the X axis to the line of centers, and ϕ the angle from this line to the line CP that joins the center of the rolling circle and the given point P. Then $DCO = \pi/2 - \theta$, and $DCP = \phi - \angle DCO = \phi + \theta - \pi/2$. Furthermore, if R is the initial position of P, the arcs RS and SP are equal. Consequently, $b\theta = a\phi$. Now the coordinates of P are

$$x = OQ = OD + EP = (b + a) \cos \theta + a \sin \left(\phi + \theta - \frac{\pi}{2} \right),$$

$$y = QP = DC - EC = (b + a) \sin \theta - a \cos \left(\phi + \theta - \frac{\pi}{2} \right).$$

Since

$$\sin \left(\phi + \theta - \frac{\pi}{2} \right) = - \cos (\phi + \theta),$$

$$\cos \left(\phi + \theta - \frac{\pi}{2} \right) = \sin (\phi + \theta), \quad \text{and} \quad \phi = b \frac{\theta}{a},$$

a parametric form of the equation of an epicycloid is

$$x = (b + a) \cos \theta - a \cos \frac{b + a}{a} \theta \quad \text{and}$$

$$y = (b + a) \sin \theta - a \sin \frac{b + a}{a} \theta$$

*if **a** and **b** are the radii of the rolling and fixed circles, respectively.*

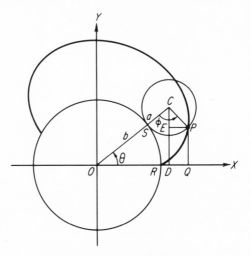

FIG. 9.5 An epicycloid.

We can obtain the equations of a hypocycloid in a similar manner. They are

$$x = (b - a) \cos \theta + a \cos \frac{b - a}{a} \theta \quad \text{and}$$

$$y = (b - a) \sin \theta - a \sin \frac{b - a}{a} \theta.$$

9.9. THE INVOLUTE OF A CIRCLE

DEFINITION. *If **A** and **B** are a fixed and a variable point, respectively, on a fixed circle and if a distance **PB** = arc **AB** is laid off on the tangent to the circle at **B**, then the locus of **P** as **B** moves around the circle is called the **involute of the circle**.*

We shall represent the angle from the X axis to the radius drawn to the point B by θ. Then angle CBP in Fig. 9.6 is also θ.

We shall obtain the parametric form of the equation of the involute of a circle of radius a with center at the origin and X axis through the point A. Hence if the variable point was originally at

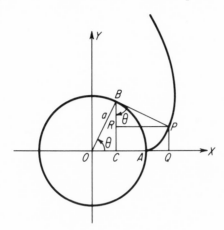

FIG. 9.6 Involute of a circle.

A and has moved to the point marked B, the arc AP of the involute has been traced and the coordinates of P are

$$x = OQ = OC + RP \quad \text{and} \quad y = QP = CB - RB.$$

Since

$$OC = a \cos \theta, \quad BP = AB = a\theta, \quad RP = BP \sin \theta = a\theta \sin \theta,$$
$$CB = a \sin \theta \quad \text{and} \quad RB = BP \cos \theta = a\theta \cos \theta,$$

a parametric form of the equation of the involute of a circle of radius a is

$$x = a \cos \theta + a\theta \sin \theta,$$
$$y = a \sin \theta - a\theta \cos \theta.$$

EXERCISE 9.3

Assume that $g = 32$ in Problems 1 through 6.

1. Find the parametric and rectangular forms of the equation of a projectile if it is fired horizontally. Vertically.

2. If a ball is thrown horizontally at 120 feet per second from a point 4 feet above horizontal ground, how long will the ball travel before being only 1.44 feet off the ground? How far will it travel horizontally?

3. If a ball is thrown horizontally at 120 feet per second from a point 4.5 feet above horizontal ground, how far from the ground will it be after traveling 60 feet? Pitcher's box and home base are 60 feet apart?

4. If a ball is thrown horizontally from a point 4.5 feet above level ground, how fast must it be thrown to be 1.5 feet above the ground after traveling 60 feet?

5. A ball is thrown at 120 feet per second at an angle of 45° with the horizontal. How long until it is the same height from level ground as when thrown? How far has it traveled horizontally in this time?

6. After how many seconds will a ball return to its original distance above level ground if thrown at an angle of 30° above the horizontal at a speed of 96 feet per second? How far has it traveled horizontally in this time?

7. Sketch the path of a projectile if its parametric equations are $x = 60t$ and $y = 60\sqrt{3}t - 16t^2$.

8. The parametric equations of the path of a projectile are $x = 120t$ and $y = 120t - 16t^2$. Sketch the path.

9. Sketch the graph of the cycloid for which the radius of the tracing circle is 2.

10. Sketch the graph of the cycloid for which the radius of the tracing circle is 3.

11. Sketch the trochoid for which $a = 3$ and $b = 4$.

12. Sketch the trochiod for which $a = 3$ and $b = 2$.

13. Sketch the epicycloid for which $a = \frac{1}{2}b$.

14. Sketch the hypocycloid for which $a = \frac{1}{4}b$. This is called the four cusped hypocycloid.

15. Sketch the involute of a circle for which $a = 2$.

16. Sketch the involute of a circle for which $a = 5$.

10 *COORDINATES IN SPACE*

10.1. COORDINATES

One of the several types of coordinates that may be used in space is the system of rectangular coordinates. If this system is used, a point is located by stating its distance and direction from each of three mutually perpendicular planes which divide space into eight parts called *octants*.

In Fig. 10.1, the planes XOY, XOZ, and YOZ are referred to as the xy-, xz-, and yz-planes. The point of intersection of the planes is called the *origin*. The line $X'X$ is the X axis, $Y'Y$ is the Y axis, and $Z'Z$ is the Z axis. The coordinates of a point are written as (x, y, z) when x, y, and z are the directed distances from the yz-, xz-, and xy-planes, respectively. The coordinates of P in Fig. 10.1 are

$$x = OM, y = MN, \quad \text{and} \quad z = NP$$

when OM is measured along the X axis (i.e., from the yz-plane) and MN and NP are measured parallel to the Y and Z axes, respectively.

The positive directions from the origin are indicated by the arrows; each negative direction is opposite to the corresponding positive one. The point $(-1, 2, 4)$ is located in Fig. 10.1.

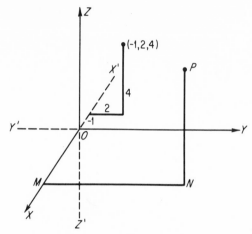

FIG. 10.1 Location of points.

10.2. *DISTANCE BETWEEN POINTS*

We can visualize the distance between two points in space and follow the derivation of a formula for it if we consider the rectangular parallelepiped shown in Fig. 10.2. The sides of the figure are parallel to the coordinate planes.

In order to derive a formula for the distance d between any two

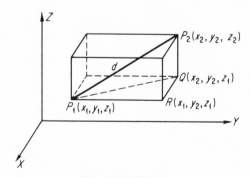

FIG. 10.2 Distance.

points, $P_1(x_1, y_1, z_1)$ and $P_2(x_2, y_2, z_2)$, we should notice that P_1P_2 is the diagonal of a right triangle with QP_2 and QP_1 as sides. Hence

$$\overline{P_1P_2}^2 = \overline{QP_1}^2 + \overline{QP_2}^2.$$

Furthermore,

$$\overline{QP_1}^2 = \overline{P_1R}^2 + \overline{QR}^2.$$

Therefore,

$$\overline{P_1P_2}^2 = \overline{P_1R}^2 + \overline{QR}^2 + \overline{QP_2}^2.$$

The coordinates of R and Q are as indicated in Fig. 10.2, since P_1R is parallel to the Y axis and QR and QP_2 are parallel to the X and Z axes, respectively. Hence putting in the values of P_1R, QR and QP_2 in terms of their coordinates and indicating that the square root is to be taken, we see that

$$P_1P_2 = d = \sqrt{(x_1 - x_2)^2 + (y_1 - y_2)^2 + (z_1 - z_2)^2}$$

is the distance between $P_1(x_1, y_1, z_1)$ *and* $P_2(x_2, y_2, z_2)$.

ILLUSTRATIVE EXAMPLE

If we substitute in the formula to obtain the distance between $(3, 2, 8)$ and $(1, -4, 5)$, we find that

$$d = \sqrt{(3 - 1)^2 + [2 - (-4)]^2 + (8 - 5)^2} = 7.$$

10.3. DIRECTION OF A LINE

The position of a directed line through the origin relative to the coordinate axes is determined if we know the angles between the positive ends of the coordinate axes and the positive direction of the given line. These angles are called the *direction angles* of the line and their cosines are known as the *direction cosines*. If the direction of the line is reversed, the direction angles are replaced by their supplements, and the direction cosines are replaced by their negatives.

If a line is undirected, its direction angles can be taken to be α, β, and γ as indicated in Fig. 10.3 or the supplements of these angles. Consequently, the direction cosines of an undirected line can be either of *two sets* of numbers. Each number of the second set is the negative of the corresponding number of the first set.

DEFINITION. *The direction angles and direction cosines of a directed line that does not pass through the origin are the same as those of the line through the origin, parallel to and directed as the given line.*

The direction angles of the line through O and P in Fig. 10.3 are α, β, and γ when P is any point in space. Their cosines are $\cos \alpha = OS/OP = RQ/OP$, $\cos \beta = OR/OP$, and $\cos \gamma = OT/OP = QP/OP$,

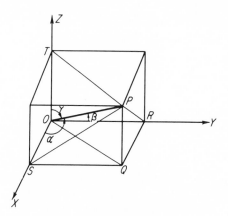

FIG. 10.3 Direction angles.

since SP, RP, and TP are perpendicular to the X, Y, and Z axes, respectively. Hence

$$RQ = OP \cos \alpha, \ OR = OP \cos \beta, \text{ and } QP = OP \cos \gamma.$$

Therefore,

$$\overline{OP}^2 = \overline{OQ}^2 + \overline{QP}^2$$
$$= \overline{RQ}^2 + \overline{OR}^2 + \overline{QP}^2$$

becomes

$$\overline{OP}^2 = \overline{OP}^2(\cos^2 \alpha + \cos^2 \beta + \cos^2 \gamma).$$

Consequently, if we take out the common factor $\overline{OP}^2$, we have the following theorem.

THEOREM 1. *The sum of the squares of the direction cosines of any line is unity.*

In Fig. 10.4, $P_1(x_1, y_1, z_1)$ and $P_2(x_2, y_2, z_2)$ are any two points. Furthermore, P_1R, P_1Q, and P_1S are parallel to the X, Y, and Z axes, respectively. Hence we obtain the following theorem by using the definition of the cosine of an angle.

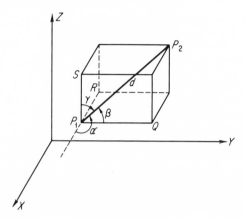

FIGURE 10.4

THEOREM 2. *The direction cosines of the segment from P_1 to P_2 are*

$$cos\ \alpha = \frac{P_1R}{d} = \frac{x_2 - x_1}{d},$$

$$cos\ \beta = \frac{P_1Q}{d} = \frac{y_2 - y_1}{d},$$

$$cos\ \gamma = \frac{P_1S}{d} = \frac{z_2 - z_1}{d}.$$

If we multiply each of these equations through by d, we see that $x_2 - x_1$, $y_2 - y_1$, and $z_2 - z_1$ are proportional to the direction cosines of the line.

DEFINITION. *Any three numbers that are proportional to the direction cosines of a line are called* **direction numbers** *of the line.*

Consequently, we have the following theorem.

THEOREM 3. *We may use* $x_2 - x_1$, $y_2 - y_1$, *and* $z_2 - z_1$ *as direction numbers of the line through the distinct points* $P_1(x_1, y_1, z_1)$ *and* $P_2(x_2, y_2, z_2)$ *regardless of its direction.*

The reader should be aware of the fact that direction numbers of a directed line and the oppositely directed one may be equal. Hence the direction cosines of a line are ambiguous in sign if only direction numbers are known.

EXAMPLE

Find the length of the segment from $P_1(3, 4, -1)$ to $P_2(5, -2, 2)$, its direction cosines and several sets of direction numbers.

Solution: The length of P_1P_2 is

$$d = \sqrt{(3 - 5)^2 + (4 + 2)^2 + (-1 - 2)^2} = 7.$$

The direction cosines of the segment from P_1 and P_2, by use of Theorem 2, are

$$\cos \alpha = \frac{5 - 3}{7} = \frac{2}{7},$$

$$\cos \beta = \frac{-2 - 4}{7} = -\frac{6}{7},$$

$$\cos \gamma = \frac{2 - (-1)}{7} = \frac{3}{7}.$$

If we use the last definition of this article, we see that $2k/7$, $-6k/7$, and $3k/7$, $k \neq 0$ are direction numbers of the line because each is k times the corresponding direction cosine.

If a, b, and c are direction numbers of a line, then $a = k \cos \alpha$, $b = k \cos \beta$, and $c = k \cos \gamma$ because direction numbers are proportional to direction cosines. Now squaring each member of each of these equations, adding corresponding new numbers, and factoring out k^2, we see that $k^2(\cos^2 \alpha + \cos^2 \beta + \cos^2 \gamma) = a^2 + b^2 + c^2$. Therefore, $k = \pm \sqrt{a^2 + b^2 + c^2}$ because $\cos^2 \alpha + \cos^2 \beta + \cos^2 \gamma = 1$.

Consequently, we have the following theorem.

THEOREM 4. *If a, b, and c are direction numbers for a line, then direction cosines are*

$$\cos \alpha = a/d, \cos \beta = b/d, \cos \gamma = c/d$$

where $d = \pm \sqrt{a^2 + b^2 + c^2}$ and the same sign is to be used with each direction cosine.

EXERCISE 10.1

Locate each pair of points in Problems 1 to 8, find the distance between each pair, and find the direction cosines for the direction from the first to the second in each case.

1. $(2, 3, -1)$, $(5, 5, 5)$ **2.** $(4, -3, 1)$, $(1, 3, -1)$

3. $(0, 0, 3)$, $(4, 0, 0)$ **4.** $(1, 7, 3)$, $(6, -5, 3)$

5. $(7, 9, 4)$, $(15, -6, 4)$ **6.** $(2, 4, 10)$, $(5, 0, -2)$

7. $(-1, -5, 7)$, $(3, -2, 1)$ **8.** $(1, -2, 5)$, $(1, 1, 1)$

Find the direction cosines for a line that has the following triples of numbers as direction numbers.

9. $a = 3, b = 2, c = 6$

10. $a = 3, b = 1, c = -2$

11. $a = -5, b = 0, c = 12$

12. $a = 2, b = -6, c = -3$

Obtain all values of the missing direction angle and each corresponding direction cosine.

13. $\alpha = 45°, \beta = 45°$ **14.** $\alpha = 60°, \gamma = 135°$

15. $\alpha = 150°, \gamma = 60°$ **16.** $\beta = 45°, \gamma = 120°$

17. Show that $(5, 0, 3)$, $(-2, 1, -2)$, and $(0, 7, 2)$ can be used as the vertices of an isosceles triangle.

18. Show that $(0, 1, -1)$, $(3, 6, 7)$, and $(8, -2, 4)$ can be used as the vertices of an equilateral triangle.

19. Show that $(1, 5, 3)$, $(3, 4, 9)$, and $(-3, 3, 4)$ can be used as the vertices of a right triangle.

20. Show that $(3, 6, 3)$, $(5, 5, 9)$, and $(-1, 4, 4)$ can be used as the vertices of a right triangle.

21. Show in two ways that $(2, 0, 5)$, $(4, 4, 2)$, and $(8, 12, -4)$ lie on a line.

22. Show in two ways that $(3, -2, -2)$, $(4, -3, 0)$, and $(1, 0, -6)$ lie on a line.

23. Show in two ways that $(2, 1, -3)$, $(1, -1, 0)$, and $(1, 3, 0)$ do not lie on a line.

24. Show in two ways that $(7, 2, -3)$, $(5, -1, -1)$, and $(9, 5, -1)$ do not lie on a line.

25. Find the coordinates of two points on the Z axis that are $\sqrt{14}$ units from $(3, 1, 2)$.

26. Find the coordinates of two points on the Y axis that are six units from $(4, 1, -4)$.

27. Find the equation of all points in the xz-plane that are four units $(2, 1, 5)$.

28. Find the equation of all points in the yz-plane that are six units from $(5, 3, -1)$.

10.4. ANGLE BETWEEN TWO LINES

We shall need the following definition in determining the angle between two lines.

DEFINITION. *The* **angle between two nonintersecting directed lines** *is equal to the angle between two intersecting lines which are parallel to and directed as them.*

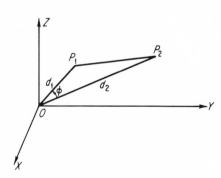

FIG. 10.5 Angle between lines.

Since the direction cosines of two intersecting directed lines are the same as those of two similarly directed lines parallel to them and passing through the origin, we need to derive only a formula for the angle ϕ between two directed lines intersecting at the origin in order to find the angle between any two lines in space. We shall let $P_1(x_1, y_1, z_1)$ and $P_2(x_2, y_2, z_2)$ be any two points and represent the direction angles of OP_1 and OP_2 by $\alpha_1, \beta_1, \gamma_1$, and $\alpha_2, \beta_2, \gamma_2$. If we use the law of cosines on the triangle P_2P_1O, we get $\overline{P_1P_2}^2 = d_1^2 + d_2^2 - 2d_1d_2 \cos \phi$. Therefore, that

$$(x_1 - x_2)^2 + (y_1 - y_2)^2 + (z_1 - z_2)^2$$
$$= x_1^2 + y_1^2 + z_1^2 + x_2^2 + y_2^2 + z_2^2 - 2d_1d_2 \cos \phi$$

is shown by use of the distance formula. If we expand the squares of the binomials, collect terms, and then solve for $\cos \phi$, we get

$$\cos \phi = \frac{x_1 x_2 + y_1 y_2 + z_1 z_2}{d_1 d_2}$$

(1)
$$= \frac{x_1 x_2}{d_1 d_2} + \frac{y_1 y_2}{d_1 d_2} + \frac{z_1 z_2}{d_1 d_2}.$$

Since

$$\cos \alpha_1 = \frac{x_1}{d_1}, \quad \cos \beta_1 = \frac{y_1}{d_1}, \quad \cos \gamma_1 = \frac{z_1}{d_1} \quad \text{and}$$

$$\cos \alpha_2 = \frac{x_2}{d_2}, \quad \cos \beta_2 = \frac{y_2}{d_2}, \quad \cos \gamma_2 = \frac{z_2}{d_2},$$

(1) can be put in the form given below.

THEOREM. *The angle between two directed lines whose direction angles are α_1, β_1, γ_1, and α_2, β_2, γ_2 is given by*

$$cos \phi = cos \alpha_1 cos \alpha_2 + cos \beta_1 cos \beta_2 + cos \gamma_1 cos \gamma_2.$$

COROLLARY 1. *Two lines are perpendicular if*

$$cos \alpha_1 cos \alpha_2 + cos \beta_1 cos \beta_2 + cos \gamma_1 cos \gamma_2 = 0,$$

and conversely.

Proof. If the angle between the lines is $90°$ or $270°$, then $\cos \phi = \cos 90° = 0$ or $\cos \phi = \cos 270° = 0$, and if $\cos \phi = 0$, then $\phi = 90°$ or $270°$ and the lines are perpendicular.

The reader should recognize the fact from Corollary 1 that, *if two lines are perpendicular, the sum of the products of their direction numbers is zero.* This is obvious if we recall that direction numbers are proportional to the direction cosines; hence the sum of the products of the direction numbers and the sum of the products of the direction cosines are both or neither zero.

COROLLARY 2. *Two directed lines are parallel and similarly directed if*

$$cos \alpha_1 cos \alpha_2 + cos \beta_1 cos \beta_2 + cos \gamma_1 cos \gamma_2 = 1;$$

they are parallel and oppositely directed if

$$\cos \alpha_1 \cos \alpha_2 + \cos \beta_1 \cos \beta_2 + \cos \gamma_1 \cos \gamma_2 = -1;$$

and conversely.

Proof. If two directed lines are parallel, the angle between them is $0°$ or $180°$. If we put these two values of ϕ in the equation of the theorem, we get the equations given in the corollary since $\cos 0° = 1$ and $\cos 180° = -1$. If $\cos \phi = \pm 1$, then $\phi = 0$ or $180°$ and the lines are parallel.

EXAMPLE 1

Find the angle between the line from the origin to $(4, 7, -4)$ and the line from $(2, 1, 5)$ to $(-4, 3, 8)$.

Solution: The lengths of the segments defined by the given points are

$$d_1 = \sqrt{(4 - 0)^2 + (7 - 0)^2 + (-4 - 0)^2} = 9,$$

and $\quad d_2 = \sqrt{(-4 - 2)^2 + (3 - 1)^2 + (8 - 5)^2} = 7.$

Hence $\qquad \cos \alpha_1 = \frac{4}{9}, \cos \beta_1 = \frac{7}{9}$ and $\cos \gamma_1 = -\frac{4}{9},$

$\qquad\qquad \cos \alpha_2 = -\frac{6}{7}, \cos \beta_2 = \frac{2}{7}$ and $\cos \gamma_2 = \frac{3}{7}.$

Therefore, $\qquad \cos \phi = \dfrac{(4)(-6) + (7)(2) + (-4)(3)}{(9)(7)}$

$$= -\tfrac{22}{63} = -.3492$$

and $\qquad\qquad\qquad = 110° \ 30'.$

Note. If either line had been oppositely directed, then $\cos \phi$ would have been .3492 and ϕ would have been $69° \ 30'$.

EXAMPLE 2

Show that the line through $P_1(3, 1, -2)$ and $P_2(5, -5, 1)$ is parallel to the one through $P_3(-4, 0, 7)$ and $P_4(-6, 6, 4)$ and perpendicular to the one through $P_5(4, 5, -1)$ and $P_6(1, 6, 3)$.

Solution: The distances between the points in the first two pairs are

$$d_{12} = \sqrt{(3 - 5)^2 + (1 + 5)^2 + (-2 - 1)^2} = 7$$

and $\quad d_{34} = \sqrt{(-4 + 6)^2 + (0 - 6)^2 + (7 - 4)^2} = 7.$

Therefore, the direction cosines of the lines through them are

$$\cos \alpha_{12} = \tfrac{2}{7}, \cos \beta_{12} = -\tfrac{6}{7}, \cos \gamma_{12} = \tfrac{3}{7}$$

and $\qquad \cos \alpha_{34} = -\tfrac{2}{7}, \cos \beta_{34} = \tfrac{6}{7}, \cos \gamma_{34} = -\tfrac{3}{7}$

or the negatives of these values. Consequently,

$$\cos \phi_{1234} = \frac{(2)(-2) + (-6)(6) + (3)(-3)}{(7)(7)} = -1$$

and the lines are parallel or $\cos \phi_{1234} = 1$, since that is the negative of -1. In this case the lines are also parallel.

In order to see if the line through P_1 and P_2 is perpendicular to the one through P_5 and P_6, we need only determine whether the sum of the products of their direction numbers is zero. Direction numbers for the lines through P_1 and P_2 and through P_5 and P_6 are

$$a_{12} = 5 - 3 = 2, b_{12} = -5 - 1 = -6, c_{12} = 1 - (-2) = 3$$

and

$$a_{56} = 1 - 4 = -3, b_{56} = 6 - 5 = 1, c_{56} = 3 - (-1) = 4.$$

Therefore, the sum of the products of the direction numbers is $(2)(-3) + (-6)(1) + (3)(4) = 0$ and the lines are perpendicular.

EXERCISE 10.2

Find the angle between the two lines in each of Problems 1 to 16.

1. The direction cosines of the lines are $1/\sqrt{2}, \tfrac{1}{2}, \tfrac{1}{2}$ and $\tfrac{1}{3}, \tfrac{2}{3}, \tfrac{2}{3}$.

2. The direction cosines of the lines are $1/\sqrt{5}, 1/\sqrt{5}, \sqrt{3}/\sqrt{5}$ and $1/\sqrt{7}, 2/\sqrt{7}, \sqrt{2}/\sqrt{7}$.

3. The direction cosines of the lines are $\tfrac{2}{7}, \tfrac{3}{7}, \tfrac{6}{7}$ and $-\tfrac{3}{7}, \tfrac{6}{7}, -\tfrac{2}{7}$.

4. The direction cosines of the lines are $\tfrac{3}{13}, -\tfrac{12}{13}, \tfrac{4}{13}$ and $-\tfrac{4}{13}, -\tfrac{3}{13}, \tfrac{12}{13}$.

5. Direction angles of the lines are $30°, 60°, 90°$ and $45°, 135°, 90°$.

6. Direction angles of the lines are $120°, 90°, 30°$ and $0°, 90°, 90°$.

7. Direction angles of the lines are $150°, 90°, 120°$ and $\arccos \tfrac{2}{7}$, $\arccos \left(-\tfrac{3}{7}\right), \arccos \tfrac{6}{7}$.

8. Direction angles of the lines are $45°, 90°, 45°$, and $\arccos \tfrac{3}{13}$, $\arccos \left(-\tfrac{4}{13}\right), \arccos \tfrac{12}{13}$.

9. Direction numbers of the lines are 2, 6, 3 and 3, 4, 12.

10. Direction numbers of the lines are 1, -2, 2 and 3, 6, -2.

11. Direction numbers of the lines are 1, 1, $-\sqrt{7}$ and $\sqrt{7}$, 1, 1.

12. Direction numbers of the lines are 3, -2, $\sqrt{2}$ and $\sqrt{2}$, 3, -2.

13. One line is through $(1, 5, -2)$ and $(4, 11, 0)$ and the other through $(3, -1, 4)$ and $(1, -7, 1)$.

14. One line is through $(5, 8, 1)$ and $(2, 2, 3)$ and the other through $(4, 0, 3)$ and $(3, -2, 1)$.

15. One line is through $(7, 2, 5)$ and $(4, -2, -7)$ and the other through $(1, -1, -2)$ and $(4, 3, 10)$.

16. One line is through $(8, 5, 4)$ and $(2, 2, 2)$ and the other through $(2, -3, 0)$ and $(3, -1, -2)$.

17. Show in two ways that the points $(1, -2, 4)$, $(2, -1, 1)$, and $(5, 0, 2)$ can be used as the vertices of an isosceles triangle.

18. Show in two ways that the points $(4, 2, -1)$, $(2, 5, 5)$, and $(1, 4, -7)$ can be used as the vertices of an isosceles triangle.

19. Show in two ways that the points $(5, -3, 2)$, $(6, -4, 4)$, and $(7, -2, 3)$ can be used as vertices of an equilateral triangle.

20. Show in two ways that the points $(3, -4, -1)$, $(4, -5, 1)$, and $(5, -3, 0)$ can be used as vertices of an equilateral triangle.

21. Is the line through $(2, 3, -1)$ and $(1, 4, 0)$ parallel or perpendicular to the one through $(7, 2, -3)$ and $(6, 3, -2)$? Why?

22. Is the line through $(2, 3, 5)$ and $(4, 1, -1)$ parallel or perpendicular to the one through $(3, 3, 3)$ and $(5, 0, -3)$? Why?

23. Is the line through $(4, -3, 0)$ and $(2, -4, 3)$ parallel or perpendicular to the one through $(1, 6, 3)$ and $(-1, 4, 1)$? Why?

24. Is the line through $(1, -2, 3)$ and $(2, 1, -1)$ parallel or perpendicular to the one through $(5, 0, 1)$ and $(6, 1, 0)$? Why?

11 *SURFACES AND CURVES*

11.1. *THE GRAPH OF AN EQUATION*

If we have an equation that involves x, y, and z and only them, we may usually assign values arbitrarily to two of them and then compute the third. In this way, we find the coordinates of a point that satisfies the given equation. The totality or set of such points forms a surface which is called the graph of the equation.

EXAMPLE

If the coordinates x, y, and z satisfy the equation

$$x^2 + y^2 + z^2 = 4,$$

then

$$\sqrt{x^2 + y^2 + z^2} = 2$$

and each point on the graph is two units from the origin. Hence the graph is the sphere with radius two and with center at the origin.

11.2. *THE PLANE*

We shall derive the equation of a plane in Article 12.1 but shall now assume the fact that it is a first-degree equation in x, y, and z.

The equation

$$z = k$$

represents a plane that is always k units in distance and direction from the xy-plane, since it is satisfied by those points and only those whose z coordinate is k. Similar results are true for $x = k$ and $y = k$. Therefore, *an equation of the first degree in only one of the variables x, y, or z represents a plane parallel to the plane of the other two variables.*

11.3. SECTIONS, TRACES, INTERCEPTS, AND SYMMETRY

We shall now familiarize ourselves with several terms used in discussing surfaces.

DEFINITION. *The curve that is determined by the intersections of a surface and a plane is called a **plane section** of the **surface.***

If the equation of the surface and the equation of the plane are used simultaneously, we have the equations of the section.

The section made by a coordinate plane is known as the *trace* on that plane and is obtained by setting the third coordinate in the given equation equal to zero. Thus, the trace on the xz-plane is obtained by setting $y = 0$.

ILLUSTRATIVE EXAMPLE 1

The trace of $x^2 + 3y^2 + z^2 + 2x + 7y + 4z - 4 = 0$ in the xz-plane is the circle $x^2 + z^2 - 2x + 4z - 4 = 0$ since that is the equation obtained by putting $y = 0$. The equations of the section made by the plane $y = -1$ are the given equation and $y = -1$. If we solve these simultaneously, we see that $(x - 1)^2 + (z + 2)^2 = 13$ is the equation of the section made by $y = -1$ and this circle is on the plane $y = -1$.

DEFINITION. *A coordinate of an intersection of a surface and a coordinate axis is an **intercept**.*

The reader should show that we can obtain the intercepts on any one of the coordinate axes by setting the other two coordinates equal to zero in the given equation, and solving for the third variable.

EXAMPLE 1

Determine the intercepts of $x^2 + y^2 + x + 2z - 5 = 0$.

Solution: If we put $x = y = 0$ and solve the resulting equation, we see that $z = \frac{5}{2}$ is the z-intercept. We can find that the y-intercepts are $y = \pm \sqrt{5}$ in a similar manner. If $y = z = 0$, we get

$$x^2 + x - 5 = 0.$$

Hence, the x-intercepts are $x = (-1 \pm \sqrt{21})/2$.

We can obtain additional useful information about a surface by use of its symmetry.

DEFINITION. *Two points are* **symmetrically located with respect to a plane** *if the line segment joining them is perpendicular to and bisected by the plane.*

DEFINITION. *A surface is* **symmetrical with respect to a plane** *if for each point on the surface the symmetrically located point with respect to the plane is also on the surface.*

The definitions of a line of symmetry and a point of symmetry as given in Article 6.3 apply in three-dimensional space. The main tests for symmetry are given below and one of them is proved.

THEOREM 1. *A surface is symmetrical with respect to the origin if the equation of the surface is unchanged or multiplied by* -1 *by replacing each of* **x, y,** *and* **z** *by its negative.*

THEOREM 2. *A surface is symmetrical with respect to a coordinate axis if the equation of the surface is unchanged or multiplied by* -1 *by replacing the two coordinates that do not occur in the name of the axis by their negatives.*

THEOREM 3. *A surface is symmetrical with respect to a coordinate plane if the equation of the surface is unaltered or is multiplied by* −1 *when the coordinate that does not occur in the name of the plane is replaced by its negative.*

Proof. In terms of symmetry with respect to the xy-plane, this theorem becomes the following: A surface $s(x, y, z) = 0$ is symmetrical with respect to the xy-plane if $s(x, y, -z) = \pm s(x, y, z)$. Similar statements can be made for symmetry with respect to the other coordinate planes. We shall prove the theorem for symmetry with respect to the xy-plane.

The points (x, y, z) and $(x, y, -z)$ are symmetrically located with respect to the xy-plane, since the line segment connecting them is perpendicular to and bisected by that plane. Hence if the equation of the surface $s(x, y, z) = 0$ is unaltered or multiplied by −1 when z is replaced by $-z$, both (x, y, z) and $(x, y, -z)$ are on the surface if either is on it.

The proof for the other two coordinate planes is analogous to the one given above and is left as an exercise for the student.

ILLUSTRATIVE EXAMPLE 2

The surface

$$f(x, y, z) = x^2 + y^2 + z^2 + 4x + 2z - 5 = 0$$

is symmetrical with respect to the xz-plane, since

$$f(x, -y, z) = x^2 + (-y)^2 + z^2 + 4x + 2z - 5$$
$$= f(x, y, z).$$

It is not symmetrical with respect to the xy- or yz-plane, since $f(x, y, -z) \neq \pm f(x, y, z)$ and $f(-x, y, z) \neq \pm f(x, y, z)$.

EXAMPLE 2

Discuss the graph of

(1) $$f(x, y, z) = y^2 + x^2 - a^2z = 0$$

by finding the sections made by planes parallel to the coordinate planes, the traces, and the intercepts, and testing for symmetry. Sketch the surface.

Solution: If $z = k$, (1) becomes $y^2 + x^2 = a^2k$. Hence each section parallel to the xy-plane is a circle if k is positive, and there are no sections parallel to that plane if k is negative because $y^2 + x^2$ cannot be negative for real values of y and x.

If $y = k$, the sections parallel to the xz-plane are parabolas since (1) becomes $x^2 = a^2z - k^2$.

If $x = k$, (1) becomes $y^2 = a^2z - k^2$; consequently, the sections parallel to the yz-plane are parabolas.

The trace in the plane of two coordinates is obtained by putting the third variable equal to zero. Hence the trace in the xy-plane is the point $f(x, y, 0) = y^2 + x^2 = 0$, that in the xz-plane is the parabola $f(x, 0, z) = x^2 - a^2z = 0$, that in the yz-plane is the parabola $f(0, y, z) = y^2 - a^2z = 0$. Each intercept is readily seen to be zero since

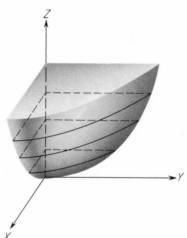

$$f(x, y, z) = y^2 + x^2 - a^2z = 0,$$
$$f(x, 0, 0) = x^2 = 0 \text{ for } x = 0,$$
$$f(0, y, 0) = y^2 = 0 \text{ for } y = 0,$$
$$f(0, 0, z) = a^2z = 0 \text{ for } z = 0.$$

Fɪɢ. 11.1 A paraboloid.

Furthermore, the surface is symmetrical with respect to the xz- and yz-planes, since

$$f(x, -y, z) = (-y)^2 + x^2 - a^2z = f(x, y, z)$$
and $$f(-x, y, z) = f(x, y, z).$$

It is not symmetrical with respect to the xy-plane since $f(x, y, -z) \neq \pm f(x, y, z)$.

A sketch of that part of the surface in the $(+, +, +)$ octant is shown in Fig. 11.1.

11.4. *USE OF PARALLEL PLANE SECTIONS IN SKETCHING*

Example 2 of Article 11.3 illustrates the use of parallel plane sections in sketching, but the method is of sufficient importance to be discussed further. If sections parallel to one coordinate plane do not give a clear enough picture, then one should sketch the surface by using sections parallel to another of the coordinate planes. It is desirable to carry out the steps used in Example 2 of Article 11.3 before making the sketch. Those steps are as follows:

(1) *determine the type of sections parallel to each coordinate plane,*

(2) *determine the traces on the coordinate planes,*

(3) *find the intercepts on the coordinate axes,*

(4) *test the equation of the surface for symmetry.*

EXAMPLE

Discuss and sketch

$$x^2 + yz - 4 = 0.$$

Solution: The sections made by $z = k$ (parallel to the xy-plane) are the parabolas $x^2 + ky - 4 = 0$. The sections made by $y = k$ are

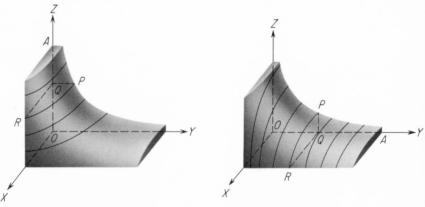

FIGURE 11.2   FIGURE 11.3

the parabolas $x^2 + kz - 4 = 0$ and those made by $x = k$ are the hyperbolas $k^2 + yz - 4 = 0$.

The trace in the xy-plane is the pair of lines $x = \pm 2$. That in the xz-plane is the pair of lines $x = \pm 2$ and the yz-trace is the hyperbola $yz - 4 = 0$.

The x-intercepts are $x = \pm 2$ and there are no y- or z-intercepts.

The surface is symmetrical with respect to the yz-plane, the X axis, and the origin.

The sketch in Fig. 11.2 uses the sections $z = k$ and is drawn as follows. Draw in the traces; lay off the interval OA that is to be used in the sketch on the coordinate axis that is perpendicular to the sections to be used and divide it into subintervals. At each point of sub-division, Q for example, draw the traces QP and QR of the cutting plane; they intersect the traces of the surface at P and R. Finally, the parabolic arc PR is the desired section.

Figure 11.3 was drawn in a similar manner but the sections $y = k$ were used. The two figures illustrate the fact that sections parallel to one coordinate plane may give a clearer or different picture of the situation than do sections parallel to another.

EXERCISE 11.1

Find the sections parallel to the coordinate planes, traces and inter-cepts of the following surfaces. Test each surface for symmetry and sketch it by use of parallel sections.

1. $x^2 + y^2 + z^2 = 9$

2. $3x^2 + 3y^2 + 3z^2 = 1$

3. $x^2 + y^2 + 2z^2 = 8$

4. $x^2 + 2y^2 + 2z^2 = 4$

5. $x^2 + 2y^2 + 3z^2 = 5$

6. $2x^2 + 5y^2 + 6z^2 = 7$

7. $3x^2 - y^2 - z^2 = 1$

8. $2x^2 + 2y^2 - z^2 = 6$

9. $z = x - xy$

10. $z = x^2 + xy$

11. $z = xy$

12. $y = 3xz - z$

13. $x^2 = 2y - 1$

14. $y^2 = 2xy - 3$

15. $z^2 = xy$

16. $x^2 = xz - y$

17. $x^2 + z^2 = 4y$

18. $y^2 - z^2 = 2x$

19. $x^2 + y^2 + z^2 - 2x = 3$

20. $x^2 - y^2 + z^2 + 4y = 5$

11.5. SURFACES OF REVOLUTION

We shall now discuss a class of surfaces which occur frequently.

DEFINITION. *A surface that can be generated by rotating a given plane curve about a fixed straight line in its plane is called a* **surface of revolution.**

The fixed line is called the *axis of revolution* and the given curve is known as the *generating curve*. A section made by a plane that is perpendicular to the axis of revolution is called a *right section.*

We should recognize the fact that there is no limit to the variety of surfaces of revolution. Consequently, we cannot study all of them, and shall list only some of the more common ones, indicating how each is generated.

Surface:	*Generated, if we rotate:*
Sphere:	A circle about any diameter;
Ellipsoid of revolution:	An ellipse about its major or minor axis;*
Hyperboloid of revolution:	A hyperbola about either of its axes;†
Paraboloid of revolution:	A parabola about its axis;
Torus (doughnut):	A circle about a line in its plane but not intersecting the circle;
Circular cylinder:	A straight line about another that is parallel to it;
Circular cone:	A straight line about another that intersects it obliquely.

* The surface is called a *prolate spheroid* (football) if we rotate about the major axis and an *oblate spheroid* (discus) if the rotation is about the minor axis.

† The surface is called a *hyperboloid of revolution of one sheet* if the rotation is about the conjugate axis and a *hyperboloid of revolution of two sheets* if the rotation is about the transverse axis.

To derive the equation of the surface of revolution when we know the equations of the fixed line and generating curve, we shall

(1) *let* **P** *represent a typical point on the generating curve,*

(2) *obtain an expression for the radius of a right section when* **P**

is in a general position **R** *on the surface* (this will be in terms of two coordinates),

(3) *get an expression for the radius of a right section when* **P** *is in the plane of the generating curve* (this can be put in terms of the third coordinate), *and*

(4) *equate these two expressions for the radius of a right section.*

EXAMPLE 1

Find the equation of the surface generated by rotating the line

$$2z + y = 4, \qquad x = 0$$

about the Y axis.

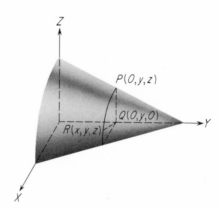

FIGURE 11.4

Solution: We shall represent a typical point on the generating curve by $P(O, y, z)$, where z is the z coordinate of the generating curve, as indicated in Fig. 11.4; furthermore, we shall represent a typical position of P on the generated surface by $R(x, y, z)$. The foot of the perpendicular from P or R to the axis of rotation (the Y axis) is $Q(0, y, 0)$.

Consequently, we want to express $QR = QP$ in terms of the coordinates of R. In order to do this, we make use of the fact that,

$$QR = \sqrt{(x - 0)^2 + (y - y)^2 + (z - 0)^2}$$
$$= \sqrt{x^2 + z^2}$$

and the fact that

$$QP = z$$
$$= (4 - y)/2, \quad \text{from the equation of the generating curve.}$$

If we now equate the expressions for QR and QP and square each member of the resulting equation, we see that the equation of the surface of revolution is

$$x^2 + z^2 = \left(\frac{4 - y}{2}\right)^2.$$

EXAMPLE 2

Find the equation of the surface generated by rotating the ellipse

$$\frac{x^2}{a^2} + \frac{y^2}{b^2} = 1$$

about the Y axis.

Solution: If $P(x, y, 0)$ represents a typical point on the generating curve, $R(x, y, z)$ a typical position of P on the generated surface, and

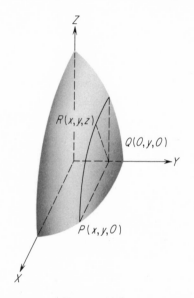

FIGURE 11.5

$Q(0, y, 0)$ the foot of the perpendicular from R or P to the axis of rotation, then

$$QR = \sqrt{x^2 + z^2}$$

and

$$QP = x$$

$$= \frac{a}{b} \sqrt{b^2 - y^2}, \quad \text{from the equation of the generating curve.}$$

Consequently, equating $\overline{QR}^2$ and $\overline{QP}^2$, we have

$$x^2 + z^2 = \frac{a^2}{b^2} (b^2 - y^2).$$

Finally, dividing by a^2 and adding y^2/b^2 to each member, we see that the equation of the surface of revolution is

$$\frac{x^2}{a^2} + \frac{y^2}{b^2} + \frac{z^2}{a^2} = 1$$

11.6. CYLINDRICAL SURFACES

We shall now consider another one of the simpler classes of surfaces.

DEFINITION. *The surface generated by a moving line that remains parallel to its original position and intersects a given plane curve at all times is called a* **cylindrical surface.**

The line or any position of it is called a *generator* of the surface and the given curve is known as the *generating curve*. The curve obtained by cutting the cylindrical surface by a plane perpendicular

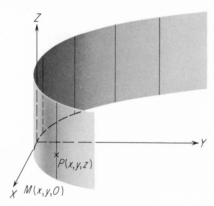

FIG. 11.6 A cylinder.

to the generators is called a *right section*. The line through the center, if any, of a right section and perpendicular to it is called the *axis* of the surface.

We shall restrict our study of cylindrical surfaces to those whose generators are parallel to one of the coordinate axes and whose generating curve is in the coordinate plane that is perpendicular to the generators. If the generating curve is in the xy-plane, it can be represented by $f(x, y) = 0$. Furthermore, the generators intersect $f(x, y) = 0$ at all times and are parallel to the Z axis; consequently, the generators are perpendicular to the xy-plane.

To study the cylindrical surface, we shall erect a generator at any point $M(x, y, O)$ on the generating curve and consider any point $P(x, y, z)$ on the generator. The coordinates of M satisfy the equation $f(x, y) = 0$ of the generating curve; hence the coordinates of P must also satisfy it because the x and y coordinates of the two points are equal and z does not enter into the equation. Hence we have the following theorem.

THEOREM. *Any equation in two variables represents in space a cylindrical surface which is perpendicular to the plane of these two variables and for which a generating curve is the plane curve whose equation is given.*

DEFINITION. *If a generating curve of a cylindrical surface is a circle, a parabola, an ellipse, or a hyperbola, the cylindrical surface is said to be* **circular, parabolic, elliptic, or hyperbolic,** *respectively.*

ILLUSTRATIVE EXAMPLE

The equation $x^2 - z^2 = 4$ represents a hyperbolic cylinder with generators perpendicular to the xz-plane, since it is an equation in x and z and the generating curve is a hyperbola.

EXERCISE 11.2

Find the equation of each surface described in Problems 1 to 24. Sketch each and, if possible, classify each.

1. The line $x + y = 2$, $z = 0$ is rotated about the X axis.

2. The line $x + y = 2$, $z = 0$ is rotated about the Y axis.

3. The line $x + 3z = 4$, $y = 0$ is rotated about the Z axis.

4. The line $x + 3z = 4$, $y = 0$ is rotated about the X axis.

5. The line $y = 3$, $z = 0$ is rotated about the X axis.

6. The line $z = 5$, $x = 0$ is rotated about the Y axis.

7. The line $2x + 3y = 4$, $z = 0$ is rotated about the X axis.

8. The line $2x + 3y = 4$, $z = 0$ is rotated about the Y axis.

9. The circle $x^2 + z^2 = a^2$, $y = 0$ is rotated about the Z axis.

10. The circle $x^2 + y^2 = a^2$, $z = 0$ is rotated about the X axis.

11. The ellipse $x^2/a^2 + y^2/b^2 = 1$, $z = 0$ is rotated about the Y axis.

12. The ellipse $x^2/a^2 + y^2/b^2 = 1$, $z = 0$ is rotated about the X axis.

13. The hyperbola $x^2/a^2 - y^2/b^2 = 1$, $z = 0$ is rotated about the X axis.

14. The hyperbola $x^2/a^2 - y^2/b^2 = 1$, $z = 0$ is rotated about the Y axis.

15. The parabola $y^2 = 4ax$, $z = 0$ is rotated about the X axis.

16. The parabola $z^2 = 4ay$, $x = 0$ is rotated about the Y axis.

17. The circle $x^2 + y^2 = a^2$, $z = 0$ is rotated about the line $y = 2a$, $z = 0$.

18. The circle $z^2 + y^2 = a^2$, $x = 0$ is rotated about the line $z = 3a$, $x = 0$.

19. The ellipse $x^2/a^2 + y^2/b^2 = 1$, $z = 0$ is rotated about the line $y = 2b$, $z = 0$.

20. The ellipse $x^2/a^2 + y^2/b^2 = 1$, $z = 0$ is rotated about the line $x = 2a$, $z = 0$.

21. The cubical parabola $y = z^3$, $x = 0$ is rotated about the Y axis.

22. The cubical parabola $y = z^3$, $x = 0$ is rotated about the Z axis.

23. The semicubical parabola $z^2 = y^3$, $x = 0$ is rotated about the Y axis.

24. The curve $zy^2 = 4$ is rotated about the Z axis.

Sketch and classify the following cylinders.

25. $x^2 + y^2 = 16$

26. $x^2 + y^2 = 9$

27. $x^2 + y^2 - 4x + 6y = 3$

28. $x^2 + z^2 + 2x + 8z = 8$

29. $x^2 + 4z^2 = 4$

30. $4y^2 + 9z^2 = 36$

31. $x^2 - 4z^2 = 4$

32. $9x^2 - y^2 = 9$

33. $y^2 = 4x$

34. $z^2 = 9y$

35. $(x - 1)^2 = 6(y - 2)$

36. $(y - 3)^2 = 4(z - 1)$

11.7. CURVES

We used the fact that a surface and a plane intersect in a plane curve in our study of sections. We shall now extend this concept by thinking of the equations

(1) $f_1(x, y, z) = 0$ and $f_2(x, y, z) = 0$

as the simultaneous equations of the curve determined by the intersections of the surfaces (1). All points of such a curve may lie in a plane and, if so, we say that we have a *plane curve*. Equations (1), however, do not necessarily determine a plane curve; we say that we have a *skew* or *twisted curve* unless it is a plane curve.

It may be possible to eliminate one of the variables, say z, from equations (1) and obtain one equation in the other two coordinates, say

$$F(x, y) = 0.$$

The graph of $F(x, y) = 0$ is called the *projection* of the curve of intersection on the xy-plane. The cylinder that has $F(x, y) = 0$ as a generating curve is known as the *projecting cylinder* of the curve of intersection. The generators of this cylinder are the perpendiculars from the skew curve to the xy-plane.

To *obtain the **xy**-projecting cylinder of a given curve, we eliminate z between the equations of the curve.* The xz- and yz-projecting cylinders can be obtained in a similar manner.

It is often useful, desirable, and relatively easy to represent a curve in space by showing it as the intersection of two of its projecting cylinders.

EXAMPLE

Find the equations of the projecting cylinders of the curve whose equations are

$$x^2 + 2y^2 - z^2 = 2$$
$$x^2 + y^2 - 2z^2 = -3$$

and sketch the curve.

Solution: If we eliminate x between the equations of the curve, we find that the yz-projecting cylinder of the curve is $y^2 + z^2 = 5$.

In a similar manner, we see that the xz- and xy-projecting cylinders are $3z^2 - x^2 = 8$ and $x^2 + 3y^2 = 7$, respectively. The curve is shown in Fig. 11.7 as the intersection of the xy- and yz-projecting cylinders. It is constructed by starting with any point Q on the Y axis, drawing parallels to the X and Z axes until they intersect the generating curves in R and S, and finally determining a point P on the curve by drawing parallels to the X and Z axes from S and R until they meet. Any desired number of points on the curve can be obtained in this manner.

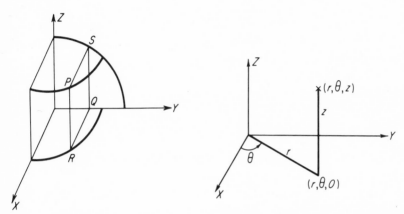

FIGURE 11.7   FIG. 11.8 Cylindrical coordinates.

11.8. CYLINDRICAL COORDINATES

There is a second type of coordinate system that is often used in locating points in space. This system uses the usual polar coordinates to locate the point in the xy-plane that is directly below or above the desired point in space; then the distance and direction from this point to the desired point is indicated by z. The coordinates of the point are (r, θ, z) and are called the *cylindrical coordinates* of the point.

The relations between them and the rectangular coordinates of the point are readily obtained from Fig. 11.8 and are

$$x = r \cos \theta, \quad y = r \sin \theta, \quad z = z$$

and

$$r = \sqrt{x^2 + y^2}, \quad \theta = \text{arc tan} \frac{y}{x}, \quad z = z.$$

11.9. SPHERICAL COORDINATES

A third type of coordinate system is often used in locating points in space. If it is used, we locate the point by stating its distance

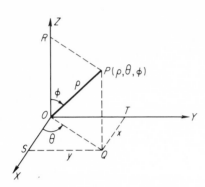

ρ (called *radius vector*) from the origin, the angle ϕ from the Z axis to the radius vector, and the angle θ from the X axis to the line which connects the origin and the point in the xy-plane that is directly below or above the point that is being located as shown in Fig. 11.9. This system is called the *spherical coordinate system* and it is convenient for use in locating points on a sphere. It can be used

FIG. 11.9 Spherical coordinates.

in giving the co-latitude and longitude of points on the surface of the earth.

We shall now derive the relations between the rectangular coordinates (x, y, z) and the spherical coordinates (ρ, θ, ϕ) of any point P. From Fig. 11.9, we see that

$$\sin \phi = \frac{RP}{\rho}$$

$$= \frac{OQ}{\rho} \qquad \text{since } OQ = RP$$

$$= \frac{y}{\rho \sin \theta} \quad \text{since } \sin \theta = \frac{y}{OQ};$$

hence, $y = \rho \sin \theta \sin \phi.$

Furthermore,

$$\sin \phi = \frac{OQ}{\rho} \qquad \text{since angle } OPQ = \phi$$

$$= \frac{x}{\rho \cos \theta} \quad \text{since } \cos \theta = \frac{OS}{OQ} = \frac{x}{OQ};$$

hence $x = \rho \cos \theta \sin \phi.$

Finally,

$$\cos \phi = \frac{OR}{\rho}$$

$$= \frac{z}{\rho} \quad \text{since } OR = QP = z$$

and
$$z = \rho \cos \phi.$$

Therefore,

$$x = \rho \cos \theta \sin \phi, \quad y = \rho \sin \theta \sin \phi, \quad and \ z = \rho \cos \phi.$$

If these equations are solved for ρ, θ, and ϕ, we get

$$\rho = \sqrt{x^2 + y^2 + z^2}, \quad \theta = \text{arc tan } \frac{y}{x},$$

$$\phi = \text{arc tan } \frac{z}{\sqrt{x^2 + y^2 + z^2}}.$$

EXAMPLE

Express

$$\rho \cos \phi = a \tan \rho$$

in terms of two other types of coordinate systems.

Solution: We shall first change the equation to rectangular and then to cylindrical form. We can replace the left member by z but must change the form of the right member before being able to replace it in terms of rectangular coordinates. Hence we put

$$\tan \theta = \frac{\sin \theta}{\cos \theta}$$

$$= \frac{\rho \sin \phi \sin \theta}{\rho \sin \phi \cos \theta} \text{ since } \rho \sin \phi / \rho \sin \phi = 1$$

$$= \frac{y}{x}.$$

Therefore, the given equation becomes

$$z = a \frac{y}{x}, \text{ or } \quad zx = ay.$$

In order to change this to cylindrical coordinates, we make direct use of the relations between rectangular and cylindrical coordinates and get

$$zr \cos \theta = ar \sin \theta$$

or
$$z = a \tan \theta.$$

EXERCISE 11.3

Express the equation in each of Problems 1 to 24 in terms of two other types of coordinate systems.

1. $z = a$ **2.** $x^2 + y^2 = a^2$

3. $x^2 + y^2 = 2ax$ **4.** $x^2 + y^2 + z^2 = a^2$

5. $x^2 - y^2 = a^2$ **6.** $yz = x$

7. $x^2 + y^2 = 2z$ **8.** $(x^2 + y^2 + z^2)^2 = 4a^2(x^2 + y^2)$

9. $z = a$ **10.** $r = a$

11. $r = 2a \cos \theta$ **12.** $r^2 + z^2 = a^2$

13. $r^2 \cos 2\theta = a^2$ **14.** $z = \cot \theta$

15. $r^2 = 2z$ **16.** $r^2 + z^2 = 2ar$

17. $\rho \cos \phi = a$ **18.** $\rho \sin \phi = a$

19. $\rho \sin \phi = 2a \cos \theta$ **20.** $\rho = a$

21. $\rho^2 \sin^2 \phi \cos 2\theta = a^2$

22. $\rho \sin \theta \cos \phi = \cos \theta$

23. $\rho \sin^2 \phi = 2 \cos \phi$

24. $\rho^2 = 4a^2 \sin^2 \phi$

Find the equations of the projection cylinders of the curves listed below. Sketch each curve.

25. $x^2 + y^2 + z^2 = 8$
$3x^2 + y^2 - z^2 = 1$

26. $x^2 + y^2 + 3z^2 = 9$
$2x^2 - y^2 + z^2 = 5$

27. $2x^2 - 3y^2 + z^2 = 7$
$x^2 + y^2 - z^2 = 6$

28. $3x^2 + 2y^2 - z^2 = 3$
$2x^2 + 3y^2 + 2z^2 = 7$

29. $x^2 - y^2 - z^2 = 4$
$x^2 + y^2 - z = 2$

30. $5x^2 - 2y^2 - z^2 = -2$
$3x^2 + y^2 + z = 8$

31. $4x^2 + y - z^2 = -1$
$3x^2 - y^2 + 2z^2 = 4$

32. $2x^2 - 3y^2 + z^2 = 6$
$x + 2y^2 + 3z^2 = 3$

33. $xz = y$
$x^2 + y^2 + z^2 = 4$

34. $xy = z$
$x^2 - y^2 - z^2 = -2$

35. $2x^2 - y^2 - 3z = 3$
$xy = z$

36. $xz = y$
$yz = x$

12 *PLANES AND LINES*

12.1. *THE NORMAL FORM OF THE EQUATION OF A PLANE*

We shall now derive the equation of a plane. In order to do this, let $P(x, y, z)$ be any point on the plane, $P_1(x_1, y_1, z_1)$ the foot of the perpendicular from the origin to the plane, the positive number p the directed distance from the origin to P_1, and α, β, γ and α_1, β_1, γ_1 the direction angles of OP and OP_1. Since P is in the plane and OP_1 is perpendicular to it, it follows that OP_1P is a right triangle with the right angle at P_1.

If in Fig. 12.1 we let angle $P_1OP = \phi$, then

$$\cos \phi = \frac{OP_1}{OP} = \frac{p}{OP}$$

and

$$OP \cos \phi = p$$

but

$$\cos \phi = \cos \alpha \cos \alpha_1 + \cos \beta \cos \beta_1 + \cos \gamma \cos \gamma_1$$

$$= \frac{x}{OP} \cos \alpha_1 + \frac{y}{OP} \cos \beta_1 + \frac{z}{OP} \cos \gamma_1.$$

213

Now, multiplying by OP and replacing $OP \cos \phi$ by p, we see that

(1) $x \cos \alpha_1 + y \cos \beta_1 + z \cos \gamma_1 = p.$

The operations performed in obtaining (1) are such that the inverse of each can be performed if P is not at the origin; that is, unless the plane passes through the origin. Furthermore, it can be

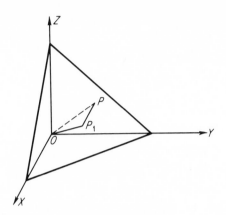

FIG. 12.1 A plane.

shown that (1) holds even though the plane passes through the origin. Hence we have the following theorem.

THEOREM. *If α_1, β_1, and γ_1 are direction angles of the normal from the origin to the plane and if p is the length of the normal, then the equation of the plane is*

$$x \cos \alpha_1 + y \cos \beta_1 + z \cos \gamma_1 = p.$$

EXAMPLE

Find the equation of the plane that is 4 units from the origin if the normal from the origin to it has $\alpha_1 = 60°$, $\beta_1 = 120°$, and $\gamma_1 = 45°$ as direction angles.

Solution: If we substitute the given values in the normal form of the equation of a plane, we get

$$x \cos 60° + y \cos 120° + z \cos 45° - 4 = 0.$$

Hence the equation of the plane becomes

$$x - y + \sqrt{2}\,z - 8 = 0$$

after multiplying by 2, since $\cos 60° = \frac{1}{2}$, $\cos 120° = -\frac{1}{2}$, and $\cos 45°$ $= \sqrt{2}/2$.

12.2. REDUCTION TO NORMAL FORM

If the values of the direction cosines are substituted in (1) of the preceding article and the equation is cleared of fractions, we get an equation of the form

$$(1) \qquad Ax + By + Cz + D = 0$$

with A, B, C, not all zero. An equation of this form represents a plane and is called the general equation of the plane. We shall now find a way to change the general linear equation to normal form. If this and the normal form of the equation represent the same plane, they must be identical, or one must be equal to a constant times the other. We shall put

$$x \cos \alpha_1 + y \cos \beta_1 + z \cos \gamma_1 - p = K(Ax + By + Cz + D)$$

and determine K so that the two members are identical. Hence it is necessary and sufficient that

$$KA = \cos \alpha_1,\ KB = \cos \beta_1,\ KC = \cos \gamma_1,\ \text{and } KD = -p.$$

If we square each member of the first three of these equations and add corresponding members of the new equations, we get

$$K^2(A^2 + B^2 + C^2) = \cos^2 \alpha_1 + \cos^2 \beta_1 + \cos^2 \gamma_1$$
$$= 1,$$

since α_1, β_1, and γ_1 are the direction angles of a line. Therefore,

$$K = \frac{1}{\pm \sqrt{A^2 + B^2 + C^2}}.$$

We must decide on a method for determining the sign to use with the radical in any particular case. The constant term in the left member of the normal form of the equation of a plane is $-p$ where p is a positive number; hence we must *choose the sign of the radical opposite to that of the constant term when in the left member.*

The constant term is zero if the plane passes through the origin; in such a case another method for determining the sign of the radical must be used. We shall *choose the sign of the radical to be that of the first one of the coefficients C, B, or A, respectively, which is different from zero.* Hence we have the theorem.

THEOREM 1. *In order to change*

$$Ax + By + Cz + D = 0 \qquad (A, B, C, \text{ not all zero})$$

to normal form, divide each term by

$$\pm \sqrt{A^2 + B^2 + C^2}$$

and choose the sign of the radical as stated above.

EXAMPLE 1

Change $6x + 2y - 3z + 14 = 0$ to normal form.

Solution: We must divide each term of the left member of the given equation by -7, since

$$\pm \sqrt{A^2 + B^2 + C^2} = \pm \sqrt{6^2 + 2^2 + (-3)^2} = \pm 7$$

and the constant term is positive. Therefore,

$$-\frac{6x}{7} - \frac{2y}{7} + \frac{3z}{7} - 2 = 0$$

is the normal form of the given equation.

The coefficients of the variables in the equation $Ax + By + Cz + D = 0$ of a plane are proportional to the direction cosines of the normal to the plane, since each coefficient is the constant $\pm \sqrt{A^2 + B^2 + C^2}$ times the corresponding direction cosine, giving the following theorem.

THEOREM 2. *If a line and a plane are perpendicular, any set of direction numbers of the line may be used as coefficients of the corresponding variables in the equation of the plane.*

EXAMPLE 2

Find the equation of a plane which passes through $P(-1, 1, 4)$ if 2, 5 and -3 are direction numbers of a line perpendicular to it.

Solution: In keeping with Theorem 2, we have $2x + 5y - 3z + D = 0$ as the equation of a plane perpendicular to the line with 2, 5 and -3 for direction numbers regardless of the value of D. We must now determine D so that the plane passes through $P(-1, 1, 4)$. We shall do this by making use of the fact that the coordinates of a point satisfy the equation of the plane if and only if the point is on the plane. Thus, substituting the coordinates of the point in the equation, we have $2(-1) + 5(1) - 3(4) + D = -9 + D = 0$; hence $D = 9$. Consequently, the equation of the plane is $2x + 5y - 3z + 9 = 0$.

EXERCISE 12.1

Find the equation of each of the following planes.

1. Five units from the origin and with 30°, 60°, and 90° as direction angles of the normal

2. Four units from the origin and with 45°, 120°, and 60° as direction angles of the normal

3. Six units from the origin and with 150°, 120°, and 90° as direction angles of the normal

4. Nine units from the origin and with 135°, 60°, and 120° as direction angles of the normal

5. Three units from the origin and with 2, -3, and 6 as direction numbers of the normal

6. Five units from the origin and with -4, -5, and $2\sqrt{2}$ as direction numbers of the normal

7. Seven units from the origin and with 2, 5, and $-\sqrt{7}$ as direction numbers of the normal

8. Six units from the origin and 6, -8, and $2\sqrt{11}$ as direction numbers of the normal

9. Through $(3, -1, 4)$ and with 1, -1, and 5 as direction numbers of the normal

10. Through $(-2, -1, 3)$ and with 2, -3, and 6 as direction numbers of the normal

11. Through $(5, 0, 7)$ and with 6, -2, and 5 as direction numbers of the normal

12. Through $(6, -2, 3)$ and with 1, -4, and -2 as direction numbers of the normal

13. Through $(4, 1, -2)$ and normal through $(5, 2, 3)$ and $(1, -1, 4)$

14. Through $(7, -2, 3)$ and normal through $(4, 0, 3)$ and $(6, 2, 1)$

15. Through $(-2, -3, 1)$ and normal through $(-2, -1, 0)$ and $(3, 4, -5)$

16. Through $(4, 5, -3)$ and normal through $(3, 4, -5)$ and $(1, 3, -2)$

Transform each of the following equations to normal form.

17. $6x - 2y + 3z - 14 = 0$ **18.** $3x + 4y - 12z - 39 = 0$

19. $4x - 12y + 3z - 26 = 0$ **20.** $2x - 3y - 6z - 21 = 0$

21. $2\sqrt{2}x + 5y - 4z - 7 = 0$ **22.** $5x + 6y - 2\sqrt{5}z + 18 = 0$

23. $5x - 3y + 6z + 9 = 0$ **24.** $3x - 5y - 6z + 14 = 0$

Make use of the fact that the distance between the plane $Ax + By + Cz + D = 0$ and the point $P_1(x_1, y_1, z_1)$ is

$$d = \frac{Ax_1 + By_1 + Cz_1 + D}{\pm \sqrt{A^2 + B^2 + C^2}}$$

and find the distance between the plane and the point in each of Problems 25 to 28.

25. $3x - 2y + 6z - 12 = 0$, $(2, -5, 4)$

26. $6x + 3y - 2z - 16 = 0$, $(-2, -3, -8)$

27. $3x + 12y - 4z - 41 = 0$, $(2, 1, 4)$

28. $4x - 3y - 12z - 72 = 0$, $(1, -5, 1)$

12.3. *THE PLANE THROUGH THREE POINTS*

Since the equation of a plane can be put in the form $Ax + By + Cz + D = 0$, with A, B, C, not all zero, and every such equation represents a plane, there are three essential constants in the equation of a plane. They are the ratios of any three of the constants A, B, C, and D to the fourth one, if it is not zero. Consequently, a plane can be made to satisfy three consistent conditions. We shall now consider the case in which each of the conditions is that the plane shall pass through a specified point.

EXAMPLE

Find the equation of the plane through $(3, 2, 1)(4, -1, -2)$, and $(0, 5, -4)$.

Solution: Substituting the coordinates of the given points in the general form $Ax + By + Cz + D = 0$ of the equation of a plane, we have

$$3A + 2B + C + D = 0,$$
$$4A - B - 2C + D = 0,$$
$$5B - 4C + D = 0.$$

Solving this system of equations simultaneously for B, C, and D in terms of A, we get $B = 7A/12$, $C = -A/4$ and $D = -47A/12$. Therefore,

$$Ax + \frac{7Ay}{12} - \frac{Az}{4} - \frac{47A}{12} = 0$$

or, dividing by A and multiplying by 12,

$$12x + 7y - 3z - 47 = 0$$

is the equation of the plane through the given points.

Note. If A is zero we must solve the system in terms of B, C, or D.

12.4. *THE ANGLE BETWEEN TWO PLANES*

The two angles between two planes are the same as the angles between the normals (perpendiculars) to them. Hence if ϕ is an angle between the normals and, consequently, an angle between the planes, we have the following theorem by use of the theorem of Article 10.4.

THEOREM. *An angle between two planes whose normals have* $\alpha_1, \beta_1, \gamma_1,$ *and* $\alpha_2, \beta_2, \gamma_2$ *as direction angles is given by*

$$cos\ \phi = cos\ \alpha_1\ cos\ \alpha_2 + cos\ \beta_1\ cos\ \beta_2 + cos\ \gamma_1\ cos\ \gamma_2.$$

If the equations of the two planes are $A_1x + B_1y + C_1z + D_1 = 0$ and $A_2x + B_2y + C_2z + D_2 = 0$, then the direction cosines of the normals to the planes are

$$\cos \alpha_1 = \frac{A_1}{\pm \sqrt{A_1^2 + B_1^2 + C_1^2}},$$

$$\cos \beta_1 = \frac{B_1}{\pm \sqrt{A_1^2 + B_1^2 + C_1^2}},$$

$$\cos \gamma_1 = \frac{C_1}{\pm \sqrt{A_1^2 + B_1^2 + C_1^2}},$$

and

$$\cos \alpha_2 = \frac{A_2}{\pm \sqrt{A_2^2 + B_2^2 + C_2^2}},$$

$$\cos \beta_2 = \frac{B_2}{\pm \sqrt{A_2^2 + B_2^2 + C_2^2}},$$

$$\cos \gamma_2 = \frac{C_2}{\pm \sqrt{A_2^2 + B_2^2 + C_2^2}},$$

respectively, where the sign of each radical is chosen as suggested in Article 12.2. Hence the theorem of this article can be put in terms of the coefficients of the equations of the planes by means of the six equations given above. If we do this, we get the following statement of the theorem.

THEOREM. *An angle ϕ between the two planes $A_1x + B_1y + C_1z + D_1 = 0$ and $A_2x + B_2y + C_2z + D_2 = 0$ is given by*

$$\cos \phi = \frac{A_1A_2 + B_1B_2 + C_1C_2}{\pm \sqrt{(A_1^2 + B_1^2 + C_1^2)(A_2^2 + B_2^2 + C_2^2)}}.$$

If we want the smaller angle between the planes, we use the positive or negative sign with the radical when the numerator is respectively positive or negative thereby obtaining a positive value for $\cos \phi$.

COROLLARY 1. *Two planes are perpendicular if and only if*

$$A_1A_2 + B_1B_2 + C_1C_2 = 0.$$

Proof. Two planes are perpendicular if and only if the angle between them is $90°$ or $270°$. Furthermore, $\cos 90° = \cos 270° = 0$; and if we replace $\cos \phi$ by 0 in the equation given in the theorem and multiply by the common denominator, we obtain the equation given in Corollary 1.

COROLLARY 2. *Two planes are parallel if and only if*

$$A_1B_2 - A_2B_1 = A_1C_2 - A_2C_1 = B_1C_2 - B_2C_1 = 0.$$

Proof. Two planes are parallel if and only if the angle between them is $0°$ or $180°$. If we put $\phi = 0°$ and $\phi = 180°$ in the equation given in the theorem and multiply through by the common denominator, we get

$$A_1A_2 + B_1B_2 + C_1C_2$$
$$= \pm \sqrt{(A_1{}^2 + B_1{}^2 + C_1{}^2)(A_2{}^2 + B_2{}^2 + C_2{}^2)}$$

since $\cos 0° = 1$ and $\cos 180° = -1$. Squaring each member of this equation and omitting terms common to both new members, we have

$$2A_1A_2B_1B_2 + 2A_1A_2C_1C_2 + 2B_1B_2C_1C_2 = (A_1B_2)^2$$
$$+ (A_1C_2)^2 + (B_1A_2)^2 + (B_1C_2)^2 + (C_1A_2)^2 + (C_1B_2)^2.$$

Hence

$$(A_1B_2 - A_2B_1)^2 + (A_1C_2 - A_2C_1)^2 + (B_1C_2 - B_2C_1)^2 = 0.$$

Therefore,

$$A_1B_2 - A_2B_1 = 0, A_1C_2 - A_2C_1 = 0 \quad \text{and} \quad B_1C_2 - B_2C_1 = 0.$$

If neither A_2, B_2 or C_2 is zero, these equations can be put in the form

$$\frac{A_1}{A_2} = \frac{B_1}{B_2} = \frac{C_1}{C_2}.$$

EXAMPLE 1

(a) Find the smaller angle between $x + 2y - 3z - 4 = 0$ and $2x - y + 5z = 7$.

(b) Prove that $x + 2y - 3z - 4 = 0$ and $11x - 4y + z + 6 = 0$ are perpendicular.

(c) Prove that $x + 2y - 3z - 4 = 0$ and $2x + 4y - 6z + 5 = 0$ are parallel.

Solution of (a): If we substitute in the formula for the cosine of the angle between two planes and choose the sign of the radical as suggested just after the second theorem of Article 12.4, we get

$$\cos \phi = - \frac{(1)(2) + (2)(-1) + (-3)(5)}{\sqrt{[1^2 + 2^2 + (-3)^2][2^2 + (-1)^2 + 5^2]}}$$

$$= \frac{15}{\sqrt{(14)(30)}} = \frac{\sqrt{105}}{14}.$$

Therefore, $\phi = \arccos \dfrac{\sqrt{105}}{14}.$

$$= 46° 50'$$

Solution of (b): If we use the data given in (b), we get

$$\cos \phi = \frac{(1)(11) + (2)(-4) + (-3)(1)}{(\sqrt{14})(\sqrt{138})} = 0.$$

Therefore, $\phi = 90°$, and the planes are perpendicular.

Solution of (c): If we substitute the data given in (c) in Corollary 2, we get

$$(1 \cdot 4) - (2 \cdot 2) = 0; (1 \cdot -6) - (2 \cdot -3) = 0; \text{ and } (2 \cdot -6) - (4 \cdot -3) = 0.$$

Therefore, the planes are parallel.

EXAMPLE 2

Find the equation of the plane parallel to $3x - 2y + 4z = 6$ and passing through $(2, 3, 1)$.

Solution: Since two planes are parallel if corresponding coefficients are proportional, we know that

$$3x - 2y + 4z = K \quad (K \text{ any constant})$$

is a plane parallel to the given one. If this plane passes through $(2, 3, 1)$, the coordinates of the point satisfy the equation of the plane.

Hence

$$3x - 2y + 4z = 3(2) - 2(3) + 4(1) = 4$$

is the equation of the plane.

EXERCISE 12.2

Find the equations of the following planes.

1. Through $(2, 1, 0)$, $(5, -1, 1)$, and $(-2, 3, -2)$

2. Through $(1, 2, 1)$, $(3, 0, -5)$, and $(-1, 3, 6)$

3. Through $(3, 3, 4)$, $(-1, 3, -2)$, and $(2, 8, 5)$

4. Through $(3, 5, 2)$, $(6, 4, 1)$, and $(5, -4, -2)$

Find the smallest angle between the pair of planes in each of Problems 5 through 12.

5. $2x - 3y + 6z = 5$, $3x + y - 2z = 4$

6. $5x + y + 2z = 8$, $x + y - 3z = 2$

7. $3x - 12y + 4z = 7$, $2x + 3y + 5z = 1$

8. $x - y + 2z = 3$, $-3x + 3y - 6z = -4$

9. $6x - 2y + 3z = 8$, $2x + 6y - 3z = 1$

10. $4x + 2y - z = 6$, $3x - 4y + 4z = 5$

11. $7x - 3y - 2z = 1$, $-14x + 6y + 4z = -5$

12. $3x - 4y = 3$, $2x - 6y + 3z = 1$

Find the equations of the following planes.

13. Parallel to $2x - y + 3z = 5$, through $(2, 1, -4)$

14. Parallel to $5x + 2y - z = 1$, through $(3, -2, 3)$

15. Parallel to $x - 3y - 5z = 8$, through $(9, 1, 1)$

16. Parallel to $3x + 2y - 7z = 4$, through $(3, -1, 1)$

17. Perpendicular to $x - y - z = 3$ and through $(1, 1, 3)$ and $(2, -1, -1)$

18. Perpendicular to $4x + 2y - 2z = 5$ and through $(1, 1, 1)$ and $(3, -3, -1)$

19. Perpendicular to $2x + 2y + 3z = 2$ and through $(8, 2, 3)$ and $(-3, 1, -1)$

20. Perpendicular to $5x + 3y + z = 4$ and through $(3, 1, 2)$ and $(5, 3, 3)$

21. Prove that the equation of the plane whose x-, y- and z- intercepts are a, b and c, respectively, is $x/a + y/b + z/c = 1$.

22. Find the equation of the plane whose x-, y- and z- intercepts are 2, -1 and 5, respectively.

23. Prove that the equation of the plane through (x_1, y_1, z_1), (x_2, y_2, z_2) and (x_3, y_3, z_3) is

$$\begin{vmatrix} x & y & z & 1 \\ x_1 & y_1 & z_1 & 1 \\ x_2 & y_2 & z_2 & 1 \\ x_3 & y_3 & z_3 & 1 \end{vmatrix} = 0$$

24. Make use of the equation given in Problem 23 and find the equation of the plane through $(2, 0, 1)$, $(3, 7, 2)$ and $(-1, 4, 3)$.

12.5. SYMMETRIC EQUATIONS OF A LINE

Since a linear equation in three variables represents a plane and two nonparallel planes meet in a line, it follows that a pair of linear equations in three variables represent a line in space provided the planes which correspond to the equations are not parallel or coincident.

We shall now find the equations of a line through a given point $P_1(x_1, y_1, z_1)$ and with given direction cosines or direction numbers. If the direction numbers are a, b, and c and each is nonzero and if $P(x, y, z)$ is any point on the line, then

$$\frac{x - x_1}{a} = \frac{y - y_1}{b} = \frac{z - z_1}{c}$$

are the equations of the line since the direction numbers are proportional to the differences between the coordinates of any two points on the line. These are called the *symmetric equations* of a line. Hence we have the following theorem.

THEOREM. *The symmetric equations of the line through* $P_1(x_1, y_1, z_1)$ *and with the nonzero numbers* a, b, *and* c *as direction numbers are*

$$\frac{x - x_1}{a} = \frac{y - y_1}{b} = \frac{z - z_1}{c}.$$

Note. If one or more direction numbers are zero, we cannot use the symmetric form given in the theorem, since division by zero is not permissible. If $P_1(x_1, y_1, z_1)$ and $P_2(x_2, y_2, z_2)$ are distinct points on the line and $a = x_2 - x_1 = 0$, we use

$$x - x_1 = 0 \quad \text{and} \quad \frac{y - y_1}{b} = \frac{z - z_1}{c}$$

in place of the symmetric equations. A similar form is used regardless of the direction number which is zero. If the two direction numbers $a = x_2 - x_1 = 0$ and $b = y_2 - y_1 = 0$, we use $x - x_1 = 0$ and $y - y_1 = 0$ as the equation of the line. A similar form is used if another pair of direction numbers is zero.

ILLUSTRATIVE EXAMPLE

The symmetric equations of the line through $(2, -3, 4)$ and with $1, 5, -6$ as direction numbers are

$$\frac{x - 2}{1} = \frac{y + 3}{5} = \frac{z - 4}{-6}.$$

If we pair the first two fractions and then the first and the third, we obtain

$$\frac{x - 2}{1} = \frac{y + 3}{5} \quad \text{or} \quad 5x - y = 13 \quad \text{and}$$

$$\frac{x - 2}{1} = \frac{z - 4}{-6} \quad \text{or} \quad 6x + z = 16$$

as another form for the pair of equations of the line.

If the second and third fractions had been paired, we would have had

$$\frac{y + 3}{5} = \frac{z - 4}{-6} \quad \text{or} \quad 6y + 5z = 2.$$

This equation is not independent of the other two, since it can be obtained from them by multiplying each member of $5x - y = 13$ by

6 and subtracting member by member from the result of multiplying $6x + z = 16$ by 5.

In general any two of the three equations obtained by equating the first and second fractions in the symmetric form, the first and third, and the second and third can be used as the equations of the line.

DEFINITION. *The point obtained by setting one of the variables equal to zero in both equations of a line and solving the resulting pair of equations for the other two variables is called the* **trace** *of the line in the plane of the two remaining variables.*

EXAMPLE 1

Find the trace in the xy-plane of the line whose equations are

$$3x - 6y + z - 3 = 0 \quad \text{and} \quad x + 2y + 3z - 5 = 0.$$

Solution: Since we want the trace in the xy-plane, we must put z equal to zero in each equation and solve for x and y. Thus we get

$$3x - 6y - 3 = 0 \quad \text{and} \quad x + 2y - 5 = 0.$$

The solution of this pair of equations is $x = 3$ and $y = 1$. Therefore, $(3, 1, 0)$ is the trace of the given line in the xy-plane.

In order to change the equations

$$A_1x + B_1y + C_1z + D_1 = 0 \quad and$$
$$A_2x + B_2y + C_2z + D_2 = 0$$

of a line to symmetric form, we shall
   (1) find the traces in any two coordinate planes
   (2) use the coordinates of these traces to get direction numbers,
   (3) use either of the traces along with the direction numbers obtained in (2) in order to write the equations.

EXAMPLE 2

Find a symmetric form of the equations of the line represented by

$$3x - 6y + z - 3 = 0 \quad \text{and} \quad x + 2y + 3z - 5 = 0.$$

Solution: The trace in the xy-plane was found to be $(3, 1, 0)$ in Example 1. We could use the trace in the yz-plane along with this to write a symmetric form of the equations but instead shall use the trace in the xz-plane. Hence we put $y = 0$ in each given equation and solve the resulting pair of equations for x and z. Thus we find that $x = \frac{1}{2}$ and $z = \frac{3}{2}$. Consequently, $(\frac{1}{2}, 0, \frac{3}{2})$ is the xz-trace.

We now know that $(3, 1, 0)$ and $(\frac{1}{2}, 0, \frac{3}{2})$ are on the line. Hence $3 - \frac{1}{2} = \frac{5}{2}$, $1 - 0 = 1$, and $0 - \frac{3}{2} = -\frac{3}{2}$ are direction numbers of the line. Consequently, if we use $(3, 1, 0)$ as (x_1, y_1, z_1), we get

$$\frac{x - 3}{\frac{5}{2}} = \frac{y - 1}{1} = \frac{z}{-\frac{3}{2}}$$

or

$$\frac{x - 3}{5} = \frac{y - 1}{2} = \frac{z}{-3}$$

as a symmetric form of the equations of the line.

12.6. THE TWO-POINT EQUATIONS OF A LINE

We shall now derive a formula for the equations of a line through any two points $P_1(x_1, y_1, z_1)$ and $P_2(x_2, y_2, z_2)$. If each is nonzero, we can use $x_1 - x_2$, $y_1 - y_2$, and $z_1 - z_2$ as direction numbers, since the differences between corresponding coordinates of two points on a line are direction numbers of the line. Hence we have the following theorem.

THEOREM. *The equations of the line through* $\boldsymbol{P}_1(\boldsymbol{x}_1, \boldsymbol{y}_1, \boldsymbol{z}_1)$ *and* $\boldsymbol{P}_2(\boldsymbol{x}_2, \boldsymbol{y}_2, \boldsymbol{z}_2)$ *are*

$$\frac{\boldsymbol{x} - \boldsymbol{x}_1}{\boldsymbol{x}_1 - \boldsymbol{x}_2} = \frac{\boldsymbol{y} - \boldsymbol{y}_1}{\boldsymbol{y}_1 - \boldsymbol{y}_2} = \frac{\boldsymbol{z} - \boldsymbol{z}_1}{\boldsymbol{z}_1 - \boldsymbol{z}_2}, \quad \text{if } x_1 \neq x_2, y_1 \neq y_2, z_1 \neq z_2.$$

This is called the two-point form of the equations of a line.

If $x_1 = x_2$, $y_1 = y_2$, or $z_1 = z_2$, we write the two-point form in a manner similar to that given in the note which follows the theorem of Article 12.5.

EXERCISE 12.3

Find the equations of the following lines.

1. With 2, 6, 3 as direction numbers, through $(1, 4, 5)$

2. With 3, 4, 12 as direction numbers, through $(2, -1, 3)$

3. With 5, 1, -3 as direction numbers, through $(5, 1, -3)$

4. With 4, 0, 7 as direction numbers, through $(4, -2, 3)$

5. With $\alpha = 45°$, $\beta = 60°$, $\gamma = 120°$, through $(2, 3, -2)$

6. With $\alpha = 135°$, $\beta = 120°$, $\gamma = 60°$, through $(6, -4, 3)$

7. With $\alpha = \beta = \gamma$, through $(-5, 2, 4)$

8. With $\alpha = \beta$, $\gamma = 45°$, through $(-1, 1, 0)$

9. Through $(2, 1, 3)$ and $(3, 3, 5)$

10. Through $(-4, 0, 5)$ and $(2, 1, 5)$

11. Through $(6, -3, 2)$ and $(-5, 4, -3)$

12. Through $(7, 5, -5)$ and $(-1, -3, 3)$

Find the traces in the coordinate planes of the following lines.

13. $x + y + z = 2$, $2x - y + z = 1$

14. $3x - 2y + 2z = 4$, $2x + 3y - z = 7$

15. $4x + 3y - 3z = 1$, $3x + y + 2z = 2$

16. $6x - 2y + 3z = 10$, $5x + 3y + 4z = -1$

Change the equations in each of the following lines to symmetric form by use of the xy- and yz-traces.

17. $x + y + z = 3$, $2x - y + 5z = 3$

18. $3x + y + 3z = 10$, $2x + 3y + 2z = 9$

19. $4x + 5y - z = 3$, $3x + 2y + z = 4$

20. $3x + 4y + 5z = -1$, $5x + 3y + 12z = -9$

21. $3x - y + 2z = 3$, $2x + 5y + 7z = 19$

22. $2x + y + 8z = 10$, $4x - 3y + 6z = 0$

23. $3x + 5y - 6z = -1$, $2x + y + 3z = 4$

24. $2x + 7y - 11z = 3$, $3x + 8y - 14z = 2$

13 *QUADRIC SURFACES*

13.1. *INTRODUCTION*

The graph of

$$Ax^2 + By^2 + Cz^2 + Dxy + Exz + Fyz + Gx + Hy + Kz + L = 0$$

is called a *quadric surface* or *conicoid* if A through F are not all zero. The first name is used because the equation is a quadratic and the second since every plane section of such a surface is a conic. We shall not study quadratic equations in general but shall restrict our discussion to some of the simpler forms to which the equation can be reduced.

13.2. *THE SPHERE*

We shall now consider one of the most commonly encountered quadric surfaces.

DEFINITION. *A **sphere** consists of all points in three-dimensional space which are at a given distance from a given point and only of such points.*

229

The given point is called the *center* of the sphere, and the given distance is known as the *radius*.

The term radius is used with either of two meanings as in the case of a circle. Ordinarily, the context will indicate whether the meaning is the line segment from the center to a point on the sphere or the length of that segment.

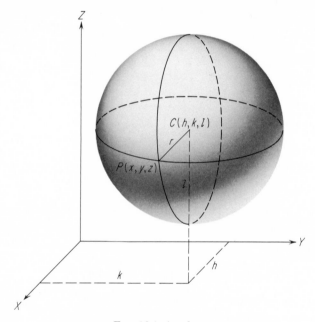

FIG. 13.1 A sphere.

We shall now derive the equation of a sphere of radius r with center at $C(h, k, l)$. If $P(x, y, z)$ is any point on the sphere, then from the definition of a sphere it follows that $CP = r$. Now $\overline{CP}^2 = r^2$ gives the same set as $CP = r$, since there are no points for which $CP = -r$. If we use the distance formula, we see that

$$(1) \qquad (x - h)^2 + (y - k)^2 + (z - l)^2 = r^2$$

is the equation of a sphere with center at **(h, k, l)** *and radius* **r**.

Equation (1) is called the *standard form* of the equation of the sphere. If the center of the sphere is at the origin, the equation reduces to

$$(2) \qquad x^2 + y^2 + z^2 = r^2.$$

If (1) is expanded, it takes the form

$$(3) \qquad x^2 + y^2 + z^2 + Hx + Ky + Lz + R = 0$$

and involves four essential constants. Hence a sphere is determined by four consistent and independent conditions. The conditions in equation (1) are that it have three given numbers for the coordinates of its center and another for its radius.

EXAMPLE 1

Find the equation of the sphere that passes through $(1, 0, 1)$, $(2, 1, 1)$, $(2, 0, -1)$, and $(1, \frac{1}{2}, 1\frac{1}{2})$.

Solution: The coordinates of the given points must satisfy the general equation

$$x^2 + y^2 + z^2 + Hx + Ky + Lz + R = 0$$

since the points are on the sphere. If we substitute the coordinates of the four points in this equation, we get the following system of four linear equations in H, K, L, and R:

$$\begin{aligned} H + L + R &= -2, \\ 2H + K + L + R &= -6, \\ 2H - L + R &= -5, \\ H + \tfrac{1}{2}K + 1\tfrac{1}{2}L + R &= -\tfrac{7}{2}. \end{aligned}$$

The solution of this system of equations is $H = 1$, $K = -5$, $L = 2$, $R = -5$. Therefore, the desired equation is

$$x^2 + y^2 + z^2 + x - 5y + 2z - 5 = 0.$$

The reader should notice that the equation (3) of a sphere has the same coefficient for each second-degree term and does not contain a product term. Equation (3) or one that can be reduced to that form by dividing each member of the equation by a constant is called the *general equation* of a sphere.

The general equation of a sphere can be reduced to the standard form by dividing by the common coefficient of x^2, y^2, and z^2 and completing the squares of the quadratics in x, y, and z.

EXAMPLE 2

Reduce

$$2x^2 + 2y^2 + 2z^2 + 6x - 8y + 10z = 3$$

to the standard form, that is, to the form (1).

Solution: In order to do this, we divide by the common coefficient of x^2, y^2, z^2 and then complete the square in each quadratic. Thus we get

$$x^2 + 3x \qquad + y^2 - 4y \qquad + z^2 + 5z = \tfrac{3}{2}$$
$$x^2 + 3x + (\tfrac{3}{2})^2 + y^2 - 4y + (-2)^2 + z^2 + 5z + (\tfrac{5}{2})^2$$
$$= \tfrac{3}{2} + \tfrac{9}{4} + 4 + \tfrac{25}{4}.$$

Therefore,

$$(x + \tfrac{3}{2})^2 + (y - 2)^2 + (z + \tfrac{5}{2})^2 = 14$$

is the standard form of the given equation. Hence the center is at $(-\tfrac{3}{2}, 2, -\tfrac{5}{2})$ and the radius is $\sqrt{14}$.

EXERCISE 13.1

Find the equations of the following spheres.

1. Center at $(2, 3, 5)$, radius 6
2. Center at $(3, 4, 7)$, radius 5
3. Center at $(6, -2, -3)$, radius 4
4. Center at $(-4, -5, 2)$, radius 3
5. Center at $(2, 7, -1)$, through $(-4, 5, 2)$
6. Center at $(4, 0, 2)$, through $(-2, 2, 5)$
7. Center at the intersection of $x + y + z = 6$, $2x - y - 3z = -6$ and $x + 2y - z = 1$, through $(5, -11, -1)$
8. Center at the intersection of $x - y + z = 0$, $3x + 2y - z = 13$ and $2x - y + 3z = -10$, through $(0, 0, 5)$
9. Passing through $(5, 3, 6)$, $(-4, 3, 3)$, $(4, -5, 3)$ and $(0, 4, -6)$
10. Passing through $(0, 1, 5)$, $(1, 0, 3)$, $(-4, 4, 0)$ and $(-3, 2, -1)$

11. Passing through $(4, 1, 5)$, $(5, 2, 3)$, $(-1, -4, -3)$ and $(4, -5, -3)$

12. Passing through $(0, 2, 3)$, $(-4, 5, 2)$, $(-7, 4, 0)$ and $(-6, 0, -5)$

Change the following equations to standard form.

13. $x^2 + y^2 + z^2 - 2x + 4y - 6z = 2$

14. $x^2 + y^2 + z^2 + 6x - 4y + 2z = -10$

15. $x^2 + y^2 + z^2 + 4x - 10y - 4z = 3$

16. $x^2 + y^2 + z^2 - 4x + 6y + 4z = -16$

17. $2x^2 + 2y^2 + 2z^2 - 6x - 4y - 2z = 1$

18. $2x^2 + 2y^2 + 2z^2 - 8x + 2y - 2z = -7$

19. $3x^2 + 3y^2 + 3z^2 - 4x + 2y + 2z = 25$

20. $3x^2 + 3y^2 + 3z^2 + 2x - 10y - 4z = -8$

13.3. *THE ELLIPSOID*

The surface represented by

$$\frac{x^2}{a^2} + \frac{y^2}{b^2} + \frac{z^2}{c^2} = 1 \qquad (a, b, \text{ and } c \text{ nonzero})$$

is called an *ellipsoid*. If two of the denominators are equal, it reduces to an ellipsoid of revolution since then cross sections parallel to one

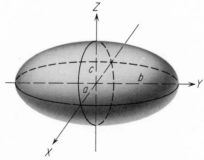

FIG. 13.2 An ellipsoid.

coordinate plane are circles. If $a = b = c$, it reduces to a sphere. Why?

The reader should verify the following statements.

The sections parallel to a coordinate plane are ellipses if they are real. The traces are ellipses.

The surface is symmetrical with respect to each coordinate plane. The x-, y-, and z-intercepts are $\pm a$, $\pm b$, and $\pm c$, respectively.

13.4. THE ELLIPTIC HYPERBOLOID OF ONE SHEET

The surface represented by $x^2/a^2 + y^2/b^2 - z^2/c^2 = 1$ is called an *elliptic hyperboloid of one sheet*. If $a = b$, the surface is a hyperboloid of revolution of one sheet.

The sections parallel to and the traces on the xz- and yz-planes are hyperbolas. Those parallel to and on the xy-plane are ellipses.

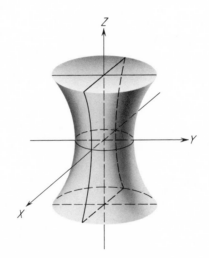

FIG. 13.3 Elliptic hyperboloid of one sheet.

The surface is symmetrical with respect to each coordinate plane. The x- and y-intercepts are $\pm a$ and $\pm b$. There are no z-intercepts.

The equation of the section of the elliptic hyperboloid made by the plane $x = a$ is $y^2/b^2 - z^2/c^2 = 0$, and it represents a pair of lines intersecting on the surface at the point (a, O, O). Similar results follow for the planes $x = -a$ and $y = \pm b$. It can be shown that through each point on the elliptic hyperboloid of one sheet there pass two lines that lie wholly in the surface.

13.5. *THE ELLIPTIC HYPERBOLOID OF TWO SHEETS*

The surface represented by

$$\frac{y^2}{a^2} - \frac{x^2}{b^2} - \frac{z^2}{c^2} = 1$$

is called an *elliptic hyperboloid of two sheets*. If $b = c$, it becomes a hyperboloid of revolution of two sheets. The surface consists of two distinct parts; one of them is in the region $y \geq a$ and the other is in the region $y \leq -a$. The surface is symmetrical with respect

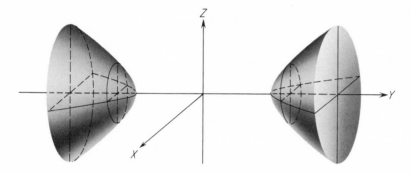

Fig. 13.4 Elliptic hyperboloid of two sheets.

to each coordinate plane. The y-intercepts are $\pm a$. There are no x- and z-intercepts. The real sections parallel to the xz-plane are ellipses. Those parallel to or on the other coordinate planes are hyperbolas.

13.6. *THE ELLIPTIC CONE*

The surface represented by

$$\frac{x^2}{a^2} + \frac{y^2}{b^2} - \frac{z^2}{c^2} = 0$$

is called an *elliptic cone*. If $a = b$, it becomes a cone of revolution. The traces on the xz- and yz-planes are intersecting straight lines. The sections parallel to the xz- and yz-planes are hyperbolas. The trace on the xy-plane is the origin. The sections parallel to the xy-plane are ellipses. The surface is symmetrical with respect to each coordinate plane. The intercepts are all zero. The surface is also a

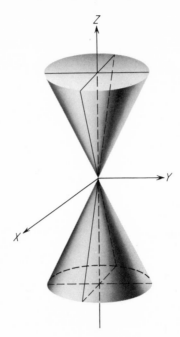

FIG. 13.5 Elliptic cone.

cone if any one of the signs is negative and the other two are positive. The traces in and sections parallel to the coordinate planes, however, are not then as given earlier in this article.

13.7. REMOVAL OF LINEAR TERMS

If an equation in three variables with a real nondegenerate graph involves all three second-degree terms and one or more linear terms but no product term, it can be put in the form of the equation of an ellipsoid, a hyperboloid, or a cone by completing the squares of the quadratics in x, y, and z and then replacing the linear terms that are squared by x', y', and z'. This is essentially a translation of the origin.

It is translated to (h, k, l) if we replace $x - h$, $y - k$, and $z - l$ by x', y', and z'.

ILLUSTRATIVE EXAMPLE

The equation

$$x^2 + 4y^2 + z^2 - 4x - 24y + 2z + 37 = 0$$

can be put in the form

$$(x - 2)^2 + 4(y - 3)^2 + (z + 1)^2 = 4$$

by completing the squares of the quadratics. Now, replacing $x - 2$ by x', $y - 3$ by y', and $z + 1$ by z' and dividing by 4, we obtain

$$\frac{x'^{\,2}}{2^2} + \frac{y'^{\,2}}{1^2} + \frac{z'^{\,2}}{2^2} = 1.$$

Hence the given equation represents an ellipsoid. The change of variable made above is equivalent to translating the origin to $(2, 3, -1)$.

EXERCISE 13.2

1. Show that $Ax^2 + By^2 + Cz^2 = D$ represents
   (a) an ellipsoid if no coefficients are negative and $D > 0$,
   (b) an elliptic hyperboloid of one sheet if one coefficient is negative and $D > 0$,
   (c) an elliptic hyperboloid of two sheets if two coefficients are negative and $D > 0$,
   (d) a cone if not all coefficients are of the same sign and $D = 0$.

By means of the statements made in Problem 1, classify the surfaces whose equations are given in Problems 2 to 17. Discuss each surface by describing the traces and sections parallel to the coordinate axes and determining the symmetry and intercepts.

2. $x^2/3^2 + y^2/2^2 + z^2/4^2 = 1$

3. $x^2/2^2 - y^2/3^2 + z^2/5^2 = 1$

4. $x^2/7^2 - y^2/3^2 - z^2/2^2 = 1$

5. $x^2/3^2 + y^2/2^2 - z^2/7^2 = 0$

6. $x^2/2^2 + y^2/4^2 - z^2/3^2 = 1$

7. $x^2/3^2 - y^2/5^2 - z^2/6^2 = 1$

8. $x^2/5^2 + y^2/3^2 - z^2/2^2 = 0$

9. $x^2/3^2 + y^2/6^2 + z^2/2^2 = 1$

10. $x^2/3^2 - y^2/1^2 - z^2/2^2 = 1$

11. $x^2/2^2 - y^2/5^2 + z^2/3^2 = 0$

12. $x^2/2^2 + y^2/6^2 + z^2/3^2 = 1$

13. $x^2/3^2 + y^2/2^2 - z^2/5^2 = 1$

14. $x^2/4^2 - y^2/3^2 + z^2/1^2 = 0$

15. $x^2/2^2 + y^2/3^2 + z^2/4^2 = 1$

16. $x^2/3^2 + y^2/2^2 - z^2/8^2 = 1$

17. $x^2/7^2 - y^2/5^2 - z^2/3^2 = 1$

Remove the linear terms and classify the surfaces whose equations are given below.

18. $\dfrac{(x-1)^2}{2^2} + \dfrac{(y-3)^2}{1^2} + \dfrac{(z-2)^2}{3^2} = 1$

19. $\dfrac{(x-2)^2}{5^2} - \dfrac{(y-7)^2}{2^2} + \dfrac{(z-3)^2}{3^2} = 1$

20. $\dfrac{(x+1)^2}{3^2} - \dfrac{(y-1)^2}{2^2} - \dfrac{(z+2)^2}{5^2} = 1$

21. $\dfrac{(x-2)^2}{3^2} + \dfrac{(y-3)^2}{6^2} - \dfrac{(z-1)^2}{2^2} = 0$

22. $\dfrac{(x-3)^2}{2^2} + \dfrac{(y+2)^2}{5^2} - \dfrac{(z+3)^2}{3^2} = 1$

23. $\dfrac{(x+4)^2}{5^2} - \dfrac{(y+3)^2}{3^2} - \dfrac{(z-5)^2}{6^2} = 1$

24. $\dfrac{(x+5)^2}{5^2} + \dfrac{(y-7)^2}{7^2} - \dfrac{(z-3)^2}{3^2} = 0$

25. $\dfrac{(x-1)^2}{2^2} + \dfrac{(y+3)^2}{4^2} + \dfrac{(z-2)^2}{3^2} = 1$

26. $9x^2 - 36y^2 - 4z^2 - 54x + 144y + 32z = 163$

27. $9x^2 - 16y^2 + 36z^2 - 108x + 160y + 288z = -500$

28. $225x^2 + 100y^2 + 36z^2 - 450x + 400y - 72z = 239$

29. $9x^2 + 4y^2 - 36z^2 + 36x - 24y + 144z = 108$
30. $100x^2 - 225y^2 + 36z^2 - 800x - 216z = -1924$
31. $4x^2 + 9y^2 + 36z^2 - 8x - 36y - 216z = -328$
32. $36x^2 + 225y^2 - 100z^2 - 144x - 450y - 200z = 631$
33. $36x^2 - 16y^2 - 9z^2 - 96y - 36z = 324$

13.8. *THE ELLIPTIC PARABOLOID*

The surface represented by

$$\frac{x^2}{a^2} + \frac{y^2}{b^2} = 4cz$$

is called an *elliptic paraboloid*. If $a = b$, it becomes a paraboloid of revolution. The sections parallel to and the traces in the xz- and

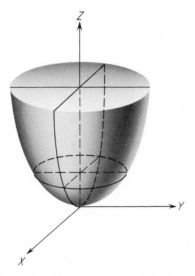

FIG. 13.6 Elliptic paraboloid.

yz-planes are parabolas. Those which are parallel to the xy-plane are ellipses. They are above the xy-plane for $c > 0$ and below it for $c < 0$. The surface is symmetrical with respect to the xz- and yz-planes. The intercepts are all zero.

13.9. *THE HYPERBOLIC PARABOLOID*

The surface represented by

$$\frac{x^2}{a^2} - \frac{y^2}{b^2} = 4cz$$

is called a *hyperbolic paraboloid*. The sections parallel to and the traces in the xz- and yz-planes are parabolas. Those parallel to the xy-plane are hyperbolas. The trace on the xy-plane is a pair of

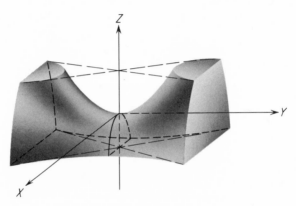

FIG. 13.7 Hyperbolic paraboloid.

intersecting lines. The surface is symmetrical with respect to the xz- and yz-planes and the intercepts are all zero.

EXERCISE 13.3

1. Show that an equation in three variables without product term represents a paraboloid if two of the variables enter to the second and possibly the first degree and the third enters only to the first degree. Show that the surface is an elliptic or hyperbolic paraboloid when the coefficients of the second-degree terms have the same or opposite signs, respectively.

Classify the following surfaces by means of the statements given in Problem 1.

2. $4x^2 + 9y^2 = 36z$　　　　**3.** $x^2 + 4z^2 = 3y$

4. $9y^2 + 16z^2 = 8x$ **5.** $3x^2 + 7y^2 = 6z$

6. $2x^2 - 3z^2 = 5y$ **7.** $5y^2 - 3z^2 = 4x$

8. $5x^2 - 8y^2 = 7z$ **9.** $9x^2 - 4y^2 = 20z$

10. $x^2 + 3y^2 - 4x - 6y - 2z + 7 = 0$

11. $4y^2 + 5z^2 + 8y - 30z - 3x + 49 = 0$

12. $7z^2 + 6x^2 - 14z + 24x - 4y + 31 = 0$

13. $2x^2 + 3y^2 - 8x + 6y - 5z + 11 = 0$

14. $3x^2 - 2y^2 - 6x - 4y - 4z + 1 = 0$

15. $5z^2 - 3y^2 + 30z + 12y - 7x - 33 = 0$

16. $7z^2 - 2x^2 + 28z + 20x - 6y - 22 = 0$

17. $2y^2 - 5x^2 + 12y + 10x - 3z + 13 = 0$

ANSWERS

Exercise 1.1, page 6

3. MH, MT, AT, MT

5. $5, \sqrt{26}, \sqrt{29}$

6. $\sqrt{13}, 13, \sqrt{274}$

7. $\sqrt{10}, \sqrt{13}, \sqrt{41}$

19. $5, -3$

21. $(2, 0)$

22. $(0, 3)$

23. $(x - 3)^2 + (y + 1)^2 = 16$

Exercise 1.2, page 10

1. $(3, 4)$

2. $(4, -4)$

3. $(4, 2.5)$

5. $(12, 6)$

6. $(-4, -14)$

7. $(1, -2)$

9. $(4, -2)$

10. $(6, -3)$

11. $(5.5, -2.5)$

14. No

15. $(4, 0)$

17. $(3, 4), (-3, 2), (1, -6)$

18. $(-4, 7), (12, 3), (0, -9)$

19. $(-2, -4)$

Exercise 1.3, page 17

1. 2

2. -5

3. 1.5

5. -1

6. 4

7. 1

9. Parallel

10. Neither

11. Perpendicular

13. Neither

14. Perpendicular

15. Neither

17. 4

18. 4

19. 9

25. $\frac{2}{11}$

26. $-19/9$

27. 23

29. $\frac{7}{3}$

30. $\sqrt{3}$

31. $-\sqrt{3}$

Exercise 1.4, page 22

1. 21.5

2. 17

3. 6

9. 3, .2

10. 2, .8

11. 2, -1

13. 2.2

14. $\frac{29}{13}$

15. $(6, -2)$, 2.5

Exercise 2.1, page 31

1. $3x - y = 5, 5x - y = 13$

2. $2x - y = 7, -4x + y = 16$

3. $4x + y = -8, 2x + y = 7$

5. $2y = 3x, y = 1$

6. $2x - y = 11, x = 2$

7. $x + y = -6, x = 7$

9. $x/2 + y/3 = 1$

10. $x/3 + y/(-5) = 1$

11. $x/(-6) + y/4 = 1$

13. $x/3 + y/2 = 1$

14. $x/4 + y/5 = 1$

15. $x/4 + y/(-3) = 1$

17. $3x - 2y = 8$

18. $2x - y = 12$

19. $x + 2y = 7$

21. $3x - 2y = 20$

22. $2x + y = 5$

23. $x = 4, y = -1$

25. $2, -5; -3, 4$

26. $5, -8; -3, -2$

27. $-\frac{2}{3}, 3; -2.5, 3.5$

29. $32° \ 30'$

30. $142° \ 10'$

31. $18° \ 30', 45°, 116° \ 30'$

33. $5x - 9y = 18$

34. $4x - 3y = 1$

35. $2x - 3y = 5$

Exercise 2.2, page 40

1. Coincident

2. Parallel

3. Intersecting

5. Intersecting

6. Intersecting and perpendicular

7. Parallel

9. $x + y - 3\sqrt{2} = 0; -\sqrt{3}x + y - 14 = 0; x - \sqrt{3}y - 4 = 0$

10. $-x + \sqrt{3}y - 8 = 0; -x - y - 5\sqrt{2} = 0; \sqrt{3}x + y - 6 = 0$

11. $-\sqrt{3}x - y - 14 = 0; x - \sqrt{3}y - 8 = 0; -x + y - 8\sqrt{2} = 0$

13. $\dfrac{-5x}{13} + \dfrac{12y}{13} - 3 = 0, \frac{3}{5}x + \frac{4}{5}y - 4 = 0$

14. $\frac{7}{25}x + \frac{24}{25}y - 4 = 0, \frac{8}{17}x - \frac{15}{17}y - 5 = 0$

15. $-\frac{4}{5}x + \frac{3}{5}y - 2 = 0, \frac{24}{25}x - \frac{7}{25}y - 6 = 0$

17. 3   **18.** 5

19. 5

21. $5x - 12y - 65 = 0, -5x + 12y - 13 = 0$

22. $8x + 15y - 102 = 0, 8x + 15y - 34 = 0$

23. $7x + 24y \pm 75 = 0$ **25.** $8x + 15y \pm 68 = 0$

26. $7x + 24y \pm 175 = 0$ **27.** $4x - 3y \mp 20 = 0$

29. 4π **30.** 25

31. On the line $5x - 12y - 13 = 0$

Exercise 2.3, page 46

1. 5, negative   **2.** 4, negative

3. 2, positive   **5.** 1, positive

6. 3, negative   **7.** 9

9. 2   **10.** 2

11. 1   **13.** 5

14. 3.5   **15.** 71

21. $\sqrt{34}$ **22.** $\sqrt{13}$

23. $\sqrt{29}$

25. $-91x + 143y + 425 = 0, 64x + 8y - 195 = 0, -19x + 399y + 442 = 0$

26. $143x + 11y = 765, 70x - 77y = 442, 27x + 99y = 65$

27. $209x + 437y + 650 = 0$

29. $x^2 + 9y^2 - 6xy + 2x + 34y + 1 = 0$

30. $16x^2 - 24xy + 9y^2 - 122x - 196y - 19 = 0$

31. $-7x + 17y - 26 = 0$ or $17x + 7y - 52 = 0$

Exercise 2.4, page 51

1. $y + 1 = m(x - 3)$ **2.** $y = 2x + b$

3. $y = mx + 6$ **5.** $x/5 + y/b = 1$

6. $x + \sqrt{3}\,y - 2p = 0$ **7.** $x \cos \omega + y \sin \omega - 4 = 0$

13. 7   **14.** 11

15. -10 **17.** ± 12

18. -12 **19.** -2

21. $y - 5 = m(x - 2), 3x - y = 1$

22. $y - 4 = m(x + 1), y = -2x + 2$

23. $y = 5x + b, y = 5x + 4$

25. $y = mx + 7, y = 5x + 7$

26. $x/a + y/(-2) = 1, x/4 + y/(-2) = 1$

27. $x/7 + y/b = 1, x/7 + y/6 = 1$

29. $x + y - \sqrt{2}\,p = 0, x + y - 10 = 0$

30. $x + \sqrt{3}\,y - 2p = 0, x + \sqrt{3}\,y - 4\sqrt{3} = 0$

31. $x \cos \omega + y \sin \omega - 6 = 0$, $\sqrt{3}\,x + y - 12 = 0$

33. $2x + 3y - 5 + k(3x - y + 2) = 0$, $19x - 10y + 19 = 0$

34. $4x - y - 10 + k(5x + 3y - 10) = 0$, $19x + 8y - 40 = 0$

35. $10x + 3y - 13 + k(-2x - 7y - 11) = 0$, $2x - y - 6 = 0$

37. $x \cos \omega + y \sin \omega - 7 = 0$, $x + y - 7\sqrt{2} = 0$

38. $y = 3x + b$, $y = 3x \pm 6$

39. $y - 2 = m(x - 1)$, $2x + y = 4$ and $x - 2y + 3 = 0$

Exercise 3.1, page 56

1. $(x - 3)^2 + (y - 2)^2 = 5^2$

2. $(x - 2)^2 + (y + 1)^2 = 4^2$

3. $(x + 5)^2 + (y - 4)^2 = 6^2$

5. $(x - 2)^2 + (y - 1)^2 = 34$

6. $(x - 3)^2 + (y + 4)^2 = 40$

7. $(x + 6)^2 + (y - 7)^2 = 289$

9. $(x - 4)^2 + (y - 5)^2 = 4$

10. $(x - 7)^2 + (y + 2)^2 = 4$

11. $(x + 1)^2 + (y - 3)^2 = 16$

13. $(x - 1)^2 + (y - 1)^2 = 25$

14. $(x - 3)^2 + (y - 2)^2 = 10$

15. $(x + 6)^2 + (y - 3)^2 = 80$

17. $(x + 1)^2 + (y - 5)^2 = 13$

18. $(x - 3)^2 + (y - 2)^2 = 29$

19. $(x - 2)^2 + (y + 4)^2 = 2$

25. $(1, -2)$, 3

26. $(-3, 2)$, 4

27. $(2, 5)$, 2

29. $(\frac{1}{2}, \frac{3}{2})$, 2

30. $(\frac{2}{3}, -\frac{4}{3})$, 1

31. $(\frac{2}{5}, \frac{3}{5})$, 2

33. $k > -10$, $k = -10$, $k < -10$

34. $k < 10$, $k = 10$, $k > 10$

35. $k > 2$, $k = 2$, $k < 2$

39. $(k^2 - 1)(x^2 + y^2) - 2(k^2 c - a)x - 2(k^2 d - b)y + k^2(c^2 + d^2)$
$- a^2 - b^2 = 0$

Exercise 3.2, page 61

1. $x^2 + y^2 - 2x - 6y = 15$

2. $x^2 + y^2 + 4x - 2y = 20$

3. $x^2 + y^2 + 6x - 14y = 111$

5. $x^2 + y^2 + 2x - 4y = 20$

6. $x^2 + y^2 + 4x + 6y = 12$

7. $x^2 + y^2 - 6x - 18y = 79$

9. $(x - 1)^2 + (y - 2)^2 = 3^2$

10. $(x + 3)^2 + (y - 2)^2 = 2^2$

11. $(x - 2)^2 + (y + 4)^2 = 5^2$

13. $(x - 5)^2 + (y - 2)^2 = 5^2$

14. $(x + 1)^2 + (y - 3)^2 = 13^2$

15. $(x - 2)^2 + (y + 1)^2 = 5^2$

17. $(x + 1)^2 + (y - 1)^2 = 1$

18. $(x - 5)^2 + (y - 3)^2 = 5^2$, $(x - 145)^2 + (y - 23)^2 = 145^2$

19. $(x - \frac{11}{3})^2 + (y - \frac{8}{3})^2 = \frac{50}{9}$

21. $(x - 2)^2 + (y - 1)^2 = 5^2$, $(x + 26)^2 + (y + 3)^2 = 25^2$

22. $(x - 2)^2 + (y - 1)^2 = 5^2$, $(x - 6)^2 + (y + 27)^2 = 25^2$

23. $(x + 3)^2 + (y - 1)^2 = 5^2$

25. $(x + 1)^2 + (y - 3)^2 = 5^2$

26. $(x - 2)^2 + (y + 9)^2 = 17^2$

27. $(x - 3)^2 + (y + 2)^2 = 5^2$

29. $3x^2 + 3y^2 - 22x + 24y + 35 = 0$

30. $3x^2 + 3y^2 - 50x + 34y + 154 = 0$

31. $x^2 + y^2 - 2x - 8y + 23 = 0$

Exercise 3.3, page 66

1. $(x - 3)^2 + (y - 2)^2 = r^2$, $(x - 3)^2 + (y - 2)^2 = 5^2$

2. $(x - 2)^2 + (y + 1)^2 = r^2$, $(x - 2)^2 + (y + 1)^2 = 4^2$

3. $(x + 5)^2 + (y - 3)^2 = r^2$, $(x + 5)^2 + (y - 3)^2 = 2^2$

5. $(x - 6)^2 + (y - 3)^2 = r^2$, $(x - 6)^2 + (y - 3)^2 = 3^2$

6. $(x - 5)^2 + (y + 1)^2 = r^2$, $(x - 5)^2 + (y + 1)^2 = 2^2$

7. $(x - 3)^2 + (y + 5)^2 = r^2$, $(x - 3)^2 + (y + 5)^2 = 5^2$

9. $(x - h)^2 + (y - 2h + 5)^2 = 5^2$, $(x + 3)^2 + (y + 11)^2 = 5^2$,
$(x - 7)^2 + (y - 9)^2 = 5^2$

10. $(x - 7 + 3k)^2 + (y - k)^2 = 3^2$, $(x - 16)^2 + (y + 3)^2 = 3^2$,
$(x + 62)^2 + (y - 23)^2 = 3^2$

11. $(x - h)^2 + (y - 3h - 1)^2 = (\pm 3h)^2$, $(x - 2)^2 + (y - 7)^2 = 6^2$,
$(x + 2)^2 + (y + 5)^2 = 6^2$

13. $(x - h)^2 + \left(y - \dfrac{41 - 12h}{5}\right)^2 = \left[\dfrac{13(h - 3)}{5}\right]^2$, $(x - 2)^2 + (y - 3.4)^2$
$= 2.6^2$

14. $\left(x - \dfrac{3k + 29}{4}\right)^2 + (y - k)^2 = 25(k + 3)^2/16$, $(x - 2)^2 + (y + 7)^2 = 25$

15. $(x - h)^2 + \left(y - \dfrac{152 - 15h}{8}\right)^2 = (\tfrac{17}{8})^2(h - 8)^2$, $x^2 + (y - 19)^2 = 17^2$

17. $x^2 + y^2 + 2x - 4y - 4 + k(x^2 + y^2 - 6x + 2y - 6) = 0$,
$4x - 3y + 1 = 0$

18. $x^2 + y^2 - 4x + 8y + 11 + k(x^2 + y^2 + 6x - 16y - 48) = 0$,
$10x - 24y - 59 = 0$

19. $x^2 + y^2 - 8x + 4y - 5 + k(x^2 + y^2 + 16x - 6y - 8) = 0$,
$24x - 10y - 3 = 0$

21. $k = 1$, $x^2 + y^2 - 2x - y - 5 = 0$

22. $k = 0$, $x^2 + y^2 + 2x - 4y - 4 = 0$

23. $k = 1$, $x^2 + y^2 - 2x - y - 5 = 0$

25. $k = 0$, $x^2 + y^2 + 2x - 4y - 4 = 0$

26. $k = 2$, $3x^2 + 3y^2 - 10x - 16 = 0$

27. $k = -5$, $2x^2 + 2y^2 - 16x + 7y - 13 = 0$

Exercise 4.1, page 74

1. $(y - 2)^2 = 4(x - 3)$ **2.** $(y + 1)^2 = -8(x - 1)$

3. $(x + 3)^2 = 12(y - 2)$ **5.** $(x + 1)^2 = -8(y - 1)$

6. $(x - 3)^2 = 12(y + 2)$ **7.** $(y + 2)^2 = -12(x - 1)$

9. $(y - 2)^2 = -8(x + 3)$ **10.** $(y - 3)^2 = 4(x + 4)$

11. $(x - 2)^2 = 8(y - 1)$

14. $(x + 2)^2 = -4(y - 1)$

17. $(y - 2)^2 = -12(x + 1)$

19. $(x - 4)^2 = -16(y + 3)$

13. $(x - 3)^2 = 12(y + 3)$

15. $(y - 5)^2 = -8(x + 3)$

18. $(y + 3)^2 = 8(x - 1)$

21. $(x - 13)^2 = 8(y + 8), (x - 1)^2 = -8(y - 2)$

22. $(x - 2)^2 = -4(y - 3), (x + 2)^2 = 4(y + 1)$

23. $(y + 3)^2 = 12(x + 1), (y - 3)^2 = -12(x - 2)$

25. $(y - 3)^2 = 8(x - 3)$

26. $(y - 5)^2 = -16x$

27. $(x - 6)^2 = 8(y + 1)$

Exercise 4.2, page 79

1. $(x - 2)^2/5^2 + (y - 1)^2/3^2 = 1$

2. $(x + 1)^2/13^2 + (y - 2)^2/5^2 = 1$

3. $(y + 3)^2/5^2 + (x + 2)^2/4^2 = 1$

5. $(y + 2)^2/25^2 + (x + 3)^2/24^2 = 1$

6. $(y - 3)^2/17^2 + (x + 4)^2/15^2 = 1$

7. $(x - 3)^2/25^2 + (y + 4)^2/7^2 = 1$

9. $(x + 5)^2/5^2 + (y - 1)^2/3^2 = 1$

10. $(x + 3)^2/17^2 + (y - 1)^2/15^2 = 1$

11. $(y - 2)^2/5^2 + (x - 3)^2/4^2 = 1$

13. $(y - 3)^2/5^2 + (x - 2)^2/2^2 = 1$

14. $(y + 2)^2/4^2 + (x + 1)^2/3^2 = 1$

15. $(x + 1)^2/3^2 + (y + 1)^2/2^2 = 1$

17. $(x + 2)^2/3^2 + (y - 1)^2/1^2 = 1$

18. $(x - 3)^2/5^2 + (y - 1)^2/4^2 = 1$

19. $(y - 1)^2/2^2 + (x + 2)^2/1^2 = 1$

21. $40x^2 + 33y^2 + 24xy - 304x - 150y + 313 = 0$

22. $35x^2 + 11y^2 - 10xy - 310x + 34y + 599 = 0$

23. $11x^2 + 27y^2 + 30xy - 4x - 12y - 16 = 0$

Exercise 4.3, page 84

1. $(x - 2)^2/4^2 - (y - 1)^2/3^2 = 1$

2. $(x + 1)^2/12^2 - (y - 2)^2/5^2 = 1$

3. $(y + 3)^2/3^2 - (x + 2)^2/4^2 = 1$

5. $(y + 2)^2/7^2 - (x + 3)^2/24^2 = 1$

6. $(y - 3)^2/8^2 - (x + 4)^2/15^2 = 1$

7. $(x - 3)^2/24^2 - (y + 4)^2/7^2 = 1$

9. $(x) + 5^2/4^2 - (y - 1)^2/3^2 = 1$

10. $(x + 3)^2/8^2 - (y - 1)^2/15^2 = 1$

11. $(y - 2)^2/3^2 - (x - 3)^2/4^2 = 1$

13. $(y - 3)^2/5^2 - (x - 2)^2/2^2 = 1$

14. $(y + 2)^2/4^2 - (x + 1)^2/3^2 = 1$
15. $(x + 1)^2/3^2 - (y + 1)^2/2^2 = 1$
17. $(x + 2)^2/3^2 - (y - 1)^2/1^2 = 1$
18. $(x - 3)^2/5^2 - (y - 1)^2/4^2 = 1$
19. $(y - 1)^2/2^2 - (x + 2)^2/1^2 = 1$
21. $7y^2 - 24xy + 24x + 70y - 113 = 0$
22. $15x^2 - 10xy - 9y^2 - 130x + 54y + 319 = 0$
23. $21x^2 - 30xy + 5y^2 + 36x - 20y - 16 = 0$

Exercise 4.4, page 89

1. $(y - 1)^2 = 4(2)(x + 1)$ **2.** $(y + 3)^2 = 4(-1)(x - 2)$
3. $(x + 2)^2 = 4(-3)(y - 1)$ **5.** $x^2/4^2 + (y - 1)^2/3^2 = 1$
6. $(x + 2)^2/12^2 + (y - 1)^2/5^2 = 1$
7. $(y - 3)^2/4^2 + (x - 1)^2/3^2 = 1$
9. $(x - 2)^2/3^2 - (y - 1)^2/2^2 = 1$
10. $(x + 1)^2/4^2 - (y - 1)^2/5^2 = 1$
11. $(y + 2)^2/3^2 - (x + 1)^2/1^2 = 1$
13. $(x - 2)^2 - (y + 1)^2 = 4$ **14.** $(x - 1)^2 - (y - 2)^2 = 16$
15. $(y - 2)^2 - (x - 3)^2 = 16$ **17.** $(y - 1)^2/4^2 - (x + 3)^2/3^2 = 1$
18. $(y - 2)^2/2^2 - (x + 1)^2/5^2 = 1$
19. $(x - 2)^2/3^2 - (y + 2)^2/5^2 = 1$
25. $\frac{1}{2}$, ellipse   **26.** 1, parabola
27. $\sqrt{3}$, hyperbola   **29.** $\sqrt{2}$, hyperbola
30. 1, parabola   **31.** $\frac{1}{3}$, ellipse

Exercise 5.1, page 94

1. $x'^2 + y'^2 = 3$ **2.** $2x'^2 - y'^2 = 2$
3. $4x'^2 + 9y'^2 = 36$ **5.** $(1, 2)$, $x'^2 + y'^2 = 4$
6. $(-1, 3)$, $x'^2 + y'^2 = 9$ **7.** $(-2, 2)$, $4x'^2 + 9y'^2 = 36$
9. $(5, -1)$, $x'^2 - 4y'^2 = 4$ **10.** $(4, 1)$, $9x'^2 - 25y'^2 = 225$
11. $(-5, 1)$, $y'^2 = 4x'$
13. The coefficient of x' does not contain h or k.
14. The coefficient of y' does not contain h or k.
15. $(-2, 2)$ **17.** $ax' + ay' + c = 0$
18. $ax' + by' = 0$ **19.** $y' = mx'$

Exercise 5.2, page 100

1. $5x'^2 - y'^2 = 4$ **2.** $5x'^2 + 3y'^2 = 18$
3. $x'^2 + 5y'^2 = 6$ **5.** $178x'^2 - 25y'^2 = 50$
6. $18x'^2 - 7y'^2 = 7$ **7.** $6x'^2 + y'^2 = 6$
9. $\sin \theta = \frac{1}{2}$, $\cos \theta = \sqrt{3}/2$
10. $\sin \theta = \sqrt{3}/2$, $\cos \theta = \frac{1}{2}$

11. $\sin \theta = \cos \theta = 1/\sqrt{2}$
13. $\sin \theta = \frac{3}{5}$, $\cos \theta = \frac{4}{5}$
14. $\sin \theta = .1\sqrt{2}$, $\cos \theta = .7\sqrt{2}$
15. $\sin \theta = 1/\sqrt{5}$, $\cos \theta = 2/\sqrt{5}$
18. $xy = -a^2$

Exercise 5.3, page 105

1. Parabola   **2.** Parabola
3. Parabola   **5.** Ellipse
6. Ellipse   **7.** Ellipse
9. Hyperbola   **10.** Hyperbola
11. Hyperbola
13. $(y' - 1)^2 = 8x'$, $y''^2 = 8x''$
14. $(x' - 2)^2 = -4y'$, $x''^2 = -4y''$
15. $4(x' - 1)^2 + (y' - 2)^2 = 4$, $4x''^2 + y''^2 = 4$
17. $4(x' + 2)^2 + 9(y' - 1)^2 = 36$, $4x''^2 + 9y''^2 = 36$
18. $4(x' + 1)^2 - (y' - 1)^2 = 4$, $4x''^2 - y''^2 = 4$
19. $(y' - 2)^2 = -8(x' + 1)$, $y''^2 = -8x''$

Exercise 6.1, page 111

1. -3 **2.** 2
3. 2.5   **5.** $2.5, -1$
6. $\frac{1}{2}, 2$ **7.** $3, -1$
9. $-2, 0, 1$ **10.** $-1, 1, 3$
11. $-3, -1, 2$ **13.** $-1, 1$
14. $2, 3$ **15.** $-2, 3$
17. $(-3 \pm \sqrt{5})/2, 1$ **18.** $1 \pm \sqrt{3}, 2$
19. -1 **21.** $-2, 0, 1, 3$
22. $-3, -1, 1, 2$ **23.** $3, 1, -1, -2$
25. $2, -1, -3$ **26.** $-1, -3, 1$
27. $1, 2, -3$ **29.** $(-3 \pm \sqrt{5})/2, 2, -1$
30. $-2, 3$ **31.** -1

Exercise 6.2, page 123

The intercepts are given first and are followed by a semicolon, the asymptotes, another semicolon and the tangents, if any, at the origin. Number 31 is symmetrical with respect to the origin.

1. $y = -\frac{3}{2}$; $x = 2$ **2.** $y = \frac{5}{3}$; $x = -3$
3. $y = -1$; $x = -1, x = 2$
5. $x = 0, y = 0$; $x = -3$; $3y = x$
6. $x = -2$; $y = 2$; $x = -1$

7. $x = 2.5$, $y = -2.5$; $x = -2$

9. $x = -2$, $y = -\frac{2}{3}$; $x = -3$, $x = 1$

10. $x = 0$, $y = 0$; $x = -1$, $x = 2$; $-2y = x$

11. $x = \frac{3}{2}$, $y = \frac{3}{2}$; $x = -2$, $x = \frac{1}{2}$

13. $x = 3$, $y = -3$

14. $x = -2$, $y = 1$

15. $x = 0$, $y = 0$; none; $y = 2x$

17. $x = 0$, $x = 2$, $y = 0$; none; $y = -x$

18. $x = 1$, $x = -\frac{3}{2}$, $y = -\frac{3}{2}$

19. $x = -\frac{3}{2}$, $x = 0$, $y = 0$; none; $2y = 3x$

21. $x = \frac{1}{2}$, $x = 2$, $y = -\frac{1}{3}$; $x = \frac{2}{3}$, $x = -3$

22. $x = -1$, $x = 3$, $y = \frac{3}{4}$; $x = -2$, $x = 2$

23. $x = -\frac{4}{3}$, $x = 1$, $y = \frac{2}{3}$; $x = \frac{3}{2}$, $x = -2$

25. $x = 0$, $x = -1$, $x = 1$, $y = 0$; $x = -2$, $x = 2$; $4y = x$

26. $x = -2$, $x = 0$, $x = 1$, $y = 0$; $x = -3$, $x = 2$; $3y = x$

27. $x = -3$, $x = -1$, $y = \frac{1}{2}$; $x = -2$, $x = 1$, $x = 3$

29. $x = 2$, $x = 1$; $x = 0$, $x = 3$

30. $y = a$; none; none

31. $x = 0$, $y = 0$; none; $a^2y = b^2x$

Exercise 6.3, page 127

Each curve is symmetrical with respect to the X axis and only 34 is symmetrical with respect to the Y axis and origin. The intercepts are given first, then a semicolon and the asymptotes. There are no asymptotes for 1 to 16.

1. $x = -2$, $x = 1$ 2. $x = -1$, $x = 3$

3. $x = 0$, $x = 2$, $y = 0$ 5. $x = -2$, $x = 1$, $x = 3$, $y = \pm \sqrt{6}$

6. $x = -3$, $x = 0$, $x = 2$, $y = 0$

7. $x = -4$, $x = -2$, $x = -1$, $y = \pm 2\sqrt{2}$

9. $x = 0$, $x = 1$, $y = 0$ 10. $x = -2$, $x = 2$

11. $x = 0$, $y = 0$

13. $x = -2$, $x = -1$, $x = 0$, $x = 3$, $y = 0$

14. $x = -1$, $x = 0$, $x = 1$, $x = 2$, $y = 0$

15. $x = -1$, $x = 1$, $x = 4$, $y = \pm 2$

17. $x = 1$; $x = -1$ 18. $x = -2$; $x = 3$

19. $x = -1$; $x = 0$, $x = 1$ 21. $x = 0$, $x = 1$, $y = 0$; $x = -2$

22. $x = -3$, $x = 2$, $y = \pm \sqrt{2}$; $x = 3$

23. $x = -2$, $x = -1$, $y = \pm \sqrt{6}/3$; $x = 1$, $x = 3$

25. $x = 0$, $y = 0$; $x = -4$, $x = 1$

26. $x = 2$; $x = 0$, $x = -1$

27. $x = -1$, $x = 1$; $x = 0$

29. $x = 0$, $x = -a$, $y = 0$; $x = a$

30. $x = 0, x = 3a, y = 0; x = -a$
31. $x = 0, y = 0; x = 2a$
33. $x = 0, y = 0$; none
34. $x = 0, y = 0; x = \pm a$
35. $x = 0, x = 2a, y = 0$; none

Exercise 6.4, page 131

17. $(3, 2), (2, 1)$
18. $(1, 3)(-\frac{3}{4}, -\frac{1}{2})$
19. $(2, -1), (4.5, 4)$
21. $(2, 2)$
22. $(3, -2), (\frac{13}{3}, -\frac{2}{3})$
23. $(2, 3), (3, 5)$
25. $(2, 3), (2, -3), (-2, 3), (-2, -3)$
26. $(2, 1), (2, -1), (-2, 1), (-2, -1)$
27. $(3, 2), (3, -2), (-3, 2), (-3, -2)$
29. $(2, -2), (-2, 2), (2\sqrt{2}, 0), (-2\sqrt{2}, 0)$
30. $(5, -1), (-5, 1)$
31. $(4, -2), (-4, 2)$
33. ± 8
34. $\pm 2\sqrt{2}$
35. ± 1

Exercise 7.2, page 144

The period is given first and is followed by the amplitude.

1. $2\pi/3, 1$
2. $\pi, 1$
3. $\pi/4, \infty$
5. $\pi/2, \infty$
6. $\pi/2, \infty$
7. $2\pi/5, 2$
9. $4\pi, 5$
10. $6\pi, 3$
11. $8\pi, 5$

The period, the amplitude and the number of units the graph of the first function is to the left of the graph of the second is the order in the answer.

13. $2\pi/3, 2, \pi/3$
14. $\pi/2, \infty, \pi/4$
15. $\pi/2, 2, \pi/4$
17. $2\pi, \infty, 2\pi$
18. $6\pi, 2, 6\pi$
19. $4\pi, \infty, 4\pi$
21. $2\pi/3, 6, -\pi/3$
22. $\pi/3, 3, -\pi/3$
23. $\pi/2, 2, -3\pi/4$

Exercise 8.2, page 157

The equations in Problems 21 to 40 are the polar forms of the equations in rectangular form in Problems 1 to 20.

Exercise 8.3, page 163

1. $r \cos \theta = 3, r \cos \theta = -3$
2. $r \sin \theta = 5, r \sin \theta = -5$
3. $r \cos (\theta - 60°) = 4$

5. $r = 12 \sin \theta$

6. $55 = r^2 - 6r \cos (\theta - 45°)$

7. $45 = r^2 - 4r \cos (\theta - 240°)$

9. $r = \dfrac{3}{1 + \cos \theta}$

10. $r = \dfrac{4}{1 - \sin \theta}$

11. $r = \dfrac{4}{1 + \frac{1}{2} \sin \theta}$

13. $r = \tan \theta$

14. $r = 3 \sin 2\theta$

15. $r = 4a \cot \theta \csc \theta$

17. A line, 2 units to the right of the normal axis

18. A line, 5 units above the polar axis

19. A line, 3 units to the left of the normal axis

21. A line, 6 units from the pole, normal to it makes an angle of 30° with the polar axis

22. A line, 3 units from the pole, normal to it makes an angle of 120° with the polar axis

23. Circle of radius 2 with center at $(3, 45°)$

25. Circle with center at the pole and radius 5

26. Circle with center at $(3, 0°)$ and radius 3

27. Circle of radius 2 with center at $(2, 270°)$

29. Parabola, focus at pole, directrix perpendicular to polar axis and 4 units to the left of the pole

30. Parabola, focus at pole, directrix perpendicular to normal axis and 6 units above the pole

31. Parabola, focus at pole, directrix perpendicular to the normal axis and 2 units below the pole

33. Ellipse, eccentricity $\frac{1}{2}$, focus at pole, directrix perpendicular to normal axis and 8 units above the pole

34. Ellipse, eccentricity $\frac{1}{3}$, focus at pole, directrix perpendicular to normal axis and 6 units below the pole

35. Ellipse, eccentricity $\frac{1}{4}$, focus at pole, directrix perpendicular to the polar axis and 4 units above the pole

37. Hyperbola, eccentricity $\frac{3}{2}$, focus at pole, directrix perpendicular to the normal axis and 2 units below the pole

38. Hyperbola, eccentricity $\frac{4}{3}$, focus at pole, directrix perpendicular to the polar axis and 3 units above the pole

39. Hyperbola, eccentricity $\frac{5}{2}$, focus at pole, directrix perpendicular to the polar axis and 2 units to the left of the pole

Exercise 8.4, page 167

1. $(3, 30°), (3, 150°)$

2. $(\sqrt{3}, 30°), (\sqrt{3}, 330°)$

3. $(4, 30°), (4, 150°)$

5. $(3, 90°), (3, 270°)$

6. $(1, 60°), (1, 120°), (1, 240°), (1, 300°)$

7. $(1, 15°), (1, 75°), (1, 195°), (1, 255°)$

9. $(a, 0°), (a, 180°)$

10. $(a, 90°), (a, 270°)$

11. $(1.5, 120°)$

13. $(\sqrt{2}/2, 45°), (-\sqrt{2}/2, 225°)$

14. $(\sqrt{2}, 22° 30'), (-\sqrt{2}, 112° 30'), (\sqrt{2}, 202° 30'), (-\sqrt{2}, 292° 30')$

15. $(1, 90°), (0, 180°)$

17. $(1.5, 60°), (1.5, 300°)$

18. $(2.5, 30°), (2.5, 150°)$

19. $(a, 90°), (a, 270°)$

21. $(0, 0°), (0, 180°), (2/\sqrt{5}, \arctan 2), (-2/\sqrt{5}, \arctan 2)$

22. $(1, 0°), (-1, 180°)$

23. $(2, 0°), (0, 90°), (0, 270°)$

Exercise 9.1, page 172

1. (a) $y = 3 \sin \theta$, (b) $x = \sqrt{6t - t^2}$

2. (a) $x = \cos t$, (b) $y = 2t$

3. (a) $y = 2t$, (b) $x = \tan t$

9. The lower half of the circle is not obtained.

10. The parts to the right of $x = a$ and to the left of $x = -a$ are not obtained.

11. Only that part to the left of $x = 2$ is obtained.

Exercise 9.2, page 176

1. $x + y = 5$

2. $y - x = 2$

3. $x + 3y = 5$

5. $y = (x - 2)^2$

6. $x^2 - 2x - y + 3 = 0$

7. $x = y^2 - y$

9. $xy = 1$

10. $xy = 2$

11. $xy - x - 1 = 0$

13. $x^2 + y^2 = 2x$

14. $x^3 + y^3 = 3xy$

15. $y^3 + 8y^2 = x^2$

17. $xy = 1$

18. $xy = 1$

19. $xy = 1$

21. $4(x + 1)^2 + (y + 1)^2 = 4$

22. $x^{2/3} + y^{2/3} = a^{2/3}$

23. $y^2 - x^2 = 4$

25. $y - x = 1$

26. $y^2 - 2y = x$

27. $y = \sqrt{x^2 - 4}$

Exercise 9.3, page 181

1. $x = V_0 t, \; 2y = -gt^2, \; gx^2 + 2V_0^2 y = 0; \; x = 0, \; y = V_0 t - gt^2/2, \; x = 0$

2. .4 sec., 48 ft.

3. .5 ft.

5. $3.75 \sqrt{2}$ sec., 450 ft.

6. 3 sec., $144 \sqrt{3}$ ft.

Exercise 10.1, page 189

1. $7; \frac{3}{7}, \frac{2}{7}, \frac{6}{7}$

2. $7; -\frac{3}{7}, \frac{6}{7}, -\frac{2}{7}$

3. $5; \frac{4}{5}, 0, -\frac{3}{5}$

5. $17; \frac{8}{17}, -\frac{15}{17}, 0$

6. $13; \frac{3}{13}, -\frac{4}{13}, -\frac{12}{13}$

7. $\sqrt{61}; 4/\sqrt{61}, 3/\sqrt{61}, -6/\sqrt{61}$

9. $\frac{3}{7}, \frac{2}{7}, \frac{6}{7}$ or $-\frac{3}{7}, -\frac{2}{7}, -\frac{6}{7}$

10. $3/\sqrt{14}, 1/\sqrt{14}, -2/\sqrt{14}$ or $-3/\sqrt{14}, -1/\sqrt{14}, 2/\sqrt{14}$

11. $-\frac{5}{13}, 0, \frac{12}{13}$ or $\frac{5}{13}, 0, -\frac{12}{13}$

13. $90°, 0$

14. $60°, 120°, \frac{1}{2}, -\frac{1}{2}$

15. $90°, 0$

25. $(0, 0, 0), (0, 0, 4)$

26. $(0, 3, 0), (0, -1, 0)$

27. $(x - 2)^2 + (z - 5)^2 = 15$

Exercise 10.2, page 193

1. $25° \ 30'$

2. $23°$

3. $90°$

5. $75°$

6. $120°$

7. $132° \ 30'$

9. $43° \ 30'$

10. $128° \ 10'$

11. $83° \ 40'$

13. $11° \ 40'$

14. $58° \ 20'$

15. $0°$

21. They are parallel since $\cos \phi = 1$.

22. They are neither since $\cos \phi$ is neither ± 1 nor zero.

23. They are perpendicular since $\cos \phi = 0$

Exercise 11.2, page 206

1. $y^2 + z^2 = (2 - x)^2$

2. $x^2 + z^2 = (2 - y)^2$

3. $x^2 + y^2 = (4 - 3z)^2$

5. $y^2 + z^2 = 9$

6. $x^2 + z^2 = 25$

7. $y^2 + z^2 = \left(\dfrac{4 - 2x}{3}\right)^2$

9. $x^2 + y^2 + z^2 = a^2$

10. $x^2 + y^2 + z^2 = a^2$

11. $b^2(x^2 + z^2) + a^2y^2 = a^2b^2$

13. $b^2x^2 - a^2(y^2 + z^2) = a^2b^2$

14. $b^2(x^2 + z^2) - a^2y^2 = a^2b^2$

15. $y^2 + z^2 = 4ax$

17. $[x^2 + (y - 2a)^2 + z^2 - 5a^2]^2 = 16a^2(a^2 - x^2)$

18. $[x^2 + y^2 + (z - 3a)^2 - 10a^2]^2 = 36a^2(a^2 - y^2)$

19. $[b^2x^2 + a^2(y - 2b)^2 + a^2z^2 - 5a^2b^2]^2 = 16a^2b^4(a^2 - x^2)$

21. $(x^2 + z^2)^3 = y^2$

22. $x^2 + y^2 = z^6$

23. $x^2 + z^2 = y^3$

Exercise 11.3, page 212

1. $z = a, \rho \cos \phi = a$

2. $r = a, \rho \sin \phi = a$

3. $r = 2a \cos \theta, \rho \sin \phi = 2a \cos \theta$

5. $r^2 \cos 2\theta = a^2$, $\rho^2 \sin^2 \phi \cos 2\theta = a^2$

6. $z = \cot \theta$, $\rho \sin \theta \cos \phi = \cos \theta$

7. $r^2 = 2z$, $\rho \sin^2 \phi = 2 \cos \phi$

9. $\rho \cos \phi = a$, $z = a$

10. $\rho \sin \phi = a$, $x^2 + y^2 = a^2$

11. $\rho \sin \phi = 2a \cos \theta$, $x^2 + y^2 = 2ax$

13. $\rho^2 \sin^2 \phi \cos 2\theta = a^2$, $x^2 - y^2 = a^2$

14. $\rho \sin \theta \cos \phi = \cos \theta$, $yz = x$

15. $\rho \sin^2 \phi = 2 \cos \phi$, $x^2 + y^2 = 2z$

17. $z = a$, $z = a$

18. $x^2 + y^2 = a^2$, $r = a$

19. $x^2 + y^2 = 2ax$, $r = 2a \cos \theta$

21. $x^2 - y^2 = a^2$, $r^2 \cos 2\theta = a^2$

22. $yz = x$, $z = \cot \theta$

23. $x^2 + y^2 = 2z$, $r^2 = 2z$

25. $4x^2 + 2y^2 = 9$, $2x^2 - 2z^2 = -7$, $2y^2 + 4z^2 = 23$

26. $5x^2 - 4y^2 = 6$, $3x^2 + 4z^2 = 14$, $3y^2 + 5z^2 = 13$

27. $3x^2 - 2y^2 = 13$, $5x^2 - 2z^2 = 25$, $5y^2 - 3z^2 = 5$

29. $x^2 - y^2 + (x^2 + y^2 - 2)^2 = 4$, $2x^2 - z^2 - z = 6$; $2y^2 + z^2 - z = -2$

30. $-5x^2 + 2y^2 + (8 - 3x^2 - y^2)^2 = 2$, $11x^2 - z^2 + 2z = 14$,
$\quad 11y^2 + 3z^2 + 5z = 46$

31. $11x^2 - y^2 + 2y = 2$, $3x^2 - (z^2 - 4x^2 - 1)^2 + 2z^2 = 4$,
$\quad 4y^2 + 3y - 11z^2 = -19$

33. $x^4 + x^2y^2 + y^2 = 4x^2$, $x^2 + x^2z^2 + z^2 = 4$, $y^2 + y^2z^2 + z^4 = 4z^2$

34. $x^2 - y^2 - x^2y^2 = -2$, $x^4 - z^2 - x^2z^2 = -2x^2$, $z^2 - y^4 - y^2z^2 = -2y^2$

35. $2x^2 - y^2 - 3xy = 3$, $2x^4 - z^2 - 3x^2z = 3x^2$, $2z^2 - y^4 - 3y^2z = 3y^2$

Exercise 12.1, page 217

1. $\sqrt{3}\,x + y = 10$

2. $\sqrt{2}\,x - y + z = 8$

3. $-x - \sqrt{3}\,y = 12$

5. $2x - 3y + 6z = 21$

6. $-4x - 5y + 2\sqrt{2}\,z = 35$

7. $2x + 5y - \sqrt{7}\,z = 42$

9. $(x - 3) - (y + 1) + 5(z - 4) = 0$

10. $2(x + 2) - 3(y + 1) + 6(z - 3) = 0$

11. $6(x - 5) - 2y + 5(z - 7) = 0$

13. $4(x - 4) + 3(y - 1) - (z + 2) = 0$

14. $(x - 7) + (y + 2) - (z - 3) = 0$

15. $(x + 2) + (y + 3) - (z - 1) = 0$

17. $\dfrac{6x}{7} - \dfrac{2y}{7} + \dfrac{3z}{7} - 2 = 0$

256   ANSWERS

18. $\dfrac{3x}{13} + \dfrac{4y}{13} - \dfrac{12z}{13} - 3 = 0$

19. $\dfrac{4x}{13} - \dfrac{12y}{13} + \dfrac{3z}{13} - 2 = 0$

21. $\dfrac{2\sqrt{2}\,x}{7} + \dfrac{5y}{7} - \dfrac{4z}{7} - 1 = 0$

22. $\dfrac{5x}{9} + \dfrac{6y}{9} - \dfrac{2\sqrt{5}\,z}{9} + 2 = 0$

23. $\dfrac{5x}{\sqrt{70}} - \dfrac{3y}{\sqrt{70}} + \dfrac{6z}{\sqrt{70}} + \dfrac{9}{\sqrt{70}} = 0$

25. 4   **26.** 3   **27.** 3

Exercise 12.2, page 223

1. $x + y - z = 3$
2. $2x - y + z = 1$
3. $3x + y - 2z = 4$
5. 69° 50′
6. 90°
7. 82° 50′
9. 79° 20′
10. 90°
11. 0°
13. $2x - y + 3z = -9$
14. $5x + 2y - z = 8$
15. $x - 3y - 5z = 1$
17. $2x + 3y - z = 2$
18. $3x - y + 5z = 7$
19. $x + 5y - 4z = 6$
22. $x/2 + y/(-1) + z/5 = 1$

Exercise 12.3, page 227

1. $(x - 1)/2 = (y - 4)/6 = (z - 5)/3$
2. $(x - 2)/3 = (y + 1)/4 = (z - 3)/12$
3. $(x - 5)/5 = (y - 1)/1 = (z + 3)/(-3)$
5. $(x - 2)/\sqrt{2} = (y - 3)/1 = (z + 2)/(-1)$
6. $(x - 6)/(-\sqrt{2}) = (y + 4)/(-1) = (z - 3)/1$
7. $(x + 5)/1 = (y - 2)/1 = (z - 4)/1$
9. $(x - 2)/1 = (y - 1)/2 = (z - 3)/2$
10. $(x + 4)/6 = y/1, z - 5 = 0$
11. $(x - 6)/11 = (y + 3)/(-7) = (z - 2)/5$
13. $(1, 1, 0), (-1, 0, 3), (0, \frac{1}{2}, \frac{3}{2})$
14. $(2, 1, 0), (\frac{18}{7}, 0, -\frac{13}{7}), (0, 4.5, 6.5)$
15. $(0, \frac{8}{9}, \frac{5}{9}), (\frac{8}{17}, 0, \frac{5}{17}), (1, -1, 0)$
17. $(x - 2)/2 = (y - 1)/(-1) = z/(-1)$
18. $(x - 3)/3 = z/(-3), y = 1$
19. $(x - 2)/2 = (y + 1)/(-2) = z/(-2)$
21. $(x - 2)/2 = (y - 3)/2 = z/(-2)$

22. $(x - 3)/3 = (y - 4)/2 = z/(-1)$
23. $(x - 3)/3 = (y + 2)/(-3) = z/(-1)$

Exercise 13.1, page 232

1. $(x - 2)^2 + (y - 3)^2 + (z - 5)^2 = 36$
2. $(x - 3)^2 + (y - 4)^2 + (z - 7)^2 = 25$
3. $(x - 6)^2 + (y + 2)^2 + (z + 3)^2 = 16$
5. $(x - 2)^2 + (y - 7)^2 + (z + 1)^2 = 49$
6. $(x - 4)^2 + y^2 + (z - 2)^2 = 49$
7. $(x - 2)^2 + (y - 1)^2 + (z - 3)^2 = 169$
9. $(x - 2)^2 + (y - 1)^2 + z^2 = 49$
10. $(x + 1)^2 + (y - 3)^2 + (z - 2)^2 = 14$
11. $(x - 2)^2 + (y + 2)^2 + (z - 1)^2 = 29$
13. $(x - 1)^2 + (y + 2)^2 + (z - 3)^2 = 16$
14. $(x + 3)^2 + (y - 2)^2 + (z + 1)^2 = 4$
15. $(x + 2)^2 + (y - 5)^2 + (z - 2)^2 = 36$
17. $(x - \frac{3}{2})^2 + (y - 1)^2 + (z - \frac{1}{2})^2 = 4$
18. $(x - 2)^2 + (y + \frac{1}{2})^2 + (z - \frac{1}{2})^2 = 1$
19. $(x - \frac{2}{3})^2 + (y + \frac{1}{3})^2 + (z + \frac{1}{3})^2 = 9$

Exercise 13.2, page 237

2. Ellipsoid
3. Elliptic hyperboloid of one sheet
5. Cone
6. Elliptic hyperboloid of one sheet
7. Elliptic hyperboloid of two sheets
9. Ellipsoid
10. Elliptic hyperboloid of two sheets
11. Cone
13. Elliptic hyperboloid of one sheet
14. Cone
15. Ellipsoid
17. Elliptic hyperboloid of two sheets
18. $x'^2/2^2 + y'^2/1^2 + z'^2/3^2 = 1$, ellipsoid
19. $x'^2/5^2 - y'^2/2^2 + z'^2/3^2 = 1$, elliptic hyperboloid of one sheet
21. $x'^2/3^2 + y'^2/6^2 - z'^2/2^2 = 0$, cone
22. $x'^2/2^2 + y'^2/5^2 - z'^2/3^2 = 1$, elliptic hyperboloid of one sheet
23. $x'^2/5^2 - y'^2/3^2 - z'^2/6^2 = 1$, elliptic hyperboloid of two sheets
25. $x'^2/2^2 + y'^2/4^2 + z'^2/3^2 = 1$, ellipsoid
26. $x'^2/2^2 - y'^2/1^2 - z'^2/3^2 = 1$, elliptic hyperboloid of two sheets
27. $x'^2/4^2 - y'^2/3^2 + z'^2/2^2 = 0$, cone

29. $x'^2/2^2 + y'^2/3^2 - z'^2/1^2 = 1$, elliptic hyperboloid of one sheet
30. $x'^2/3^2 - y'^2/2^2 + z'^2/5^2 = 0$, cone
31. $x'^2/3^2 + y'^2/2^2 + z'^2/1^2 = 1$, ellipsoid
33. $x'^2/2^2 - y'^2/3^2 - z'^2/4^2 = 1$, elliptic hyperboloid of two sheets

Exercise 13.3, page 240

2. Elliptic paraboloid
5. Elliptic paraboloid
7. Hyperbolic paraboloid
10. Elliptic paraboloid
13. Elliptic paraboloid
15. Hyperbolic paraboloid
3. Elliptic paraboloid
6. Hyperbolic paraboloid
9. Hyperbolic paraboloid
11. Elliptic paraboloid
14. Hyperbolic paraboloid
17. Hyperbolic paraboloid

TABLE OF NATURAL
TRIGONOMETRIC FUNCTION
TO FOUR PLACES

	Sin	Cos	Tan	Cot	
0° 00′	.0000	1.0000	.0000		**90° 00′**
10	029	000	029	343.8	50
20	058	000	058	171.9	40
30	.0087	1.0000	.0087	114.6	30
40	116	.9999	116	85.94	20
50	145	999	145	68.75	10
1° 00′	.0175	.9998	.0175	57.29	**89° 00′**
10	204	998	204	49.10	50
20	233	997	233	42.96	40
30	.0262	.9997	.0262	38.19	30
40	291	996	291	34.37	20
50	320	995	320	31.24	10
2° 00′	.0349	.9994	.0349	28.64	**88° 00′**
10	378	993	378	26.43	50
20	407	992	407	24.54	40
30	.0436	.9990	.0437	22.90	30
40	465	989	466	21.47	20
50	494	988	495	20.21	10
3° 00′	.0523	.9986	.0524	19.08	**87° 00′**
10	552	985	553	18.07	50
20	581	983	582	17.17	40
30	.0610	.9981	.0612	16.35	30
40	640	980	641	15.60	20
50	669	978	670	14.92	10
4° 00′	.0698	.9976	.0699	14.30	**86° 00′**
10	727	974	729	13.73	50
20	756	971	758	13.20	40
30	.0785	.9969	.0787	12.71	30
40	814	967	816	12.25	20
50	843	964	846	11.83	10
5° 00′	.0872	.9962	.0875	11.43	**85° 00′**
10	901	959	904	11.06	50
20	929	957	934	10.71	40
30	.0958	.9954	.0963	10.39	30
40	987	951	992	10.08	20
50	.1016	948	.1022	9.788	10
6° 00′	.1045	.9945	.1051	9.514	**84° 00′**
10	074	942	080	9.255	50
20	103	939	110	9.010	40
30	.1132	.9936	.1139	8.777	30
40	161	932	169	8.566	20
50	190	929	198	8.345	10
7° 00′	.1219	.9925	.1228	8.144	**83° 00′**
10	248	922	257	7.953	50
20	276	918	287	7.770	40
30	.1305	.9914	.1317	7.596	30
40	334	911	346	7.429	20
50	363	907	376	7.269	10
8° 00′	.1392	.9903	.1405	7.115	**82° 00′**
10	421	899	435	6.968	50
20	449	894	465	6.827	40
30	.1478	.9890	.1495	6.691	30
40	507	886	524	6.561	20
50	536	881	554	6.435	10
9° 00′	.1564	.9877	.1584	6.314	**81° 00′**
	Cos	Sin	Cot	Tan	

	Sin	Cos	Tan	Cot	
9° 00′	.1564	.9877	.1584	6.314	81° 00′
10	593	872	614	197	50
20	622	868	644	084	40
30	.1650	.9863	.1673	5.976	30
40	679	858	703	871	20
50	708	853	733	769	10
10° 00′	.1736	.9848	.1763	5.671	80° 00′
10	765	843	793	576	50
20	794	838	823	485	40
30	.1822	.9833	.1853	5.396	30
40	851	827	883	309	20
50	880	822	914	226	10
11° 00′	.1908	.9816	.1944	5.145	79° 00′
10	937	811	974	066	50
20	965	805	.2004	4.989	40
30	.1994	.9799	.2035	4.915	30
40	.2022	793	065	843	20
50	051	787	095	773	10
12° 00′	.2079	.9781	.2126	4.705	78° 00′
10	108	775	156	638	50
20	136	769	186	574	40
30	.2164	.9763	.2217	4.511	30
40	193	757	247	449	20
50	221	750	278	390	10
13° 00′	.2250	.9744	.2309	4.331	77° 00′
10	278	737	339	275	50
20	306	730	370	219	40
30	.2334	.9724	.2401	4.165	30
40	363	717	432	113	20
50	391	710	462	061	10
14° 00′	.2419	.9703	.2493	4.011	76° 00′
10	447	696	524	3.962	50
20	476	689	555	914	40
30	.2504	.9681	.2586	3.867	30
40	532	674	617	821	20
50	560	667	648	776	10
15° 00′	.2588	.9659	.2679	3.732	75° 00′
10	616	652	711	689	50
20	644	644	742	647	40
30	.2672	.9636	.2773	3.606	30
40	700	628	805	566	20
50	728	621	836	526	10
16° 00′	.2756	.9613	.2867	3.487	74° 00′
10	784	605	899	450	50
20	812	596	931	412	40
30	.2840	.9588	.2962	3.376	30
40	868	580	994	340	20
50	896	572	.3026	305	10
17° 00′	.2924	.9563	.3057	3.271	73° 00′
10	952	555	089	237	50
20	979	546	121	204	40
30	.3007	.9537	.3153	3.172	30
40	035	528	185	140	20
50	062	520	217	108	10
18° 00′	.3090	.9511	.3249	3.078	72° 00′
	Cos	Sin	Cot	Tan	

	Sin	Cos	Tan	Cot	
18° 00'	.3090	.9511	.3249	3.078	**72° 00'**
10	118	502	281	047	50
20	145	492	314	018	40
30	.3173	.9483	.3346	2.989	30
40	201	474	378	960	20
50	228	465	411	932	10
19° 00'	.3256	.9455	.3443	2.904	**71° 00'**
10	283	446	476	877	50
20	311	436	508	850	40
30	.3338	.9426	.3541	2.824	30
40	365	417	574	798	20
50	393	407	607	773	10
20° 00'	.3420	.9397	.3640	2.747	**70° 00'**
10	448	387	673	723	50
20	475	377	706	699	40
30	.3502	.9367	.3739	2.675	30
40	529	356	772	651	20
50	557	346	805	628	10
21° 00'	.3584	.9336	.3839	2.605	**69° 00'**
10	611	325	872	583	50
20	638	315	906	560	40
30	.3665	.9304	.3939	2.539	30
40	692	293	973	517	20
50	719	283	.4006	496	10
22° 00'	.3746	.9272	.4040	2.475	**68° 00'**
10	773	261	074	455	50
20	800	250	108	434	40
30	.3827	.9239	.4142	2.414	30
40	854	228	176	394	20
50	881	216	210	375	10
23° 00'	.3907	.9205	.4245	2.356	**67° 00'**
10	934	194	279	337	50
20	961	182	314	318	40
30	.3987	.9171	.4348	2.300	30
40	.4014	159	383	282	20
50	041	147	417	264	10
24° 00'	.4067	.9135	.4452	2.246	**66° 00'**
10	094	124	487	229	50
20	120	112	522	211	40
30	.4147	.9100	.4557	2.194	30
40	173	088	592	177	20
50	200	075	628	161	10
25° 00'	.4226	.9063	.4663	2.145	**65° 00'**
10	253	051	699	128	50
20	279	038	734	112	40
30	.4305	.9026	.4770	2.097	30
40	331	013	806	081	20
50	358	001	841	066	10
26° 00'	.4384	.8988	.4877	2.050	**64° 00'**
10	410	975	913	035	50
20	436	962	950	020	40
30	.4462	.8949	.4986	2.006	30
40	488	936	.5022	1.991	20
50	514	923	059	977	10
27° 00'	.4540	.8910	.5095	1.963	**64° 00'**
	Cos	Sin	Cot	Tan	

	Sin	Cos	Tan	Cot	
27° 00′	.4540	.8910	.5095	1.963	**63° 00′**
10	566	897	132	949	50
20	592	884	169	935	40
30	.4617	.8870	.5206	1.921	30
40	643	857	243	907	20
50	669	843	280	894	10
28° 00′	.4695	.8829	.5317	1.881	**62° 00′**
10	720	816	354	868	50
20	746	802	392	855	40
30	.4772	.8788	.5430	1.842	30
40	797	774	467	829	20
50	823	760	505	816	10
29° 00′	.4848	.8746	.5543	1.804	**61° 00′**
10	874	732	581	792	50
20	899	718	619	780	40
30	.4924	.8704	.5658	1.767	30
40	950	689	696	756	20
50	975	675	735	744	10
30° 00′	.5000	.8660	.5774	1.732	**60° 00′**
10	025	646	812	720	50
20	050	631	851	709	40
30	.5075	.8616	.5890	1.698	30
40	100	601	930	686	20
50	125	587	969	675	10
31° 00′	.5150	.8572	.6009	1.664	**59° 00′**
10	175	557	048	653	50
20	200	542	088	643	40
30	.5225	.8526	.6128	1.632	30
40	250	511	168	621	20
50	275	496	208	611	10
32° 00′	.5299	.8480	.6249	1.600	**58° 00′**
10	324	465	289	590	50
20	348	450	330	580	40
30	.5373	.8434	.6371	1.570	30
40	398	418	412	560	20
50	422	403	453	550	10
33° 00′	.5446	.8387	.6494	1.540	**57° 00′**
10	471	371	536	530	50
20	495	355	577	520	40
30	.5519	.8339	.6619	1.511	30
40	544	323	661	501	20
50	568	307	703	1.492	10
34° 00′	.5592	.8290	.6745	1.483	**56° 00′**
10	616	274	787	473	50
20	640	258	830	464	40
30	.5664	.8241	.6873	1.455	30
40	688	225	916	446	20
50	712	208	959	437	10
35° 00′	.5736	.8192	.7002	1.428	**55° 00′**
10	760	175	046	419	50
20	783	158	089	411	40
30	.5807	.8141	.7133	1.402	30
40	831	124	177	393	20
50	854	107	221	385	10
36° 00′	.5878	.8090	.7265	1.376	**54° 00′**
	Cos	Sin	Cot	Tan	

	Sin	Cos	Tan	Cot	
36° 00′	.5878	.8090	.7265	1.376	**54° 00′**
10	901	073	310	368	50
20	925	056	355	360	40
30	.5948	.8039	.7400	1.351	30
40	972	021	445	343	20
50	995	004	490	335	10
37° 00′	.6018	.7986	.7536	1.327	**53° 00′**
10	041	969	581	319	50
20	065	951	627	311	40
30	.6088	.7934	.7673	1.303	30
40	111	916	720	295	20
50	134	898	766	288	10
38° 00′	.6157	.7880	.7813	1.280	**52° 00′**
10	180	862	860	272	50
20	202	844	907	265	40
30	.6225	.7826	.7954	1.257	30
40	248	808	.8002	250	20
50	271	790	050	242	10
39° 00′	.6293	.7771	.8098	1.235	**51° 00′**
10	316	753	146	228	50
20	338	735	195	220	40
30	.6361	.7716	.8243	1.213	30
40	383	698	292	206	20
50	406	679	342	199	10
40° 00′	.6428	.7660	.8391	1.192	**50° 00′**
10	450	642	441	185	50
20	472	623	491	178	40
30	.6494	.7604	.8541	1.171	30
40	517	585	591	164	20
50	539	566	642	157	10
41° 00′	.6561	.7547	.8693	1.150	**49° 00′**
10	583	528	744	144	50
20	604	509	796	137	40
30	.6626	.7490	.8847	1.130	30
40	648	470	899	124	20
50	670	451	952	117	10
42° 00′	.6691	.7431	.9004	1.111	**48° 00′**
10	713	412	057	104	50
20	734	392	110	098	40
30	.6756	.7373	.9163	1.091	30
40	777	353	217	085	20
50	799	333	271	079	10
43° 00′	.6820	.7314	.9325	1.072	**47° 00′**
10	841	294	380	066	50
20	862	274	435	060	40
30	.6884	.7254	.9490	1.054	30
40	905	234	545	048	20
50	926	214	601	042	10
44° 00′	.6947	.7193	.9657	1.036	**46° 00′**
10	967	173	713	030	50
20	988	153	770	024	40
30	.7009	.7133	.9827	1.018	30
40	030	112	884	012	20
50	050	092	942	006	10
45° 00′	.7071	.7071	1.000	1.000	**45° 00′**
	Cos	Sin	Cot	Tan	

INDEX